THE CANTERBURY TALES

The pilgrims outside the walls of the city of Canterbury, an illustration from an edition of Lydgate's poems. John Lydgate (1370?-1449), a monk at Bury St Edmunds, was a great admirer of Chaucer and wrote his own contribution to 'The Canterbury Tales'.

THE CANTERBURY TALES

GEOFFREY CHAUCER

Translated into Modern English by
NEVILL COGHILL

Foreword by
MELVYN BRAGG

Introduction by
JOHN WAIN

CRESSET PRESS

Copyright © the Estate of Nevill Coghill
1951, 1958, 1960, 1975, 1977, 1986, 1992
All rights reserved

This edition first published 1986
by arrangement with Penguin Books Limited
by Century Hutchinson Limited
This 1992 edition published by Cresset Press
20 Vauxhall Bridge Road, London SW1V 2SA

Edited, designed and produced by
Shuckburgh Reynolds Limited

Editor: Gila Falkus
Designer: David Fordham
Picture research: Philippa Lewis

Typeset by SX Composing Limited, Rayleigh, Essex
Printed and bound in Italy by New Interlitho,
S.p.a., Milan

British Library Cataloguing in Publication Data
Chaucer, Geoffrey
  [Canterbury tales. *English*]   The illustrated
  Canterbury tales.
  I. [Canterbury tales. *English*]   II. Title
  821'.1   PR1870.A1

ISBN 0 09 177223 0

CONTENTS

FOREWORD

BY MELVYN BRAGG

I READ *The Canterbury Tales* for the first time thirty years ago. It was like biting through the sweetest crust to a new taste you had somehow always known. The simple seeming words were in a foreign English which was not unlike the Northern dialect I then spoke and they rustled around the quiet small town school-room luxuriantly, beckoning and binding us into the world of the first major English poet. It is a world which has stayed with us. For Chaucer's gifts of story-telling and character drawing, his ear for the music of a line and his spectrum of humour from the ironic to the wincingly bawdy have appeared and reappeared in our literature ever since. Indeed they have helped to shape it. And Nevill Coghill's easy, seductive translation ensures that this, the most popular work in English Literature – now 600 years old – will run through yet more centuries, beguiling yet more readers, shaping more writers.

For Chaucer pierced the root of Englishness. A few others may have surpassed him: none can challenge his claim to have invented a whole company, even a community, coarse and fine, graceful and appalling, sly, solid, anarchic – it is like a first rainbow of English writing and all the colours are in it. In any English community to this day, you will find your Knight, your Miller, your Franklin, your Yeoman and always your Wife of Bath, even to the gap-teeth.

But besides being a book of character and marvellous stories, it is also a book of its time: of that rich embroidery of cultures in the Middle Ages in which the pagan met on the field with the Christian, the chivalric code coexisted with wholesale clerical corruption, illiteracy was widespread, scholarship rare. Europe was in many ways the single place it has not been since, and societies further off, especially to the East, were listened to in the conch shells of their stories.

It was a world, for instance, where the Prioress, most dainty of them all, eats with her fingers, even putting them in the sauce. It is a world in which everyone wears much of their character and place in society on their backs. Chaucer is at great pains to describe the dress. It is a world where few can read but all can see and see keenly. The great age of the stained glass window, the time of brilliantly decorated Books of Hours, of tapestries and the language of flowers.

It is here that the illustrations are such a major extension of *The Canterbury Tales*. As well as their intrinsic beauty and spell-binding freshness of vision, they place Chaucer's work in its precise period and by giving it that locality help us to appreciate how great a leap it has made into universality. It is a nice irony too, that Nevill Coghill's twentieth-century translation should be balanced by medieval reproduction.

For those of us who know *The Canterbury Tales*, this is as near as we will ever get to being able to afford it as the illuminated manuscript it might, in fancy, have been. For those of you who do not know the work, I envy the pleasure coming your way.

The Gough Map of the British Isles was acquired by the British Museum in 1809 from the collection of the antiquarian, Richard Gough. An anonymous manuscript map on vellum, dated c.1360, it is the first map to show roads.

INTRODUCTION

BY JOHN WAIN

HUMAN history is stained all too frequently with crimes so enormous in scale that we find them ungraspable: genocides, pogroms, mass deportations, crimes against whole races and whole nationalities. These outrages are, literally, unimaginable: the mind slips from them as the foot slips from a cake of ice. Individuals, on the other hand, attract attention; we can identify with them. And no crime against an individual has ever set moving such an immediate wave of horror and indignation as the event that took place in Canterbury Cathedral on the evening of 29 December 1170, when four knights of Henry II burst in as the Archbishop Thomas Becket was celebrating Mass and beat him to death, there in front of the altar. As far east as the Levant, as far north as the Arctic Circle, wherever there were people of the Christian faith, the shock-waves were felt. Becket had shown his worth in many ways. He had been a brave commander on the battlefield; he had held high office in the state, being no less than Lord Chancellor of England; and he was a pious and merciful prelate.

In the following February Becket was canonized. The Pope evidently pushed through this normally rather slow procedure at a phenomenal rate, but not fast enough for the common people. They decided immediately that Thomas was a saint, a 'holy blissful martyr', and pilgrims began arriving at the Cathedral almost as soon as the body was interred. By some quirk of hagiographical thinking, St Thomas became particularly associated with the miraculous healing of the sick. *'Optimus egrorum, medicus fit Thomas bonorum'*, ran the Latin tag: "For good people that are sick, St Thomas is the best doctor."

Pilgrimages occupied a central place in the life of the Middle Ages. All the elements of medieval Catholic Christianity are seen there in high relief: the beautiful piety and dedication, and also the superstition, fraudulence and rascality. After confessing one's sins, one might be ordered by one's priest to go on a pilgrimage as a penance. Or, in serious illness or dire peril, the sufferer might make a vow to undertake a pilgrimage if spared. And, at the other extreme, there must have been many who went on pilgrimages out of a thirst for adventure and to see the world. If, by doing so, they could pick up a little spiritual merit that would stand them in good stead when they came face to face with St Peter, so much the better. The thought must have helped them to bear up against the discomforts and disappointments that travel always brings with it.

In an age when good roads and reliable maps were scarce, a traveller's best chance of being reasonably safe and provided for lay in following one of the principal routes of pilgrimage. For to take care of pilgrims, to see that they had somewhere to sleep and some kind of nourishment, was accounted a charitable act that earned merit in Heaven, much like the pilgrimage itself, and many religious houses made it their business not only to offer rest and hospitality but to keep roads and bridges in repair. Thus looked after, even people with very little money (no more, in some cases, than could be gathered by a whip-round in their native village, the donor of a few pence also clocking up some celestial merit) could travel long distances. The four most frequently visited foreign shrines were Rome, Jerusalem, St James's of Galicia, and the Spanish shrine at Compostela. Within England, the most visited shrines were that of the Virgin Mary at Walsingham, where the church and chapel, destroyed at the Reformation, had been built up by generations of gifts into a blaze of gold and jewels; and, as we have seen, the shrine of Thomas in Canterbury.

For this journey, Londoners like Chaucer would hire horses at Southwark and change them for fresh ones at Rochester, the cost being twelve pence for each stage. To stop people stealing the horses, they were identified with the branding-iron, exactly like the Lazy S and Bar H of the Wild West stories we used to read in our youth.

Left: Geoffrey Chaucer reading a manuscript (probably his 'Troilus and Criseyde') to the assembled court of Richard II and his Queen, Anne of Bohemia.

Chaucer parades his pilgrims before our eyes with un- forgettable clarity. His writing has retained its freshness across six hundred years. Small wonder, since he built it out of non-perishable materials. It is highly visual, but always in a hard-edged, unsentimental way with no blurring of one effect into the next. He presents his characters, diverse as they are, in clear outline and primary colours, deliberately making them as vivid and memorable as the figures on a pack of cards; except that where the card-figures are frozen into two-dimensional immobility, Chaucer's people are in constant movement, riding along, talking, laughing, gesticulating, quarrelling. The scene he puts before us in the Prologue is all energy, variety and colour; it is the great verbal pageant of the Middle Ages. This method of pre- sentation was no doubt the result of conscious and skilful decision-making on Chaucer's part, for he was a meticulous artist, with a lifetime of work behind him, and as interested in the form of what he wrote as in its content. And yet, granted all this, it seems to me probable that this fresh, vivid way of seeing the human scene, like a photographer who waits for a moment of strong sunlight before clicking the shutter, is temperamental; Chaucer saw people like that, and described them like that, because he was that kind of man; just as Ben Jonson, using something of the Chaucerian technique of plastic hardness, made his comedies into a similar verbal pageant, depicting a society in the first phase of unrestrained captialism as Chaucer had depicted the last moment of the high Middle Ages.

Pilgrimages brought together devout people and cynics, the blameless and the rascally. As well as the gentle clerk of Oxford, the cultivated and sensitive Prioress, the saintly village parson and the honest ploughman, one encountered such social dregs as the Pardoner, a man licensed to sell papal pardons and indulgences. The Church imposed penances for sin; in time the custom arose of commuting these penances for a cash payment; and at first, if adminis- tered through the proper channels, there was something to be said for it. As John Middleton Murry remarked, it was at least 'a tax on sin', and the money so collected was often used to help the needy. But by the time such figures as Chaucer's Pardoner arose, the sale of pardons had become simply a racket, and such a man would unhesitatingly put the money into his own pocket. Almost as low in public esteem was his companion the Summoner, whose job was to summon de- linquents to appear in ecclesiastical courts, to enforce payments of the tithes and church dues, and to have disciplinary powers in punishing adultery, fornication and perjury, none of which came under the common law. Opportunities for petty bribery were of course numerous, and a man like Chaucer's Summoner would seize them with both hands.

Honest people, then, mingled with crooks and charla- tans. But then, the pilgrimage mingled people of every kind, however contrasting. The pilgrimage was a great social leveller. Not that feudal England consciously proposed social levelling as a good to be aimed at. The organization of society was quite frankly along lines of rank, and the time was far distant when the nation as a whole would become ashamed of this; in Chaucer's day it seemed natural. But it was also natural for these sharply differentiated classes to mix with a closeness and familiarity that have become un- known. The most socially exalted of Chaucer's pilgrims is, of course, the Knight, a man presented to us in all serious- ness as worthy of the highest respect not only for his rank but for his personal qualities of courtesy and gallantry; a man fit to associate with noblemen and kings. Fittingly, he is given the longest and the best of the Tales. It is a story of courtly love in the medieval manner, and as a rule such tales have lost their appeal in our world and their conventions are withered. But the Knight's Tale, with its urgency, pace, and philosophical weight, is one of the peaks of Chaucer's work. Of all the poems of *amour courtois*, it is the one that has the best chance of being understood by the reader who cares nothing for the historical dimension but is capable of responding to a story of love and suffering, for in it we enter that region of emotional pressure in which differences be- tween modes of passion are merged. The characters in it are no more dated than the characters in the Prologue itself.

By giving his Knight the best story, Chaucer was setting us an example of the respect we ought to pay him. At the other end of the social scale, his humblest character is the village ploughman, the very bottom of the ladder, the country labourer in a pre-industrial age. But if he is the lowest in formal social classification, he is by no means the lowest in the eyes of his creator, whether we take that creator to be God or Geoffrey Chaucer. The poet respects him. And we know – to leave literature for everyday fact – that he rode along, often, beside the Knight; that when the pilgrims reached the Cathedral they threw themselves down on their knees, or prone, and prayed with an abandon that took no note of who came first and who last. The ploughman might as easily be jammed up against the knight as against the cook or the shipman. In that feudal world which had never heard of 'equality', it was easier for a poor man to be close to an aristocrat, to eat the same food, to endure the same mud and weather, and to pray at the same shrine, than it has ever been in our chain-store democracy.

The pilgrimage thus had many effects on medieval society, too complex and ramifying to be traced. But one of its effects that, as it happens, we *are* in a position to trace is this: it gave England's greatest medieval poet an opportunity to show the full range of his genius. Without the institution of the pilgrimage, Chaucer's supreme work, *The Canterbury Tales*, would not have had its framework. And without its framework it would lose half its magic. For where, in the world as it was at that time, could he have found another that would have served the same complex and multiple purposes?

That Chaucer should sooner or later have embarked on a large-scale compilation of tales was only to be expected. A travelled man with an international outlook, insatiably curious about life, he had an ear for a good story and was besides a voracious reader. Part of his life's work was to channel some of the richness of Continental European narrative into the nascent literature of England. In his young days as a poet he had been a great devotee of French literature, and was in fact the intermediary by which the French poetic genius learnt to speak to English ears. When the amalgam of Anglo-Saxon and Norman-French reached a stage, some time in the thirteenth century, at which it had set, so to speak, into the firmness necessary for a recognizably independent language, poets began to make verses in it, and one of the new features of these verses was that they rhymed. English had already had a poetry for some six centuries before that, but it was a poetry without rhyme; it got its disciplined effects from contrapuntal alliteration and felt no more need of rhyme than Homer or Virgil had. But once rhyme came in – and its primal originators may have been Arabic poets, who started it on its journey round the Mediterranean littoral till it reached Provence and spread from there to all Western Europe – it so enchanted people's ears that a poet who did not use rhyme would have seemed a strange being until the innovations of the twentieth century. (And even those innovations have not succeeded in putting anything very decisive in its place.)

Fourteenth-century England had two great poets, Geoffrey Chaucer and William Langland. Langland, though bookish and probably a cleric, was a man of the people. He came out of a more conservative culture rooted in the old ways, and he wrote his masterpiece, *Piers Plowman*, in the old alliterative verse with no concession to these new-fangled Frenchified ways. All the better that Chaucer was a different kind of man from a different kind of background, for it would have been a waste to have two great poets trying to cultivate the same strip of ground. Chaucer's deep sympathy with common humanity, his true democracy of the spirit, is not in conflict with the fact that he is a courtier, the friend of kings and great noblemen, and that the literary culture he represents is sophisticated and international. On a government mission to Florence and Genoa in 1372, he met Boccaccio and perhaps also Petrarch, was exposed to the dazzling brilliance of an Italy already entering the Renaissance, and began to show Italian influence on his work, just as such poets as Milton and Shelley were to do after him. In the years following that eye-opening visit, many of the separate works that make up the *Tales* must have been written; but though they form a rich and varied testimony to his genius, he was evidently haunted by the thought that he could do something better with them than merely let them lie in a heap, however fascinating a heap it was. We know that in 1388, when he was forty-eight, he went on the Canterbury pilgrimage; did it come to him then, the brilliant idea of a collection of tales recounted by a party of pilgrims to while away their long journey and the better to enjoy one another's company? We cannot say, across six centuries, when this or that idea popped into a man's head; but we can say with certainty that Chaucer's idea for the framework of *The Canterbury Tales* was an original one. Nothing exactly like it had been done before.

And this, in spite of the fact that the collection or compendium of stories was one of the most familiar kinds of reading in the medieval, and for that matter the ancient, world. A collection of stories sewn up into one large manuscript book was obviously a good idea in the Middle Ages when people had to spend the long winter in a chilly castle, not only with no TV or radio or gramophone but also no card games, so that they must have been ready after about the third month to welcome almost anything that could be read aloud to the company. Many of the collections in use were mere rag-bag accumulations, but building on this simple foundation came the writer who claimed to set his own stamp on all the diverse material, to tell each story in his own way, and to orchestrate the whole into a unified work. Such would be, in Chaucer's time, the *Confessio Amantis* by John Gower, a friend of Chaucer's; and his own *Monk's Tale*, a collection of tragedies. Side by side with this was the compendium containing any old kind of story, but claiming to be useful in supplying material for sermons and religious instruction generally. These 'example-books' increased in number as preaching to the laity became more common after the establishment of the orders of friars. The cynical Pardoner, proud of his skill in manipulating his audience, actually offers his story as an '*exemplum*' under the heading of "gluttony, luxurie and hasardrie".

All this Chaucer knew. And his Italian exposure had brought him into the magic world of Boccaccio, whose *Decameron*, written about forty years before *The Canterbury Tales*, adopts the containing device of having a group of noble Florentines taking refuge in a castle because an outbreak of plague is raging in the city, and occupying the time with stores. (Chaucer does not actually mention this work and there is no direct influence from it in *The Canterbury Tales*, but this surely matters less than the fact that he had been in the kitchen where such things were cooked.)

The Canterbury Tales were planned on such a huge scale that we can tell Chaucer in his later forties must have felt himself to be in the prime of life and full of vigour. Many of the tales could be taken from stock, and he expected to knock out the rest in the next few years. Interesting, to see that after all his experience and with all his wisdom and maturity, he was still making the mistake that every writer makes! Still underestimating the time, and the exhausting effort, needed for a long work! If thirty pilgrims were to tell four stories each, that would make 120, and no doubt the dinner given to celebrate the winner before they all break up would furnish an amusing scene. As it turned out, when the poet died at the age of sixty, he had completed only nine segments of the wide circle he planned; and obviously the material as we have it is not fully revised, since it has some slips and anomalies (the Shipman appears to class himself among the women, the Second Nun refers to herself as an 'unworthy son of Eve', and the Nun's Priest, who tells one of the most amusing of the Tales, an animal-fable to set beside *The Wind in the Willows* or *Animal Farm*, is not mentioned in the Prologue and suddenly bobs up from nowhere.

No matter. What we have is enough to show us the range of Chaucer's genius; so that we remember how the great seventeenth-century poet John Dryden, faced with the task of describing the full variety of what he found in Chaucer's work, in the end gave up and simply said, 'Here is God's plenty.'

As well as contributing to the tradition of the collection of tales, Chaucer enriched it by a new idea – a breath-takingly simple innovation that suddenly transforms the whole tradition: the notion of first presenting a vivid, closely observed portrait-gallery of his tale-tellers and culling them from every social class and walk of life – a far better idea than merely having a group of friends taking refuge in a castle, who would necessarily be of the same class and type – and then fitting the stories to the personality of the tellers. It seems such a simple idea in retrospect, but then so did the flying-machine invented by a couple of bicycle mechanics named Orville and Wilbur Wright. Surely someone ought to have thought before of a machine with flat wings that canted over on the turns like a bicycle, but oddly enough no one had. And of all the people who wrote or gathered collections of stories, no one before Chaucer had though of introducing the element of dramatization that makes each tale two things at once – a story in itself, and a piece of self-revelation by the character who tells it.

Once he had this idea, it was natural to elaborate it. He has the pilgrims react to the stories – to quarrel, to take offence; he has the Host, as master of ceremonies, comment spontaneously on the stories and take action to protect the company from excessive boredom from story-tellers who are incompetent or long-winded; and, by a delicious stroke of irony, he makes himself the one who is interrupted with the least ceremony. Chaucer, the master story-teller, represents himself as the one who is unable to hold the attention of his hearers.

The joke becomes richer still when Chaucer, mildly but insistently claiming his right to be heard, obtains the Host's grudging permission and launches into the Tale of Melibee, *in prose*. Chaucer the great story-teller had bored his audience, and now it is Chaucer the magical poet who descends to jog-trot prose – Chaucer, who had honed the skills of poetry to the point where he could achieve any effect in verse: compose haunting lyrics ('*Thyn eyen two wol sleye me sodeinly*') or sinewy narrative, who could write dialogue in verse and make it sound natural, who could manage any kind of stanza; and who knew so unerringly how to make a light, feathery music out of an English line by exploiting the fact that in the English of his day many words had a final *e* that was sounded lightly but perceptibly.

Indeed, it was Nevill Coghill's sorrow that, in adapting

Chaucer's verse for the modern reader, he had to sacrifice the music we most particularly associate with it. In his valuable book, *The Poet Chaucer*, Coghill wrote:

'There is an ever-present liquidness of movement in his language, now unrecapturable in poetry because those gliding terminations that he knew so well how to use have vanished from our language. We can no longer make the music of such a line as

And smalë fowles maken melodyë.

We can make other music, but this kind is lost to us for ever.'

Nevill Coghill was scholar enough, and poet enough, to be well aware that in putting Chaucer into twentieth-century English some beauty, some magic, will inevitably be lost; and he was always the first to admit that for anyone who really comes to love Chaucer and wants to get close to him, the slight effort of getting used to his own language is well worth it. But a good modern adaptation can lead many people to form that initial interest, to become Chaucerians in two stages, as the pilgrim changed horses at Rochester. And Nevill's is good. How could it not be? He knew so much about Chaucer, studied him so deeply, loved his work so much. More than that. He was a man who shared much of the Chaucerian outlook on life. He shared the poet's Christian beliefs, and also his preference for kindliness and humour and tolerance as against spite and envy. Chaucer, who particularly admired courtesy and largeness of mind, would have found them in Neville, for

He never yet no vileinye ne sayde
In all his lyfe, un-to no maner wight.
He was a verray parfit gentil knight,

and this splendidly produced book is a fitting reminder of him as well as of his great original.

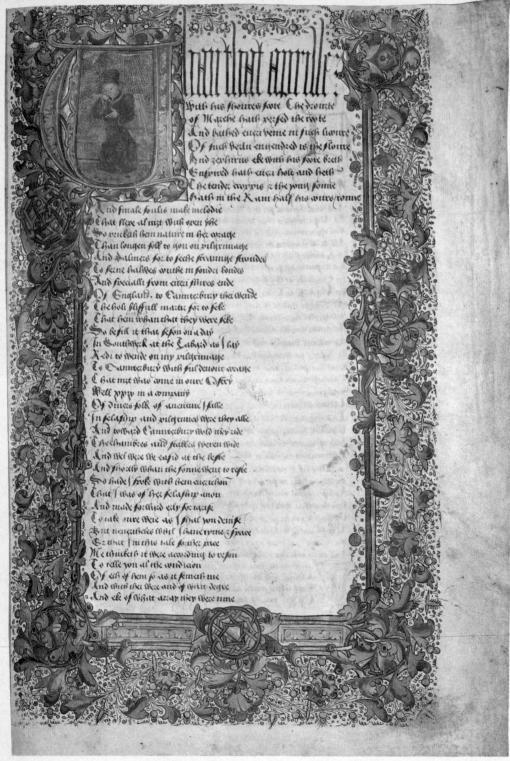

The beginning of the Prologue of 'The Canterbury Tales'
from a mid-fifteenth-century manuscript.

ᛏHE ᛈROLOGUE

ᛅHEN in April the sweet showers fall
And pierce the drought of March to the root,
  and all
    The veins are bathed in liquor of such power
As brings about the engendering of the flower,
When also Zephyrus with his sweet breath
Exhales an air in every grove and heath
Upon the tender shoots, and the young sun
His half-course in the sign of the *Ram* has run,
And the small fowl are making melody
That sleep away the night with open eye
(So nature pricks them and their heart engages)
Then people long to go on pilgrimages
And palmers long to seek the stranger strands
Of far-off saints, hallowed in sundry lands,
And specially, from every shire's end
Of England, down to Canterbury they wend
To seek the holy blissful martyr, quick
To give his help to them when they were sick.

ᛁt happened in that season that one day
In Southwark, at *The Tabard*, as I lay
  Ready to go on pilgrimage and start
For Canterbury, most devout at heart,
At night there came into that hostelry
Some nine and twenty in a company
Of sundry folk happening then to fall
In fellowship, and they were pilgrims all
That towards Canterbury meant to ride.
The rooms and stables of the inn were wide;
They made us easy, all was of the best.
And, briefly, when the sun had gone to rest,
I'd spoken to them all upon the trip
And was soon one with them in fellowship,
Pledged to rise early and to take the way
To Canterbury, as you heard me say.

ᛒut none the less, while I have time and space,
Before my story takes a further pace,
  It seems a reasonable thing to say
What their condition was, the full array
Of each of them, as it appeared to me,

According to profession and degree,
And what apparel they were riding in;
And at a Knight I therefore will begin.
There was a *Knight*, a most distinguished man,
Who from the day on which he first began
To ride abroad had followed chivalry,
Truth, honour, generousness and courtesy.
He had done nobly in his sovereign's war
And ridden into battle, no man more,
As well in Christian as in heathen places,
And ever honoured for his noble graces.

The Knight was the highest ranking pilgrim; his Tale is the longest.

ᛅhen we took Alexandria, he was there.
He often sat at table in the chair
  Of honour, above all nations, when in Prussia.
In Lithuania he had ridden, and Russia,
No Christian man so often, of his rank.
When, in Granada, Algeciras sank
Under assault, he had been there, and in
North Africa, raiding Benamarin;

17

In Anatolia he had been as well
And fought when Ayas and Attalia fell,
For all along the Mediterranean coast
He had embarked with many a noble host.
In fifteen mortal battles he had been
And jousted for our faith at Tramissene
Thrice in the lists, and always killed his man.
This same distinguished knight had led the van
Once with the Bey of Balat, doing work
For him against another heathen Turk;
He was of sovereign value in all eyes.
And though so much distinguished, he was wise
And in his bearing modest as a maid.
He never yet a boorish thing had said
In all his life to any, come what might;
He was a true, a perfect gentle-knight.

Speaking of his equipment, he possessed
Fine horses, but he was not gaily dressed.
He wore a fustian tunic stained and dark
With smudges where his armour had left mark;
Just home from service, he had joined our ranks
To do his pilgrimage and render thanks.

He had his son with him, a fine young *Squire*,
A lover and cadet, a lad of fire
With locks as curly as if they had been pressed.
He was some twenty years of age, I guessed.
In stature he was of a moderate length,
With wonderful agility and strength.
He'd seen some service with the cavalry
In Flanders and Artois and Picardy
And had done valiantly in little space
Of time, in hope to win his lady's grace.

Caxton's fine woodcut of the Squire with his daintily curled locks.

He was embroidered like a meadow bright
And full of freshest flowers, red and white.
Singing he was, or fluting all the day;
He was as fresh as is the month of May.
Short was his gown, the sleeves were long and wide;

He knew the way to sit a horse and ride.
He could make songs and poems and recite,
Knew how to joust and dance, to draw and write.
He loved so hotly that till dawn grew pale
He slept as little as a nightingale.
Courteous he was, lowly and serviceable,
And carved to serve his father at the table.

The Yeoman is one of the characters who never tell a Tale.

There was a *Yeoman* with him at his side,
No other servant; so he chose to ride.
This Yeoman wore a coat and hood of green,
And peacock-feathered arrows, bright and keen
And neatly sheathed, hung at his belt the while
– For he could dress his gear in yeoman style,
His arrows never drooped their feathers low –
And in his hand he bore a mighty bow.
His head was like a nut, his face was brown.
He knew the whole of woodcraft up and down.
A saucy brace was on his arm to ward
It from the bow-string, and a shield and a sword
Hung at one side, and at the other slipped
A jaunty dirk, spear-sharp and well-equipped.
A medal of St Christopher he wore
Of shining silver on his breast, and bore
A hunting-horn, well slung and burnished clean,
That dangled from a baldrick of bright green.
He was a proper forester, I guess.

There also was a *Nun*, a Prioress,
Her way of smiling very simple and coy.
Her greatest oath was only 'By St Loy!'
And she was known as Madam Eglantyne.
And well she sang a service, with a fine
Intoning through her nose, as was most seemly,
And she spoke daintily in French, extremely,
After the school of Stratford-atte-Bowe;
French in the Paris style she did not know.
At meat her manners were well taught withal;
No morsel from her lips did she let fall,

The fashionable Prioress, the first of Chaucer's female pilgrims.

A manly man, to be an Abbot able;
Many a dainty horse he had in stable.
His bridle, when he rode, a man might hear
Jingling in a whistling wind as clear,
Aye, and as loud as does the chapel bell
Where my lord Monk was Prior of the cell.
The Rule of good St Benet or St Maur
As old and strict he tended to ignore;
He let go by the things of yesterday
And took the modern world's more spacious way.
He did not rate that text at a plucked hen
Which says that hunters are not holy men
And that a monk uncloistered is a mere
Fish out of water, flapping on the pier,
That is to say a monk out of his cloister.
That was a text he held not worth an oyster;
And I agreed and said his views were sound;
Was he to study till his head went round
Poring over books in cloisters? Must he toil
As Austin bade and till the very soil?
Was he to leave the world upon the shelf?
Let Austin have his labour to himself.

The robust Monk, one of the eight ecclesiastics among the pilgrims.

Nor dipped her fingers in the sauce too deep;
But she could carry a morsel up and keep
The smallest drop from falling on her breast.
For courtliness she had a special zest,
And she would wipe her upper lip so clean
That not a trace of grease was to be seen
Upon the cup when she had drunk; to eat,
She reached a hand sedately for the meat.
She certainly was very entertaining,
Pleasant and friendly in her ways, and straining
To counterfeit a courtly kind of grace,
A stately bearing fitting to her place,
And to seem dignified in all her dealings
As for her sympathies and tender feelings,
She was so charitably solicitous
She used to weep if she but saw a mouse
Caught in a trap, if it were dead or bleeding.
And she had little dogs she would be feeding
With roasted flesh, or milk, or fine white bread.
And bitterly she wept if one were dead
Or someone took a stick and made it smart;
She was all sentiment and tender heart.
Her veil was gathered in a seemly way,
Her nose was elegant, her eyes glass-grey;
Her mouth was very small, but soft and red,
Her forehead, certainly, was fair of spread,
Almost a span across the brows, I own;
She was indeed by no means undergrown.
Her cloak, I noticed, had a graceful charm.
She wore a coral trinket on her arm,
A set of beads, the gaudies tricked in green,
Whence hung a golden brooch of brightest sheen
On which there first was graven a crowned A,
And lower, *Amor vincit omnia.*

nother *Nun*, the secretary at her cell,
Was riding with her, and *three Priests* as well.

Monk there was, one of the finest sort
Who rode the country; hunting was his sport.

his Monk was therefore a good man to horse;
Greyhounds he had, as swift as birds, to course.
Hunting a hare or riding at a fence
Was all his fun, he spared for no expense.
I saw his sleeves were garnished at the hand
With fine grey fur, the finest in the land,
And on his hood, to fasten it at his chin
He had a wrought-gold cunningly fashioned pin;
Into a lover's knot it seemed to pass.
His head was bald and shone like looking-glass;
So did his face, as if it had been greased.
He was a fat and personable priest;
His prominent eyeballs never seemed to settle.
They glittered like the flames beneath a kettle;
Supple his boots, his horse in fine condition.
He was a prelate fit for exhibition,
He was not pale like a tormented soul.
He liked a fat swan best, and roasted whole.

His palfrey was as brown as is a berry.
There was a *Friar*, a wanton one and merry,
A Limiter, a very festive fellow.
In all Four Orders there was none so mellow,
So glib with gallant phrase and well-turned speech.
He'd fixed up many a marriage, giving each
Of his young women what he could afford her.
He was a noble pillar to his Order.
Highly beloved and intimate was he
With County folk within his boundary,
And city dames of honour and possessions;
For he was qualified to hear confessions,
Or so he said, with more than priestly scope;
He had a special licence from the Pope.

Chaucer's Friar is a hypocrite who cynically exploits religion.

Sweetly he heard his penitents at shrift
With pleasant absolution, for a gift.
He was an easy man in penance-giving
Where he could hope to make a decent living;
It's a sure sign whenever gifts are given
To a poor Order that a man's well shriven,
And should he give enough he knew in verity
The penitent repented in sincerity.
For many a fellow is so hard of heart
He cannot weep, for all his inward smart.
Therefore instead of weeping and of prayer
One should give silver for a poor Friar's care.
He kept his tippet stuffed with pins for curls,
And pocket-knives, to give to pretty girls.
And certainly his voice was gay and sturdy,
For he sang well and played the hurdy-gurdy.
At sing-songs he was champion of the hour.
His neck was whiter than a lily-flower
But strong enough to butt a bruiser down.
He knew the taverns well in every town
And every innkeeper and barmaid too
Better than lepers, beggars and that crew,
For in so eminent a man as he
It was not fitting with the dignity
Of his position, dealing with a scum

Of wretched lepers; nothing good can come
Of commerce with such slum-and-gutter dwellers,
But only with the rich and victual-sellers.
But anywhere a profit might accrue
Courteous he was and lowly of service too.
Natural gifts like his were hard to match.
He was the finest beggar of his batch,
And, for his begging-district, paid a rent;
His brethren did no poaching where he went.
For though a widow mightn't have a shoe,
So pleasant was his holy how-d'ye-do
He got his farthing from her just the same
Before he left, and so his income came
To more than he laid out. And how he romped,
Just like a puppy! He was ever prompt
To arbitrate disputes on settling days
(For a small fee) in many helpful ways,
Not then appearing as your cloistered scholar
With threadbare habit hardly worth a dollar,
But much more like a Doctor or a Pope.
Of double-worsted was the semi-cope
Upon his shoulders, and the swelling fold
About him, like a bell about its mould
When it is casting, rounded out his dress.
He lisped a little out of wantonness
To make his English sweet upon his tongue.
When he had played his harp, or having sung,
His eyes would twinkle in his head as bright
As any star upon a frosty night.
This worthy's name was Hubert, it appeared.
There was a *Merchant* with a forking beard
And motley dress; high on his horse he sat,
Upon his head a Flemish beaver hat
And on his feet daintily buckled boots.
He told of his opinions and pursuits
In solemn tones, he harped on his increase
Of capital; there should be sea-police
(He thought) upon the Harwich-Holland ranges;
He was expert at dabbling in exchanges.
This estimable Merchant so had set

The Merchant too is hypocritical and greedy.

His wits to work, none knew he was in debt,
He was so stately in administration,
In loans and bargains and negotiation.
He was an excellent fellow all the same;
To tell the truth I do not know his name.

*A*n *Oxford Cleric*, still a student though,
One who had taken logic long ago,
Was there; his horse was thinner than a rake,
And he was not too fat, I undertake,
But had a hollow look, a sober stare;
The thread upon his overcoat was bare.
He had found no preferment in the church
And he was too unworldly to make search
For secular employment. By his bed
He preferred having twenty books in red
And black, of Aristotle's philosophy,
Than costly clothes, fiddle or psaltery.
Though a philosopher, as I have told,
He had not found the stone for making gold.
Whatever money from his friends he took
He spent on learning or another book
And prayed for them most earnestly, returning
Thanks to them thus for paying for his learning.

The Man of Law is characterized by his professional qualities.

All was fee-simple to his strong digestion,
Not one conveyance could be called in question.
Though there was nowhere one so busy as he,
He was less busy than he seemed to be.
He knew of every judgement, case and crime
Ever recorded since King William's time.
He could dictate defences or draft deeds;
No one could pinch a comma from his screeds
And he knew every statute off by rote.
He wore a homely parti-coloured coat,
Girt with a silken belt of pin-stripe stuff;
Of his appearance I have said enough.

*T*here was a *Franklin* with him, it appeared;
White as a daisy-petal was his beard.
A sanguine man, high-coloured and benign,
He loved a morning sop of cake in wine.
He lived for pleasure and had always done,
For he was Epicurus' very son,
In whose opinion sensual delight
Was the one true felicity in sight.
As noted as St Julian was for bounty
He made his household free to all the County.
His bread, his ale were finest of the fine

The Clerk is one of the few unworldly pilgrims.

His only care was study, and indeed
He never spoke a word more than was need,
Formal at that, respectful in the extreme,
Short, to the point, and lofty in his theme.
A tone of moral virtue filled his speech
And gladly would he learn, and gladly teach.

A Serjeant at the Law who paid his calls,
Wary and wise, for clients at St Paul's
There also was, of noted excellence.
Discreet he was, a man to reverence,
Or so he seemed, his sayings were so wise.
He often had been Justice of Assize
By letters patent, and in full commission.
His fame and learning and his high position
Had won him many a robe and many a fee.
There was no such conveyancer as he;

The Franklin was a freeholder who ranked next below the gentry.

And no one had a better stock of wine.
His house was never short of bake-meat pies,
Of fish and flesh, and these in such supplies
It positively snowed with meat and drink
And all the dainties that a man could think.
According to the seasons of the year
Changes of dish were ordered to appear.
He kept fat partridges in coops, beyond,
Many a bream and pike were in his pond.
Woe to the cook unless the sauce was hot
And sharp, or if he wasn't on the spot!
And in his hall a table stood arrayed
And ready all day long, with places laid.
As Justice at the Sessions none stood higher;
He often had been Member for the Shire.
A dagger and a little purse of silk
Hung at his girdle, white as morning milk.
As Sheriff he checked audit, every entry.
He was a model among landed gentry.

A *Haberdasher*, a *Dyer*, a *Carpenter*,
A *Weaver* and a *Carpet-maker* were
Among our ranks, all in the livery
Of one impressive guild-fraternity.
They were so trim and fresh their gear would pass
For new. Their knives were not tricked out with brass
But wrought with purest silver, which avouches
A like display on girdles and on pouches.

The Carpenter and the other gildsmen do not reappear.

Each seemed a worthy burgess, fit to grace
A guild-hall with a seat upon the dais.
Their wisdom would have justified a plan
To make each one of them an alderman;
They had the capital and revenue,
Besides their wives declared it was their due.
And if they did not think so, then they ought;
To be called '*Madam*' is a glorious thought,
And so is going to church and being seen
Having your mantle carried, like a queen.

They had a *Cook* with them who stood alone
For boiling chicken with a marrow-bone,
Sharp flavouring-powder and a spice for savour.

The Cook is later too drunk to complete his Tale.

He could distinguish London ale by flavour,
And he could roast and seethe and broil and fry,
Make good thick soup and bake a tasty pie.
But what a pity – so it seemed to me,
That he should have an ulcer on his knee.
As for blancmange, he made it with the best.

There was a *Skipper* hailing from far west;
He came from Dartmouth, so I understood.
He rode a farmer's horse as best he could,
In a woollen gown that reached his knee.
A dagger on a lanyard falling free
Hung from his neck under his arm and down.
The summer heat had tanned his colour brown,
And certainly he was an excellent fellow.
Many a draught of vintage, red and yellow,
He'd drawn at Bordeaux, while the trader snored.
The nicer rules of conscience he ignored.
If, when he fought, the enemy vessel sank,
He sent his prisoners home; they walked the plank.
As for his skill in reckoning his tides,
Currents and many another risk besides,
Moons, harbours, pilots, he had such dispatch
That none from Hull to Carthage was his match.
Hardy he was, prudent in undertaking;
His beard in many a tempest had its shaking,
And he knew all the havens as they were
From Gottland to the Cape of Finisterre,
And every creek in Brittany and Spain;
The barge he owned was called *The Maudelayne*.

A *Doctor* too emerged as we proceeded;
No one alive could talk as well as he did
On points of medicine and of surgery,
For, being grounded in astronomy,
He watched his patient closely for the hours
When, by his horoscope, he knew the powers
Of favourable planets, then ascendent,
Worked on the images for his dependent.
The cause of every malady you'd got
He knew, and whether dry, cold, moist or hot;

He knew their seat, their humour and condition.
He was a perfect practising physician.
These causes being known for what they were,
He gave the man his medicine then and there.
All his apothecaries in a tribe
Were ready with the drugs he would prescribe
And each made money from the other's guile;
They had been friendly for a goodish while.
He was well-versed in Aesculapius too
And what Hippocrates and Rufus knew
And Dioscorides, now dead and gone,
Galen and Rhazes, Hali, Serapion,
Averroes, Avicenna, Constantine,

The Wife of Bath is one of Chaucer's most enduring figures.

For all his learning, the Doctor, too, is motivated by avarice.

Scotch Bernard, John of Gaddesden, Gilbertine.
In his own diet he observed some measure;
There were no superfluities for pleasure,
Only digestives, nutritives and such.
He did not read the Bible very much.
In blood-red garments, slashed with bluish grey
And lined with taffeta, he rode his way;
Yet he was rather close as to expenses
And kept the gold he won in pestilences.
Gold stimulates the heart, or so we're told.
He therefore had a special love of gold.

A worthy *woman* from beside *Bath* city
Was with us, somewhat deaf, which was a pity.
In making cloth she showed so great a bent
She bettered those of Ypres and of Ghent.
In all the parish not a dame dared stir
Towards the altar steps in front of her,
And if indeed they did, so wrath was she
As to be quite put out of charity.
Her kerchiefs were of finely woven ground;
I dared have sworn they weighed a good ten pound,
The ones she wore on Sunday, on her head.
Her hose were of the finest scarlet red
And gartered tight; her shoes were soft and new.
Bold was her face, handsome, and red in hue.
A worthy woman all her life, what's more

She'd had five husbands, all at the church door,
Apart from other company in youth;
No need just now to speak of that, forsooth.
And she had thrice been to Jerusalem,
Seen many strange rivers and passed over them;
She'd been to Rome and also to Boulogne,
St James of Compostella and Cologne,
And she was skilled in wandering by the way.
She had gap-teeth, set widely, truth to say.
Easily on an ambling horse she sat
Well wimpled up, and on her head a hat
As broad as is a buckler or a shield;
She had a flowing mantle that concealed
Large hips, her heels spurred sharply under that.
In company she liked to laugh and chat
And knew the remedies for love's mischances,
An art in which she knew the oldest dances.

A holy-minded man of good renown
There was, and poor, the *Parson* to a town,
Yet he was rich in holy thought and work.
He also was a learned man, a clerk,
Who truly knew Christ's gospel and would preach it
Devoutly to parishioners, and teach it.
Benign and wonderfully diligent,
And patient when adversity was sent
(For so he proved in much adversity)
He hated cursing to extort a fee,
Nay rather he preferred beyond a doubt
Giving to poor parishioners round about
Both from church offerings and his property;
He could in little find sufficiency.
Wide was his parish, with houses far asunder,
Yet he neglected not in rain or thunder,
In sickness or in grief, to pay a call
On the remotest, whether great or small,
Upon his feet, and in his hand a stave.
This noble example to his sheep he gave
That first he wrought, and afterwards he taught;
And it was from the Gospel he had caught
Those words, and he would add this figure too,

That if gold rust, what then will iron do?
For if a priest be foul in whom we trust
No wonder that a common man should rust;
And shame it is to see – let priests take stock –
A shitten shepherd and a snowy flock.
The true example that a priest should give
Is one of cleanness, how the sheep should live.
He did not set his benefice to hire
And leave his sheep encumbered in the mire
Or run to London to earn easy bread
By singing masses for the wealthy dead,
Or find some Brotherhood and get enrolled.
He stayed at home and watched over his fold
So that no wolf should make the sheep miscarry.
He was a shepherd and no mercenary.
Holy and virtuous he was, but then
Never contemptuous of sinful men,
Never disdainful, never too proud or fine,
But was discreet in teaching and benign.
His business was to show a fair behaviour
And draw men thus to Heaven and their Saviour,
Unless indeed a man were obstinate;
And such, whether of high or low estate,
He put to sharp rebuke, to say the least.
I think there never was a better priest.
He sought no pomp or glory in his dealings,
No scrupulosity had spiced his feelings.
Christ and His Twelve Apostles and their lore
He taught, but followed it himself before.

⊂Ｔ here was a *Plowman* with him there, his brother;
    Many a load of dung one time or other
    He must have carted through the morning dew.
He was an honest worker, good and true,
Living in peace and perfect charity,
And, as the gospel bade him, so did he,
Loving God best with all his heart and mind
And then his neighbour as himself, repined
At no misfortune, slacked for no content,
For steadily about his work he went
To thrash his corn, to dig or to manure
Or make a ditch; and he would help the poor

For love of Christ and never take a penny
If he could help it, and, as prompt as any,
He paid his tithes in full when they were due
On what he owned, and on his earnings too.
He wore a tabard smock and rode a mare.

⊂Ｔ here was a *Reeve*, also a *Miller*, there,
    A College *Manciple* from the Inns of Court,
    A papal *Pardoner* and, in close consort,
A Church-Court *Summoner*, riding at a trot,
And finally myself – that was the lot.

⊂Ｔ he *Miller* was a chap of sixteen stone,
    A great stout fellow big in brawn and bone.
    He did well out of them, for he could go
And win the ram at any wrestling show.
Broad, knotty and short-shouldered, he would boast
He could heave any door off hinge and post,
Or take a run and break it with his head.
His beard, like any sow or fox, was red
And broad as well, as though it were a spade;
And, at its very tip, his nose displayed
A wart on which there stood a tuft of hair
Red as the bristles in an old sow's ear.
His nostrils were as black as they were wide.
He had a sword and buckler at his side,
His mighty mouth was like a furnace door.

The brutish Miller is almost more of an animal than a human.

A wrangler and buffoon, he had a store
Of tavern stories, filthy in the main.
His was a master-hand at stealing grain.
He felt it with his thumb and thus he knew
Its quality and took three times his due –
A thumb of gold, by God, to gauge an oat!
He wore a hood of blue and a white coat.
He liked to play his bagpipes up and down
And that was how he brought us out of town.

⊂Ｔ he *Manciple* came from the Inner Temple;
    All caterers might follow his example
    In buying victuals; he was never rash
Whether he bought on credit or paid cash.
He used to watch the market most precisely
And got in first, and so he did quite nicely.

The lowly Ploughman has a simple dignity and integrity.

Now isn't it a marvel of God's grace
That an illiterate fellow can outpace
The wisdom of a heap of learned men?
His masters – he had more than thirty then –
All versed in the abstrusest legal knowledge,
Could have produced a dozen from their College
Fit to be stewards in land and rents and game
To any Peer in England you could name,
And show him how to live on what he had
Debt-free (unless of course the Peer were mad)
Or be as frugal as he might desire,
And make them fit to help about the Shire
In any legal case there was to try;
And yet this Manciple could wipe their eye.

 he *Reeve* was old and choleric and thin;
   His beard was shaven closely to the skin,
   His shorn hair came abruptly to a stop
Above his ears, and he was docked on top
Just like a priest in front; his legs were lean,
Like sticks they were, no calf was to be seen.
He kept his bins and garners very trim;
No auditor could gain a point on him.
And he could judge by watching drought and rain
The yield he might expect from seed and grain.
His master's sheep, his animals and hens,
Pigs, horses, dairies, stores and cattle-pens
Were wholly trusted to his government.
He had been under contract to present
The accounts, right from his master's earliest years.
No one had ever caught him in arrears.
No bailiff, serf or herdsman dared to kick,
He knew their dodges, knew their every trick;
Feared like the plague he was, by those beneath.

A Reeve superintended the estates and tenants of a landowner.

He had a lovely dwelling on a heath,
Shadowed in green by trees above the sward.
A better hand at bargains than his lord,
He had grown rich and had a store of treasure
Well tucked away, yet out it came to pleasure
His lord with subtle loans or gifts of goods,

To earn his thanks and even coats and hoods.
When young he'd learnt a useful trade and still
He was a carpenter of first-rate skill.
The stallion-cob he rode at a slow trot
Was dapple-grey and bore the name of Scot.
He wore an overcoat of bluish shade
And rather long; he had a rusty blade
Slung at his side. He came, as I heard tell,
From Norfolk, near a place called Baldeswell.
His coat was tucked under his belt and splayed.
He rode the hindmost of our cavalcade.

 here was a *Summoner* with us at that Inn,
   His face on fire, like a cherubin,
   For he had carbuncles. His eyes were narrow,
He was as hot and lecherous as a sparrow.
Black scabby brows he had, and a thin beard.
Children were afraid when he appeared.
No quicksilver, lead ointment, tartar creams,
No brimstone, no boracic, so it seems,
Could make a salve that had the power to bite,
Clean up or cure his whelks of knobby white
Or purge the pimples sitting on his cheeks.
Garlic he loved, and onions too, and leeks,
And drinking strong red wine till all was hazy.
Then he would shout and jabber as if crazy,
And wouldn't speak a word except in Latin
When he was drunk, such tags as he was pat in;
He only had a few, say two or three,
That he had mugged up out of some decree;
No wonder, for he heard them every day.
And, as you know, a man can teach a jay
To call out 'Walter' better than the Pope.
But had you tried to test his wits and grope
For more, you'd have found nothing in the bag.
Then *'Questio quid juris'* was his tag.
He was a noble varlet and a kind one,
You'd meet none better if you went to find one.
Why, he'd allow – just for a quart of wine -
Any good lad to keep a concubine
A twelvemonth and dispense him altogether!
And he had finches of his own to feather:
And if he found some rascal with a maid
He would instruct him not to be afraid
In such a case of the Archdeacon's curse
(Unless the rascal's soul were in his purse)
For in his purse the punishment should be.
'Purse is the good Archdeacon's Hell,' said he.
But well I know he lied in what he said;
A curse should put a guilty man in dread,
For curses kill, as shriving brings, salvation.
We should beware of excommunication.
Thus, as he pleased, the man could bring duress
On any young fellow in the diocese.
He knew their secrets, they did what he said.
He wore a garland set upon his head
Large as the holly-bush upon a stake
Outside an ale-house, and he had a cake,
A round one, which it was his joke to wield

As if it were intended for a shield.

He and a gentle *Pardoner* rode together,
A bird from Charing Cross of the same feather,
Just back from visiting the Court of Rome.
He loudly sang *'Come hither, love, come home!'*
The Summoner sang deep seconds to this song,
No trumpet ever sounded half so strong.

The Pardoner earns his living by selling holy relics and indulgences.

This Pardoner had hair as yellow as wax,
Hanging down smoothly like a hank of flax.
In driblets fell his locks behind his head
Down to his shoulders which they overspread;
Thinly they fell, like rat-tails, one by one.
He wore no hood upon his head, for fun;
The hood inside his wallet had been stowed,
He aimed at riding in the latest mode;
But for a little cap his head was bare
And he had bulging eye-balls, like a hare.
He'd sewed a holy relic on his cap;
His wallet lay before him on his lap,
Brimful of pardons come from Rome, all hot.
He had the same small voice a goat has got.
His chin no beard had harboured, nor would harbour,
Smoother than ever chin was left by barber.
I judge he was a gelding, or a mare.
As to his trade, from Berwick down to Ware
There was no pardoner of equal grace,
For in his trunk he had a pillow-case
Which he asserted was Our Lady's veil.
He said he had a gobbet of the sail
Saint Peter had the time when he made bold
To walk the waves, till Jesu Christ took hold.
He had a cross of metal set with stones
And, in a glass, a rubble of pigs' bones.
And with these relics, any time he found
Some poor up-country parson to astound,
In one short day, in money down, he drew
More than the parson in a month or two,
And by his flatteries and prevarication
Made monkeys of the priest and congregation.

But still to do him justice first and last
In church he was a noble ecclesiast.
How well he read a lesson or told a story!
But best of all he sang an Offertory,
For well he knew that when that song was sung
He'd have to preach and tune his honey-tongue
And (well he could) win silver from the crowd.
That's why he sang so merrily and loud.

Now I have told you shortly, in a clause,
The rank, the array, the number and the cause
Of our assembly in this company
In Southwark, at that high-class hostelry
Known as *The Tabard*, close beside *The Bell*.
And now the time has come for me to tell
How we behaved that evening; I'll begin
After we had alighted at the Inn,
Then I'll report our journey, stage by stage,
All the remainder of our pilgrimage.
But first I beg of you, in courtesy,
Not to condemn me as unmannerly
If I speak plainly and with no concealings
And give account of all their words and dealings,
Using their very phrases as they fell.
For certainly, as you all know so well,
He who repeats a tale after a man
Is bound to say, as nearly as he can,
Each single word, if he remembers it,
However rudely spoken or unfit,
Or else the tale he tells will be untrue,
The things pretended and the phrases new.
He may not flinch although it were his brother,
He may as well say one word as another.
And Christ Himself spoke broad in Holy Writ,
Yet there is no scurrility in it,
And Plato says, for those with power to read,
'The word should be as cousin to the deed.'
Further I beg you to forgive it me
If I neglect the order and degree
And what is due to rank in what I've planned.
I'm short of wit as you will understand.

Our *Host* gave us great welcome; everyone
Was given a place and supper was begun.
He served the finest victuals you could think,
The wine was strong and we were glad to drink.
A very striking man our Host withal,
And fit to be a marshal in a hall.
His eyes were bright, his girth a little wide;
There is no finer burgess in Cheapside.
Bold in his speech, yet wise and full of tact,
There was no manly attribute he lacked,
What's more he was a merry-hearted man.
After our meal he jokingly began
To talk of sport, and, among other things
After we'd settled up our reckonings,
He said as follows: 'Truly, gentlemen,
You're very welcome and I can't think when
– Upon my word I'm telling you no lie –
I've seen a gathering here that looked so spry,

The pilgrims enjoy a boar's head, a fowl and a pitcher of wine.

No, not this year, as in this tavern now.
I'd think you up some fun if I knew how.
And, as it happens, a thought has just occurred
To please you, costing nothing, on my word.
You're off to Canterbury – well, God speed!
Blessed St Thomas answer to your need!
And I don't doubt, before the journey's done
You mean to while the time in tales and fun.
Indeed, there's little pleasure for your bones
Riding along and all as dumb as stones.
So let me then propose for your enjoyment,
Just as I said, a suitable employment.
And if my notion suits and you agree
And promise to submit yourselves to me
Playing your parts exactly as I say
Tomorrow as you ride along the way,
Then by my father's soul (and he is dead)
If you don't like it you can have my head!
Hold up your hands, and not another word.'

'W ell, our opinion was not long deferred,
It seemed not worth a serious debate;
We all agreed to it at any rate
And bade him issue what commands he would.
'My lords,' he said, 'now listen for your good,
And please don't treat my notion with disdain.
This is the point. I'll make it short and plain.
Each one of you shall help to make things slip
By telling two stories on the outward trip
To Canterbury, that's what I intend,
And, on the homeward way to journey's end
Another two, tales from the days of old;
And then the man whose story is best told,
That is to say who gives the fullest measure
Of good morality and general pleasure,
He shall be given a supper, paid by all,
Here in this tavern, in this very hall,
When we come back again from Canterbury.

And in the hope to keep you bright and merry
I'll go along with you myself and ride
All at my own expense and serve as guide.
I'll be the judge, and those who won't obey
Shall pay for what we spend upon the way.
Now if you all agree to what you've heard
Tell me at once without another word,
And I will make arrangements early for it.'

'O f course we all agreed, in fact we swore it
Delightedly, and made entreaty too
That he should act as he proposed to do,
Become our Governor in short, and be
Judge of our tales and general referee,
And set the supper at a certain price.
We promised to be ruled by his advice
Come high, come low; unanimously thus
We set him up in judgement over us.
More wine was fetched, the business being done;
We drank it off and up went everyone
To bed without a moment of delay.

'E arly next morning at the spring of day
Up rose our Host and roused us like a cock,
Gathering us together in a flock,
And off we rode at slightly faster pace
Than walking to St Thomas' watering-place;
And there our Host drew up, began to ease
His horse, and said, 'Now, listen if you please,
My lords! Remember what you promised me.
If evensong and mattins will agree
Let's see who shall be first to tell a tale.
And as I hope to drink good wine and ale
I'll be your judge. The rebel who disobeys,
However much the journey costs, he pays.
Now draw for cut and then we can depart;
The man who draws the shortest cut shall start.
My Lord the Knight,' he said, 'step up to me
And draw your cut, for that is my decree.
And come you near, my Lady Prioress,
And you, Sir Cleric, drop your shamefastness,
No studying now! A hand from every man!'
Immediately the draw for lots began
And to tell shortly how the matter went,
Whether by chance or fate or accident,
The truth is this, the cut fell to the Knight,
Which everybody greeted with delight.
And tell his tale he must, as reason was
Because of our agreement and because
He too had sworn. What more is there to say?
For when this good man saw how matters lay,
Being by wisdom and obedience driven
To keep a promise he had freely given,
He said, 'Since it's for me to start the game,
Why, welcome be the cut in God's good name!
Now let us ride, and listen to what I say.'
And at the word we started on our way
And in a cheerful style he then began
At once to tell his tale, and thus it ran.

A French miniature of Emily being watched by the two captive knights. Chaucer began his writing career as a court poet and 'The Knight's Tale' is a thoroughly aristocratic poem, dealing with the two main preoccupations of medieval courtiers – love and war.

THE KNIGHT'S TALE

PART I

STORIES of old have made it known to us
That there was once a Duke called Theseus,
Ruler of Athens, Lord and Governor,
And in his time so great a conqueror
There was none mightier beneath the sun.
And many a rich country he had won,
What with his wisdom and his troops of horse.
He had subdued the Amazons by force
And all their realm, once known as Scythia,
But then called Femeny. Hippolyta,
Their queen, he took to wife, and, says the story,
He brought her home in solemn pomp and glory,
Also her younger sister, Emily.
And thus victorious and with minstrelsy
I leave this noble Duke for Athens bound
With all his host of men-at-arms around.

And were it not too long to tell again
I would have fully pictured the campaign
In which his men-at-arms and he had won
Those territories from the Amazon
And the great battle that was given then
Between those women and the Athenian men,
Or told you how Hippolyta had been
Besieged and taken, fair courageous queen,
And what a feast there was when they were married,
And after of the tempest that had harried
Their home-coming. I pass these over now
Having, God knows, a larger field to plough.
Weak are my oxen for such mighty stuff;
What I have yet to tell is long enough.
I won't delay the others of our rout,
Let every fellow tell his tale about
And see who wins the supper at the Inn.
Where I left off, let me again begin.

This Duke I mentioned, ere alighting down
And on the very outskirts of the town
In all felicity and height of pride
Became aware, casting an eye aside,
That kneeling on the highway, two by two,
A company of ladies were in view

All clothed in black, each pair in proper station
Behind the other. And such lamentation
And cries they uttered, it was past conceiving
The world had ever heard such noise of grieving,
Nor did they hold their misery in check
Till they grasped bridle at his horse's neck.

The Greek women in mourning, from the Lydgate Manuscript. John Lydgate was a monk who greatly admired Chaucer and who later, 'by a merry conceit', wrote his own contribution to 'The Canterbury Tales'.

Who may you be that, at my coming, so
Perturb my festival with cries of woe?'
Said Theseus. 'Do you grudge the celebration
Of these my honours with your lamentation?
Who can have injured you or who offended?
And tell me if the matter may be mended
And why it is that you are clothed in black?'

The eldest of these ladies answered back,
Fainting a little in such deadly fashion
That but to see and hear her stirred compassion,
And said, 'O Sir, whom Fortune has made glorious

In conquest and is sending home victorious,
We do not grudge your glory in our grief
But rather beg your mercy and relief.
Have pity on our sorrowful distress!
Some drop of pity, in your nobleness,
On us unhappy women let there fall!
For sure there is not one among us all
That was not once a duchess or a queen,
Though wretches now, as may be truly seen,
Thanks be to Fortune and her treacherous wheel
That suffers no estate on earth to feel
Secure, and, waiting on your presence, we,
Here at the shrine of Goddess Clemency,
Have watched a fortnight for this very hour.
Help us, my Lord, it lies within your power.
I, wretched Queen, that weep aloud my woe,
Was wife to King Capaneus long ago
That died at Thebes, accursed be the day!
And we in our disconsolate array
That make this sorrowful appeal to pity
Lost each her husband in that fatal city
During the siege, for so it came to pass.
Now old King Creon – O alas, alas! –
The Lord of Thebes, grown cruel in his age
And filled with foul iniquity and rage,
For tyranny and spite as I have said
Does outrage on the bodies of our dead,

'Creon forbids the burial of the dead.' Like a medieval painter,
Chaucer portrays the appearance and behaviour of his classical
characters in medieval terms. His account of Theseus's campaign
against Creon follows the medieval code of war precisely.

On all our husbands, for when they were slain
Their bodies were dragged out on to the plain
Into a heap, and there, as we have learnt,

They neither may have burial nor be burnt,
But he makes dogs devour them, in scorn.'
At that they all at once began to mourn,
And every woman fell upon her face
And cried, 'Have pity, Lord, on our disgrace
And let our sorrow sink into your heart.'
The Duke, who felt a pang of pity start
At what they spoke, dismounted from his steed;
He felt his heart about to break indeed,
Seeing how piteous and disconsolate
They were, that once had been of high estate!
He raised them in his arms and sought to fill
Their hearts with comfort and with kind good will,
And swore on oath that as he was true knight,
So far as it should lie within his might,
He would take vengeance on this tyrant King,
This Creon, till the land of Greece should ring
With how he had encountered him and served
The monster with the death he had deserved.
Instantly then and with no more delay,
He turned and with his banners in display
Made off for Thebes with all his host beside,
For not a step to Athens would he ride,
Nor take his ease so much as half a day,
But marched into the night upon his way.
But yet he sent Hippolyta the Queen
And Emily her sister, the serene,
On into Athens, where they were to dwell,
And off he rode; there is no more to tell.
The figure of red Mars with spear and targe
So shone upon his banners white and large,
That all the meadows glittered up and down,
And close by them his pennon of renown
Shone rich with gold, emblazoned with that feat,
His slaying of the Minotaur in Crete.
Thus rode this Duke, thus rode this conqueror
And led his flower of chivalry to war,
Until he came to Thebes, there to alight
In splendour on a chosen field to fight.
And, to speak briefly of so great a thing,
He conquered Creon there, the Theban king,
And slew him manfully, as became a knight,
In open battle, put his troops to flight,
And by assault captured the city after
And rent it, roof and wall and spar and rafter;
And to the ladies he restored again
The bones belonging to their husbands slain,
To do, as custom was, their obsequies.
But it were all too long to speak of these,
Or of the clamorous complaint and yearning
These ladies uttered at the place of burning
The bodies, or of all the courtesy
That Theseus, noble in his victory,
Showed to the ladies when they went their way;
I would be brief in what I have to say.
Now when Duke Theseus worthily had done
Justice on Creon and when Thebes was won,
That night, camped in the field, he took his rest,

Having disposed the land as he thought best.
Crawling for ransack among heaps of slain
And stripping their accoutrements for gain,
The pillagers went busily about
After the battle on the field of rout.
And so befell among the heaps they found,
Thrust through with bloody wounds upon the ground,
Two pale young knights there, lying side by side,
Wearing the self-same arms in blazoned pride.
Of these Arcita was the name of one,
That of the other knight was Palamon;
And they were neither fully quick nor dead.
By coat of arms and crest upon the head
The heralds knew, for all the filth and mud,
That they were Princes of the Royal Blood;
Two sisters of the House of Thebes had borne them.
Out of the heap these pillagers have torn them
And gently carried them to Theseus' tent.
And he decreed they should at once be sent
To Athens, and gave order they be kept
Perpetual prisoners – he would accept
No ransom for them. This was done, and then
The noble Duke turned homeward with his men
Crowned with the laurel of his victory,
And there in honour and felicity
He lived his life; what more is there to say?
And in a tower, in grief and anguish lay
Arcite and Palamon, beyond all doubt
For ever, for no gold could buy them out.
Year after year went by, day after day,
Until one morning in the month of May
Young Emily, that fairer was of mien
Than is the lily on its stalk of green,
And fresher in her colouring that strove
With early roses in a May-time grove
– I know not which was fairer of the two –
Ere it was day, as she was wont to do,
Rose and arrayed her beauty as was right,
For May will have no sluggardry at night,
Season that pricks in every gentle heart,
Awaking it from sleep, and bids it start,
Saying, 'Arise! Do thine observance due!'
And this made Emily recall anew
The honour due to May and she arose,
Her beauties freshly clad. To speak of those,
Her yellow hair was braided in a tress
Behind her back, a yard in length, I guess,
And in the garden at the sun's uprising,
Hither and thither at her own devising,
She wandered gathering flowers, white and red,
To make a subtle garland for her head,
And like an angel sang a heavenly song.
The great, grim tower-keep, so thick and strong,
Principal dungeon at the castle's core
Where the two knights, of whom I spoke before
And shall again, were shut, if you recall,
Was close-adjoining to the garden wall
Where Emily chose her pleasures and adornings.

The month of May from the Bedford Hours. A garden in May was the conventional setting for love and 'The Knight's Tale' seems to unfold in perpetual May. There is no sign that anyone is less youthful by the end than when the knights first see Emily 'in a May-time grove'.

Bright was the sun this loveliest of mornings
And the sad prisoner Palamon had risen,
With licence from the jailer of the prison,
As was his wont, and roamed a chamber high
Above the city, whence he could descry
The noble buildings and the branching green
Where Emily the radiant and serene
Went pausing in her walk and roaming on.
This sorrowful prisoner, this Palamon,
Was pacing round his chamber to and fro
Lamenting to himself in all his woe.
'Alas,' he said, 'that ever I was born!'
And so it happened on this May day morn,
Through a deep window set with many bars
Of mighty iron squared with massive spars,
He chanced on Emily to cast his eye
And, as he did, he blenched and gave a cry
As though he had been stabbed, and to the heart.
And, at the cry, Arcita gave a start
And said, 'My cousin Palamon, what ails you?
How deadly pale you look! Your colour fails you!
Why did you cry? Who can have given offence?
For God's love, take things patiently, have sense,
Think! We are prisoners and shall always be.
Fortune has given us this adversity,
Some wicked planetary dispensation,
Some Saturn's trick or evil constellation
Has given us this, and Heaven, though we had sworn
The contrary, so stood when we were born.
We must endure it, that's the long and short.'
And Palamon in answer made retort,
'Cousin, believe me, your opinion springs
From ignorance and vain imaginings.
Imprisonment was not what made me cry.
I have been hurt this moment through the eye,

Into my heart. It will be death to me.
The fairness of the lady that I see
Roaming the garden yonder to and fro
Is all the cause, and I cried out my woe.
Woman or Goddess, which? I cannot say.
I guess she may be Venus – well she may!'
He fell upon his knees before the sill
And prayed: 'Oh Venus, if it be thy will
To be transfigured in this garden thus
Before two wretched prisoners like us,
O help us to escape, O make us free!
Yet, if my fate already is shaped for me
By some eternal word, and I must pine
And die in prison, have pity on our line
And kindred, humbled under tyranny!'

'I have been hurt this moment through the eye, Into my heart.' In this Flemish illumination the God of Love takes aim at a lover. The medieval Cupid was a tyrant with terrifying power.

Now, as he spoke, Arcita chanced to see
This lady as she roamed there to and fro,
And, at the sight, her beauty hurt him so
That if his cousin had felt the wound before,
Arcite was hurt as much as he, or more,
And with a deep and piteous sigh he said:
'The freshness of her beauty strikes me dead,
Hers that I see, roaming in yonder place!
Unless I gain the mercy of her grace,
Unless at least I see her day by day,
I am but dead. There is no more to say.'
On hearing this young Palamon looked grim
And in contempt and anger answered him,
'Do you speak this in earnest or in jest?'
'No, in good earnest,' said Arcite, 'the best!

So help me God, I mean no jesting now.'
Then Palamon began to knit his brow:
'It's no great honour, then,' he said, 'to you
To prove so false, to be a traitor too
To me, that am your cousin and your brother,
Both deeply sworn and bound to one another,
Though we should die in torture for it, never
To loose the bond that only death can sever,
And when in love neither to hinder other,
Nor in what else soever, dearest brother,
But truly further me in all I do
As faithfully as I shall further you.
This was our oath and nothing can untie it,
And well I know you dare not now deny it.
I trust you with my secrets, make no doubt,
Yet you would treacherously go about
To love my lady, whom I love and serve
And ever shall, till death cut my heart's nerve.
No, false Arcite! That you shall never do!
I loved her first and told my grief to you
As to the brother and the friend that swore
To further me, as I have said before,
So you are bound in honour as a knight
To help me, should it lie within your might;
Else you are false, I say, your honour vain!'
Arcita proudly answered back again:
'You shall be judged as false,' he said, 'not me;
And false you are, I tell you, utterly!
I loved her as a woman before you.
What can you say? Just now you hardly knew
If she were girl or goddess from above!
Yours is a mystical, a holy love,
And mine is love as to a human being,
And so I told you at the moment, seeing
You were my cousin and sworn friend. At worst
What do I care? Suppose you loved her first,
Haven't you heard the old proverbial saw
"Who ever bound a lover by a law"?
Love is law unto itself. My hat!
What earthly man can have more law than that?
All man-made law, all positive injunction
Is broken every day without compunction
For love. A man must love, for all his wit;
There's no escape though he should die for it,
Be she a maid, a widow or a wife.
Yet you are little likely, all your life,
To stand in grace with her; no more shall I.
You know yourself, too well, that here we lie
Condemned to prison both of us, no doubt
Perpetually. No ransom buys us out.
We're like two dogs in battle on their own;
They fought all day but neither got the bone,
There came a kite above them, nothing loth,
And while they fought he took it from them both.
And so it is in politics, dear brother,
Each for himself alone, there is no other.
Love if you want to; I shall love her too,
And that is all there is to say or do.

We're prisoners and must endure it, man,
And each of us must take what chance he can.'
Great was the strife for many a long spell
Between them had I but the time to tell,
But to the point. It happened that one day,
To tell it you as briefly as I may,
A certain famous Duke, Perotheus,
Friend and companion of Duke Theseus
Since they were little children, came to spend
A holiday in Athens with his friend,
Visiting him for pleasure as of yore,
For there was no one living he loved more.
His feelings were as tenderly returned;
Indeed they were so fond, as I have learned,
That when one died (so ancient authors tell)
The other went to seek him down in Hell;
But that's a tale I have no time to treat.
Now this Perotheus knew and loved Arcite
In Theban days of old for many years,
And so, at his entreaty, it appears,
Arcita was awarded his release
Without a ransom; he could go in peace
And was left free to wander where he would
On one condition, be it understood,
And the condition, to speak plain, went thus,
Agreed between Arcite and Theseus,
That if Arcite were ever to be found
Even for an hour, in any land or ground
Or country of Duke Theseus, day or night,
And he were caught, it would to both seem right
That he immediately should lose his head,
No other course or remedy instead.
Off went Arcite upon the homeward trek.
Let him beware! For he has pawned his neck.
What misery it cost him to depart!
He felt the stroke of death upon his heart,
He wept, he wailed. How piteously he cried
And secretly he thought of suicide.
He said, 'Alas the day that gave me birth!
Worse than my prison is the endless earth,
Now I am doomed eternally to dwell
Not in Purgatory, but in Hell.
Alas that ever I knew Perotheus!
For else I had remained with Theseus.
Fettered in prison and without relief
I still had been in bliss and not in grief.
Only to see her whom I love and serve,
Though it were never granted to deserve
Her favour, would have been enough for me.
O my dear cousin Palamon,' said he,
'Yours is the victory in this adventure.
How blissfully you serve your long indenture
In prison – prison? No, in Paradise!
How happily has Fortune cast her dice
For you! You have her presence, I the loss.
For it is possible, since your paths may cross
And you're a knight, a worthy one, and able,
That by some chance – for Fortune is unstable –

'The Lover faces Fortune' from an illuminated manuscript of the influential French poem, the 'Roman de la Rose', which set out the art of love for its aristocratic readers and which Chaucer translated.

You may attain to your desire at last.
But I, that am an exile and outcast,
Barren of grace and in such deep despair
That neither earth nor water, fire nor air,
Nor any creature that is made of these
Can ever bring me help, or do me ease,
I must despair and die in my distress.
Farewell my life, my joy, my happiness!
Alas, why is it people so dispraise
God's providence or Fortune and her ways,
That oft and variously in their scheme
Includes far better things than they could dream?
One man desires to have abundant wealth,
Which brings about his murder or ill-health;
Another, freed from prison as he'd willed,
Comes home, his servants catch him, and he's killed.
Infinite are the harms that come this way;
We little know the things for which we pray.
Our ways are drunkard ways – drunk as a mouse;
A drunkard knows quite well he has a house,
But how to get there puts him in a dither,
And for a drunk the way is slip and slither.
Such is our world indeed, and such are we.
How eagerly we seek felicity,
Yet are so often wrong in what we try!
Yes, we can all say that, and so can I,
In whom the foolish notion had arisen
That if I only could escape from prison
I should be well, in pure beatitude,
Whereas I am an exile from my good,
For since I may not see you, Emily,
I am but dead and there's no remedy.'
Now, on the other hand, poor Palamon,
When it was told him that Arcite had gone,
Fell in such grief, the tower where he was kept

Resounded to his yowling as he wept.
The very fetters on his mighty shins
Shine with his bitter tears as he begins,
'Alas, Arcite, dear cousin! In our dispute
And rivalry God knows you have the fruit.
I see you now in Thebes, our native city,
As free as air, with never a thought of pity
For me! You, an astute, determined man
Can soon assemble all our folk and clan
For war on Athens, make a sharp advance,
And by some treaty or perhaps by chance
She may become your lady and your wife
For whom, needs must, I here shall lose my life.
For, in the way of possibility,
As you're a prisoner no more, but free,
A Prince, you have the advantage to engage
In your affair. I perish in a cage,
For I must weep and suffer while I live
In all the anguish that a cell can give
And all the torment of my love, O care
That doubles all my suffering and despair.'

With that he felt the fire of jealousy start,
Flame in his breast and catch him by the heart
So madly that he seemed to fade and fail,
Cold as dead ashes, or as box-wood pale.
He cried, 'O cruel Gods, whose government
Binds all the world to your eternal bent,
And writes upon an adamantine table
All that your conclave has decreed as stable,
What more is man to you than to behold
A flock of sheep that cower in the fold?
For men are slain as much as other cattle,
Arrested, thrust in prison, killed in battle,
In sickness often and mischance, and fall,
Alas, too often, for no guilt at all.
Where is right rule in your foreknowledge, when
Such torments fall on innocent, helpless men?
Yet there is more, for added to my load,
I am to pay the duties that are owed
To God, for Him I am to curb my will
In all the lusts that cattle may fulfil.
For when a beast is dead, he feels no pain,
But after death a man must weep again
That living has endured uncounted woe;
I have no doubt that it may well be so.
I leave the answer for divines to tell,
But that there's pain on earth I know too well.

I have seen many a serpent, many a thief
Bring down the innocent of heart to grief,
Yet be at large and take what turn they will.
But I lie languishing in prison still.
Juno and Saturn in their jealous rage
Have almost quelled our Theban lineage;

Left: The inscription on the scroll of this Flemish parade shield reads 'Vous où la mort'. According to the rules of courtly love, the knight has to beg his lady for mercy. His love is like a mortal wound and if, like Arcite, he is banished, he will perish.

Thebes stands in waste, her walls are broken wide.
And Venus slays me on the other side
With jealous fears of what Arcite is doing.'
Now I will turn a little from pursuing
Palamon's thoughts, and leave him in his cell,
For I have something of Arcite to tell.
The summer passes, and long winter nights
Double the miseries and appetites
Of lover in jail and lover free as air.
I cannot tell you which had most to bear.
To put it shortly, Palamon the pale
Lies there condemned to a perpetual jail,

Chained up in fetters till his dying breath;
Arcita is exiled on pain of death
For ever from the long-desired shore
Where lives the lady he will see no more.
You lovers, here's a question I would offer,
Arcite or Palamon, which had most to suffer?
The one can see his lady day by day,
But he must dwell in prison, locked away.
The other's free, the world lies all before,
But never shall he see his lady more.
Judge as you please between them, you that can,
For I'll tell on my tale as I began.

PART II

NOW when Arcita got to Thebes again
Daylong he languished, crying out in pain
'Alas!' for never could he hope to see
His lady more. To sum his misery,
There never was a man so woe-begone,
Nor is, nor shall be while the world goes on.
Meat, drink and sleep – he lay of all bereft,
Thin as a shaft, as dry, with nothing left.
His eyes were hollow, grisly to behold,
Fallow his face, like ashes pale and cold,
And he went solitary and alone,
Wailing away the night and making moan;

*The God of Love strikes a mortal wound in the lover's heart in
another illumination from the 'Roman de la Rose'. Both Palamon
and Arcite feel their love as a sudden sickness or wound.*

And if the sound of music touched his ears
He wept, unable to refrain his tears.
So feeble were his spirits and so low,
And changed so much, one could not even know
Him by his voice; one heard and was in doubt.

And so for all the world he went about
Not merely like a lover on the rack
Of Eros, but more like a maniac
In melancholy madness, under strain
Of fantasy – those cells that front the brain.
Briefly, his love had turned him upside-down
In looks and disposition, toe to crown,
This poor distracted lover, Prince Arcite.
But I shall take all day if I repeat
All that he suffered for the first two years,
In cruel torment and in painful tears
At Thebes, in his home-country, as I said.
Now as he lay one night asleep in bed
The winged god Mercury, he thought, came near
And stood before him, bidding him have good cheer.
His sleep-imbuing wand he held in air,
He wore a hat upon his golden hair,
Arrayed (Arcita noticed) in the guise
He wore when closing up the hundred eyes
Of Argus, and he said, 'You are to go
To Athens. There shall be an end to woe.'
He spoke; Arcita started and woke up.
'Truly, however bitter be my cup,
To Athens I will go at once!' he said,
'Nor will I change my purpose for the dread
Of death, for I will see her. I can die
Gladly enough, if she be standing by.'
He rose and snatched a mirror from its place
And saw what change had come upon his face,
The colour gone, the features redesigned,
And instantly it came into his mind
That being so disfigured and so wan
From the long sickness he had undergone,
He might, if he assumed a humble tone,
Live out his life in Athens unbeknown
And see his lady almost every day.
So, on the spot, he doffed his lord's array,
And dressed as a poor labourer seeking hire.

Then all alone, except for a young squire,
Who knew the secret of his misery
And was disguised as wretchedly as he,
He went to Athens by the shortest way
And came to Court. And on the following day
Arcita proffered at the gate for hire
To do what drudgery they might require.
And briefly (there is little to explain)
He fell in service with a chamberlain
Who had his dwelling there with Emily.
The man was cunning and was quick to see
What work the servants did and which were good.
Arcite could carry water or hew wood,
For he was young and powerfully grown,
A tall young fellow too, and big of bone,
Fit to do any work that was ordained.

Thus, for a year or two, Arcite remained
With Emily the bright, her page-of-state,
And gave it out his name was Philostrate.
And half so well beloved a man as he
There never was at Court, of his degree.
He was so much a gentleman by breed
He grew quite famous through the Court indeed,
And it would be a charitable notion
(They said) if Theseus offered him promotion
And put him to a service less despised
In which his virtues might be exercised.
Thus in a little while his fame had sprung
Both for good deeds and for a courteous tongue,
And Theseus took him and advanced him higher,
Made him his personal and chamber-squire,
And gave him money to maintain his station.
There came, moreover, men of his own nation
Secretly, year by year, and brought his dues.
He spent them cunningly, these revenues,
But honestly; none wondered at his wealth.
Three years went by in happiness and health;
He bore himself so well in peace and war
That there was no one Theseus valued more.
I leave him there in bliss, though bliss is brittle,
And turn to speak of Palamon a little.

In darkness horrible and prison tears
Poor Palamon has sat for seven years,
Pining away in sorrow and distress.
Who feels a two-fold grief and heaviness
But Palamon, whom love oppresses so
That he has lost his very wits for woe?
Added to which, he must lie prisoner there
Perpetually, not only for a year.

Who could make rhymes in English fit to vie
With martyrdom like that? Indeed, not I.
Let me pass lightly over it and say
It happened in the seventh year, in May,
The third of May (my ancient sources give
This detail in their fuller narrative),
Whether by accident or destiny,
For as events are shaped they have to be,
Soon after midnight, ere the sun had risen,

Helped by a friend, Palamon broke from prison
And fled the town as fast as he could go.
A drink had proved his jailer's overthrow,
A kind of honeyed claret he had fixed
With Theban opium and narcotics mixed.
The jailer slept all night; had he been shaken
He would have been impossible to waken.
So off runs Palamon as best he may.
The night was short and it was nearly day,
So it was necessary he should hide.
Into a grove that flanked the city's side
Palamon stalked with terror-stricken feet.
Here was, in his opinion, a retreat
In which he could conceal himself all day
And whence at nightfall he could make his way
On towards Thebes and rally at his back
A host of friends all eager to attack
Duke Theseus. He would either lose his life
Or conquer and win Emily to wife.
That was his whole intention, fair and plain.

I turn my story to Arcite again.
He little knew how close he was to care
Till Fortune brought him back into the snare.

The busy lark, the messenger of day,
Sings salutation to the morning grey,
And fiery Phoebus rising up so bright
Sets all the Orient laughing with the light,
And with his streams he dries the dewy sheaves
And silver droplets hanging on the leaves.
And now Arcita, at the royal court,
Principal squire to Theseus, seeking sport
Has risen from bed and greets the merry day.
Thinking to do observances to May,
And musing on the point of his desires
He rode a courser full of flickering fires
Into the fields for pleasure and in play
A mile or two from where the palace lay,
And to the very grove you heard me mention
He chanced to hold his course, with the intention
To make himself a garland. There he weaves
A hawthorn-spray and honeysuckle leaves
And sings aloud against the sunny sheen,
'O Month of May, with all thy flowers and green,
Welcome be thou, O fairest, freshest May,
Give me thy green, in hope of happy day!'

Quickly dismounting from his horse, he started
To thrust his way into the grove, light-hearted,
And roamed along the pathway, on and on,
Until he came by chance where Palamon
Crouched in a bush, scarce daring to draw breath
Lest he be seen, in deadly fear of death.
He little knew it was Arcite he heard,
It would have seemed incredible, absurd;
Yet there's a saying, known these many years:
Fields have their eyes, and forests have their ears.
It's well to be upon one's guard, I mean,
Since all day long we meet the unforeseen.
And little knew Arcite that there, beside him,

Richard Pynson, like William Caxton, was one of the first English printers and he too produced an edition of 'The Canterbury Tales' with woodcut illustrations, as well as printing editions of many of Chaucer's other works. This is an illustration to his 1526 edition.

Palamon lay, with but a bush to hide him,
So close to him, and hearing all he said
But keeping still and silent as the dead.
Now when at last Arcite had roamed his fill
And sung his roundel with a lusty will
He felt a change of humour, for the nonce,
And fell into a study all at once,
As do these lovers in their quaint desires,
Now on the spray, now down among the briars,
Now up, now down, like buckets in a well,
Just as upon a Friday, truth to tell,
It shines one moment, and the next rains fast;
For thus can whimsical Venus overcast
The spirits of her folk, just as her day,
Friday is changeable, and so too are they,
Seldom is Friday like the rest of the week.
And, having sung, Arcite began to speak,
And sat him down, unutterably forlorn.
'Alas!' he said, 'the day that I was born!
How long, O Juno, in thy cruelty,
Wilt thou make war and bring to misery
The city of Thebes, and those that played the lion,
The royal blood of Cadmus and Amphion!
Cadmus, the first of men to win renown

By building Thebes, or first in laying down
Her strong foundations, first to be crowned her king;
And I that share his lineage, I that spring
By right descent out of the royal stock,
Have fallen captive and am made a mock,
Slave to my mortal enemy, no higher
Than a contemptible, a menial squire!
Yet Juno does me even greater shame;
I dare no more acknowledge my own name.
Time was Arcita was my name by right;
Now I'm called Philostrate, not worth a mite!
Alas, fell Mars! Ah, Juno, stern of face,
You have undone our lineage and our race
Save for myself and Palamon, who dwells
In martyrdom, poor wretch, in Theseus' cells.
On top of this, to slay me utterly,
The fiery dart of love so burningly
Thrusts through my faithful heart with deadly hurt!
My death was shaped for me before my shirt.
You kill me with your eyes, my Emily,
You are the cause that brings my death on me!
All the remainder of my cares and needs
I'd rate no higher than a mound of weeds
Could I but please or earn a grateful glance!'
And on the word he fell into a trance
A long, long time, then woke and moved apart.

Palamon felt a cleaving in his heart
As of a cold sword suddenly gliding through.
He quaked with anger; hiding would not do
Now that he'd listened to Arcita's tale,
And with a madman's face, extinct and pale,
He started up out of his bushy thicket
And cried, 'Arcita! Traitor! False and wicked,
Now you are caught that love my lady so,
For whom I suffer all this pain and woe,
And of my blood – sworn friend – for so we swore
As I have told you many times before,
And you have cheated Theseus with this game,
False as you are, of a pretended name!
Let it be death for you or death for me.
You shall not love my lady Emily.
I, no one else, will love her! Look and know
That I am Palamon your mortal foe.
And though I have no weapon in this place,
Having escaped from prison by God's grace,
I doubt it not you shall be slain by me
Or else yield up the love of Emily.
You shan't escape me, therefore choose your part!'
Arcite, however, full of scorn at heart,
Knowing his face and hearing what he said,
Fierce as a lion drew his sword instead
And answered him, 'By God that sits above,
Were you not sick, and lunatic for love,
And weaponless moreover in this place,
You never should so much as take a pace
Beyond this grove, but perish at my hand.
And I denounce all covenants that stand

37

Or are alleged, as between you and me.
Fool that you are, remember love is free
And I will love her! I defy your might.
Yet, as you are an honourable knight
Willing by battle to decide your claim,
Tomorrow, by the honour of my name
I will not fail you, nor will make it known
To anyone. To-morrow, here, alone
You'll find me as a knight, and on my oath
I shall bring arms and harness for us both;
And you shall have the right of choosing first,
Taking the best and leaving me the worst.
I'll bring you meat and drink, let that be said,
Enough for you, and clothes to make your bed.
As for my lady, should you chance to win
And kill me in this thicket we are in,
Then you can have your lady, as for me.'
And Palamon gave answer, 'I agree.'
And thus they parted at the coppice-edge
Until the morning. Each had given pledge.
O Cupid, Cupid, lost to charity!
O realm that brooks no fellow-king in thee!
Well is it said that neither love nor power
Admit a rival, even for an hour.
Arcite and Palamon had found that out.
So back to town Arcite turned about,
And the next morning, ere the day was light,
He filched two suits of armour by a sleight,
Fully sufficient for the work in hand,
The battle in the fields, that they had planned.
Alone as at his birth Arcita rode
And carried all the armour in a load.
There in the grove where time and place were set
This Palamon and this Arcite are met.
Then slowly changed the colour in each face
Just as when hunters in the realm of Thrace
That standing in the gap will poise a spear
And wait for bear or lion to appear,
Then hear him coming, breaking through the branches,
And hear the swish of leaves upon his haunches,
And think, 'Here comes my mortal enemy!
It's either death for him or death for me.
For either I must slay him at this gap
Or he slay me, if I should have mishap.'
Just so these knights changed colour when they met,
Knowing each other and the purpose set.
There was no salutation, no 'Good day',
But without word or prelude straight away
Each of them gave his help to arm the other
As friendly as a brother with his brother;
And after that with spears of sharpened strength
They fought each other at amazing length.
You would have thought, seeing Palamon engage,
He was a lion fighting-mad with rage,
Arcite a cruel tiger, as they beat
And smote each other, or as boars that meet
And froth as white as foam upon the flood.
They fought till they were ankle-deep in blood.

And in this rage I leave them fighting thus
And turn once more to speak of Theseus.
Now Destiny, that Minister-General
Who executes on earth and over all
What God, from everlasting, has foreseen,
Is of such strength, that though the world had been
Sure of the contrary, by Yea and Nay,
That thing will happen on a certain day,
Though never again within a thousand years.
And certainly our appetites and fears,
Whether in war or peace, in hate or love,
Are governed by a providence above.
Thus must explain why mighty Theseus found
A sudden wish to hunt with horse and hound
Especially the hart in early May.
About his bed there never dawned a day
But he was up and ready dressed to ride
With horn and hound and hunter at his side.
Hunting to him was such a keen delight
It was his ruling joy and appetite
To be a stag's destroyer, for the stars
Ruled he should serve Diana after Mars.

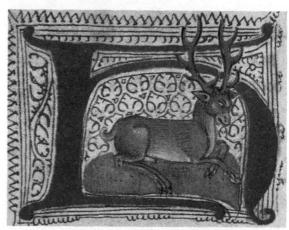

The hart was thought to be an especially noble quarry. Again Theseus is acting in a characteristically medieval manner.

Clear was the day, as I have told ere this,
And Theseus, bathed in happiness and bliss,
With fair Hippolyta, his lovely Queen,
And Emily, who was arrayed in green,
Rode out to hunt; it was a royal band.
And to the coppice lying near at hand
In which a hart – or so they told him – lay,
He led his gathering by the shortest way.
And pressing on towards a glade in sight
Down which the hart most often took to flight
Over a brook and off and out of view,
The Duke had hopes to try a course or two
With certain hounds that he had singled out;
And when he reached the glade he looked about.
Glancing towards the sun he thereupon
Beheld Arcita fighting Palamon.

*The quarrel between the two rivals becomes progressively more
ceremonial. Palamon first draws his sword in anger; they then agree
to a duel; but Theseus substitutes a public tournament.*

They fought like boars in bravery. There go
The shining swords in circle, to and fro,
So hideously that with their lightest stroke
It seemed as if they would have felled an oak.
What they could be he did not know, of course,
But he clapped spur at once into his horse
And, at a bound, he parted blow from blow,
And pulling out his sword he shouted, 'Ho!
No more on pain of death! Upon your head!
By mighty Mars, he is as good as dead
That dares to strike a blow in front of me!
Tell me, what sort of fellows may you be
That have the impudence to combat here
Without a judge or other overseer,
Yet as if jousting at a royal tilt?'

Palamon answered quickly and in guilt,
'O Sir, what need of further word or breath?
Both of us have deserved to die the death,
Two wretched men, your captives, met in strife,
And each of them encumbered with his life.
If to judge righteously has been your fashion,
Show neither of us mercy or compassion,
And kill me first for holy charity!
But kill my fellow too, the same as me.
Or kill him first, for little though you know,
This is Arcita and your mortal foe,
Banished by you on forfeit of his head,
For which alone he merits to be dead.
This is the man that waited at your gate
And told you his name was Philostrate.
This is the man that mocked you many a year,
And you have made him chief equerry here.
This is the man who dares love Emily.
Now, since my day of death has come to me,
I will make full confession and go on
To say I am that woeful Palamon
That broke out of your jail feloniously.

And it is I, your mortal enemy,
That am in love with Emily the Bright
And glad to die this moment in her sight.
And so I ask for judgement and for death;
But slay my fellow in the self-same breath,
Since we have both deserved that we be slain!'

And noble Theseus answered back again,
'This is a short conclusion. It shall stand.
Your own confession damns you out of hand.
I shall record your sentence as it stood;
There needs no torturing to make it good.
Death you shall have, by mighty Mars the Red!'

On hearing this, the Queen began to shed
Her womanly tears, and so did Emily
And all the ladies in the company.
It seemed so very piteous to them all
That ever such misfortune should befall
For they were noblemen of great estate
And love the only cause of their debate.
They saw their bloody gashes gaping wide
And, from the greatest to the least, they cried,
'Have mercy, Lord, upon us women all!'
Down on their knees they then began to fall,
Ready to kiss his feet as there he stood.

Abated in the end his angry mood;
Pity runs swiftly in a noble heart.
Though he had quaked with anger at the start
He had reflected, having time to pause,
Upon their trespass and upon its cause,
And though his anger at their guilt was loth
To pardon either, reason pardoned both.
For thus he argued: almost any man
Will help himself to love, if so he can,
And anyone will try to break from prison;
And then compassion in his heart had risen
Seeing these ladies weeping there together,
And in his noble heart he wondered whether
He should not show his clemency, and 'Fie,'
He thought, 'on lords who show no mercy! Why,
To be a lion both in word and deed
To a penitent in fear, is not to heed
His change of heart, and equal him with one
Proudly persisting in an evil done.
A lord will lack discretion among his graces
Who does not make distinction in such cases,
But weighs humility and pride as one.'
And, to be brief, his anger being done,
His eyes began to sparkle and uncloud
And having taken thought he said aloud:
'The God of Love! Ah, *Benedicite!*
How mighty and how great a lord is he!
No obstacles for him make any odds;
His miracles proclaim his power a God's.
Cupid can make of every heart and soul
Just what he pleases, such is his control.
Look at Arcita here and Palamon!
Both had escaped scot-free and could have gone
To Thebes and lived there royally; they know

That I have ever been their mortal foe;
Their lives are mine, they can make no defence;
Yet Cupid in the teeth of common sense
Has brought them here to die in melancholy!
Consider, is it not the height of folly?
What is so foolish as a man in love?
Look at them both! By God that sits above
See how they bleed! Are they not well arrayed?
Thus has their lord, the God of Love, repaid
Their services; these are his fees and wages!
And yet, in spite of that, they pose as sages,
These devotees of Love, as I recall.
But still this is the finest stroke of all,
That she, the cause of all these jolly pranks,
Has no more reason to return them thanks
Than I, and knows no more of this affair,
By God, than does a cuckoo or a hare!
Well, well, try anything once, come hot, come cold!
If we're not foolish young, we're foolish old.
I long have known myself what Love can do,
For, in my time, I was a lover too.
And therefore, knowing something of love's pain,
How violently it puts a man to strain,
As one so often caught in the same snare
I readily forgive the whole affair,
Both at the Queen's request, that on her knees
Petitions, and my sister Emily's.
But you shall swear to me and give your hands
Upon it never to attack my lands,
Or levy war on me by night or day,
But be my friends in everything you may.
I pardon you your fault. You are forgiven.'

They swore as he had asked, and, having striven
To gain his patronage and further grace,
Were satisfied, and Theseus summed the case:
So far as riches go, and nobleness,
Were she a queen in question, or princess,
You would be worthy when the moment came,
Either of you, to marry. All the same,
Speaking as for my sister Emily,
The cause of all your strife and jealousy,
You are aware yourselves that she can never
Wed both at once, though you should fight for ever.
And one of you, come joy to him or grief,
Must go pipe tunes upon an ivy-leaf;
That is to say she cannot have you both,
However jealous you may be, or loth.
And so, to put the matter in good order,
Let Destiny herself be your Awarder,
And shape your fortune. Listen to the close,
For here is the solution I propose.

My will is this, to make a flat conclusion
And end all counterpleading and confusion,
(And you will please to take it for the best)
That each shall take his freedom, east or west,
And without ransom or constraint of war;
And, a year later, neither less nor more,
Each shall return, bringing a hundred knights,

Emily is a personification of spring.

Armed for the lists and everything to rights,
Ready by battle to decide his claim
To Emily. To this I give my name,
My faith and honour, as I am a knight.
Whichever of you proves of greater might,
Or, more precisely, whether you or he,
Backed by the hundred knights allowed by me,
Can drive his foe to stake, or take his life,
To him I shall give Emily to wife,
To whom kind Fortune gives so fair à grace.
I'll build the lists upon this very place,
And God in wisdom deal my soul its due
As I shall prove an even judge and true.
There is no other way, let that be plain;
One of you must be taken or else slain.
And if this seems to you to be well said,
Think yourselves lucky, sirs, and nod your head.
That's the conclusion I've decided on.'

Who looks delighted now but Palamon?
And who springs up rejoicing but Arcite?
And who could tell, what poetry repeat
The joy of all those present in the place
That Theseus had vouchsafed so fair a grace?
Down on their knees went everyone in sight
Returning thanks with all their heart and might,
Especially the Thebans, time on time.
Thus in good hope, with beating heart a-climb,
Each took his leave, and they began to ride
To Thebes and to her ancient walls and wide.

PART III

I JUDGE it would be held for negligence
If I forgot to tell of the dispense
Of money by the Duke who set about
To make the lists a royal show throughout.
A theatre more noble in its plan
I dare well say was never seen by man.
It had a circuit of a mile about,
Well walled with stone; there was a ditch without.
Shaped like a circle there it stood complete
In tier on tier, the height of sixty feet,
So that a man set in a given row
Did not obstruct his neighbour from below.
Eastward there stood a gate of marble white,
And westward such another rose to sight;
Briefly, there was never upon the face
Of earth so much within so small a space.
No craftsmen in the land that had the trick
Of pure geometry, arithmetic,
Portraiture, carving and erecting stages,
But Theseus found him and supplied his wages
To build this theatre and carve devices.
And, to observe due rites and sacrifices,
Eastward he built upon the gate, above,
An oratory to the Queen of Love,
To Venus and her worship, and he dressed
An altar there; and like it, to the west,
In reverence to Mars he built a second;
The cost in gold was hardly to be reckoned.
Yet, northward, in a turret on the wall
He built a third, an oratory tall
And rich, of whitest alabaster, set
With crimson coral, to discharge the debt
Of worship to Diana of Chastity.
And it was thus that Theseus built these three
Temples in great magnificence of style.
But yet I have forgotten all this while
To tell you of the portraits that there were,
The shapes, the carvings and the figures there
To grace these temples high above the green.
First, in the temple of Venus, you had seen
Wrought on the wall, and piteous to behold,
The broken sleeps and sighings manifold,
The sacred tears and the lamenting songs
And every fiery passion that belongs
To those that suffer love, the long-endured,
Their taken oaths, their covenants assured,
Pleasure and Hope, Desire, Foolhardiness,
Beauty and Youth, Lasciviousness, Largesse,
Philtres and Force, Falsehood and Flattery,
Extravagance, Intrigue and Jealousy
Gold-garlanded, with many a yellow twist,
That had a cuckoo sitting on her wrist.
Stringed instruments, and carols, feasts and dances,
Joy and display, and all the circumstances

Of love, as I have told you and shall tell,
Were in due order painted there as well,
And more than I can mention or recount.
Truly the whole of Citherea's Mount,
Where Venus has her dwelling above all
Her other playgrounds, figured on the wall
With all her garden in its joyful dress.
Nor was forgotten her porter, Idleness,
Nor yet Narcissus, beauty's paragon
In times gone by, nor doting Solomon,
Nor the unmastered strength of Hercules.
Medea and her enchantments next to these,
And Circe's too, and Turnus fierce and brave,
And rich King Croesus, captive and a slave,

Another illumination from the 'Roman de la Rose'. Rich King Croesus, like the other famous figures listed by Chaucer, did come to a bad end but Chaucer's learning for once lets him down since Croesus's fate had nothing to do with Venus.

That men might see that neither wit nor wealth,
Beauty or cunning, bravery or health
Can challenge Venus or advance their worth
Against that goddess who controls the earth.
And all these people captured in her noose
Cried out, 'Alas!' but it was little use.
Suffice these few examples, but the score
Could well be reckoned many thousands more.
Her statue, glorious in majesty,
Stood naked, floating on a vasty sea,
And from the navel down there were a mass
Of green and glittering waves as bright as glass.
In her right hand a cithern carried she
And on her head, most beautiful to see,
A garland of fresh roses, while above
There circles round her many a flickering dove.

As 'The Knight's Tale' develops and preparations begin for the great climax, the public tournament, it is the gods of classical mythology who increasingly take control of the characters' destinies. This is a late-medieval representation of Mars, god of war; and Venus, goddess of love, from a manuscript of Chaucer's poem, 'The Compaint of Mars'.

Cupid her son was standing to behold her
Fronting her statue, winged on either shoulder,
And he was blind, as it is often seen;
He bore a bow with arrows bright and keen.

Why should I not go on to tell you all
The portraiture depicted on the wall
Within the Temple of Mighty Mars the Red?
The walls were painted round and overhead
Like the recesses of that grisly place
Known as the Temple of Great Mars in Thrace,
That frosty region under chilling stars
Where stands the sovereign mansion of King Mars.

First on the walls a forest with no plan
Inhabited by neither beast nor man
Was painted – tree-trunks, knotted, gnarled and old,
Jagged and barren, hideous to behold,
Through which there ran a rumble and a soughing
As though a storm should break the branches bowing
Before it. Downwards from a hill there went
A slope; the Temple of Armipotent
Mars was erected there in steel, and burnished.
The Gateway, narrow and forbidding, furnished
A ghastly sight, and such a rushing quake
Raged from within, the portals seemed to shake.
In at the doors a northern glimmer shone
Onto the walls, for windows there were none;
One scarce discerned a light, it was so scant.
The doors were of eternal adamant,
And vertically clenched, and clenched across
For greater strength with many an iron boss,
And every pillar to support the shrine
Weighed a full ton of iron bright and fine.

And there I saw the dark imaginings
Of felony, the stratagems of kings,
And cruel wrath that glowed an ember-red,
The pick-purse and the image of pale Dread,
The smiler with the knife beneath his cloak,
The out-houses that burnt with blackened smoke;
Treason was there, a murder on a bed,
And open war, with wounds that gaped and bled;
Dispute, with bloody knife and snarling threat;
A screaming made the place more dreadful yet.
The slayer of himself, I saw him there
With all his heart's blood matted in his hair;
The driven nail that made the forehead crack,
Cold Death, with gaping mouth, upon its back.

And in the middle of the shrine Mischance
Stood comfortless with sorry countenance.
There I saw madness cackling his distress,
Armed insurrection, outcry, fierce excess,
The carrion in the undergrowth, slit-throated,
And thousands violently slain. I noted
The raping tyrant with his prey o'ertaken,
The levelled city, gutted and forsaken,
The ships on fire dancingly entangled,
The luckless hunter that wild bears had strangled,
The sow, munching the baby in the cradle,
The scalded cook, in spite of his long ladle –

Nothing forgotten of the unhappy art
Of Mars: the carter crushed beneath his cart,
Flung to the earth and pinned beneath the wheel;
Those also on whom Mars has set his seal,
The barber and the butcher and the smith
Who forges things a man may murder with.
And high above, depicted in a tower,
Sat Conquest, robed in majesty and power,
Under a Sword that swung above his head,
Sharp-edged and hanging by a subtle thread.

And Caesar's slaughter stood in effigy
And that of Nero and Mark Antony;
Though to be sure they were as yet unborn,
Their deaths were there prefigured to adorn
This Temple with the menaces of Mars,
As is depicted also in the stars
Who shall be murdered, who shall die for love;
Such were the portraits on the walls above.
Let these examples from the past hold good,
For all I cannot reckon, though I would.

The statue of Mars was in a cart, and clad
In armour, grim and staring, like the mad,
Above his head there shone with blazing looks
Two starry figures, named in ancient books,
Puella one, the other Rubeus.
The God of Battles was encompassed thus:
There stood a wolf before him at his feet,
His eyes glowed red, he had a man to eat.
Subtle the pencil was that told this story
Picturing Mars in terror and in glory.

To the temple of Diana, now, the Chaste,
I briefly turn, for I will use what haste
I can in trying to describe it all.
Here there were many paintings on the wall
Of hunting and of shamefast chastity.
There I perceived the sad Callisto, she
Whom in her rage Diana did not spare
But changed her from a woman to a bear,
Then to a star, and she was painted so
(She is the lode-star, that is all I know;
Her son, too, is a star, as one can see).
There I saw Dana, turned into a tree
(No, not Diana, she was not the same,
But Penneus' daughter, Dana was her name).
I saw Actaeon turned into a stag;
This was Diana's vengeance, lest he brag
Of having seen her naked. There they show him
Caught and devoured – his own hounds did not know him.
Close by there was a painting furthermore
Of Atalanta hunting a wild boar,
And Meleager; there were others too
Diana chose to harry and undo,
And many other wonders on the wall
Were painted, that I need not now recall.

High on a stag the Goddess held her seat,
And there were little hounds about her feet;
Below her feet there was a sickle moon,
Waxing it seemed, but would be waning soon.

Her statue bore a mantle of bright green,
Her hand a bow with arrows cased and keen;
Her eyes were lowered, gazing as she rode
Down to where Pluto has his dark abode.
A woman in her travail lay before her,
Her child unborn; she ceased not to implore her
To be delivered and with piteous call
Cried, 'Help, Lucina, thou the best of all!'
It was a lively painting, every shade
Had cost the painter many a florin paid.

So now the lists were made, and Theseus
Who, at huge cost, had bidden them produce
These temples in a theatre so stately,
Saw it was finished, and it pleased him greatly.
No more of Theseus now; I must pass on
To speak of Arcite and of Palamon.

The day approached for trial of their rights
When each should bring with him a hundred
knights

The late-medieval fondness for ceremonial is fully indulged in the elaborate tournament arranged by Theseus, with the precise equality of the two sides, the heralds and the definite rules of procedure.

To settle all by battle, as I said;
So, back to Athens each of them had led
His hundred knights, all helmeted and spurred
And armed for war. They meant to keep their word.
And it was said indeed by many a man
That never since the day the world began
In all God's earth, wide seas and reach of land,
Had so few men made such a noble band
As in respect of knighthood and degree.

Everyone with a taste for chivalry
And keen (you bet!) to win a glorious name
Had begged to be allowed to join the game.
Lucky the man to whom they gave the word!
And if, tomorrow, such a thing occurred
You know quite well that every lusty knight
Who loved the ladies and had strength to fight,
Whether in England here, or anywhere,
Would wish – you cannot doubt it – to be there.
Fight for a lady? *Benedicite!*
That would be something for a man to see.

And that was just the case with Palamon.
With him there rode his comrades – many a one;
Some were in coat of mail and others wore
A breastplate and a tunic, little more.
Some carried heavy plating, front and back,
And some a Prussian shield to ward attack;
Some cased their legs in armour, thigh to heel,
Some bore an axe and some a mace of steel
– There's never a new fashion but it's old -
And so they armed themselves as I have told.
Each man according to his own opinion.

You might have seen arrive from his dominion
Mighty Lycurgus, famous King of Thrace;
Black was his beard and manly was his face.
To see the circling eye-balls of the fellow
Set in his head and glowing red and yellow!
And like a gryphon he would stare and rouse
The shaggy hair upon his beetling brows.
Huge were his limbs, his muscles hard and strong,
His back was broad, his bulging arms were long.
True to his country's custom from of old
He towered in a chariot of gold
And four white bulls were harnessed in the traces.
Over his armour, which in many places
Was studded with bright nails of yellow gold,
He wore a coal-black bear-skin, fold on fold,
Instead of surcoat, and behind his back
His fell of hair was combed and shone as black
As raven's feather, and a golden wreath,
Thick as your arm, weighted the head beneath.
It was immensely heavy, and was bright
With many precious stones of fiery light,
With finest rubies and with diamonds.
About his chariot, white enormous hounds,
Twenty and more, each larger than a steer,
And trained to hunt the lion and the deer,
Went following him. Their muzzles were fast bound;
Their collars were of gold with rings set round.
He had a hundred nobles in his rout
Armed to the teeth; their hearts were stern and stout.

Right: 'There's never new fashion but it's old.' Perhaps this was Chaucer's apology for once again dressing his classical knights in medieval armour. This exquisite illumination from the Luttrell Psalter, written for an East Anglian knight, Sir Geoffrey Luttrell in the middle of the fourteenth century, shows him being handed his knightly equipment by his wife, Agnes.

pudore : + operiantur sicut diploide
confusione sua
Confitebor domino nimis in
ore meo : et in medio multorum
laudabo eum
Qui astitit a dextris paupens :
ut saluam faceret a persequentibz
animam meam.
Gloria patri
Dñs Galfridus louterell me fieri
fecit

And with Arcita, so the poets sing,
Went great Emetrius the Indian king
On a bay steed whose trappings were of steel
Covered in cloth of gold from haunch to heel
Fretted with diaper. Like Mars to see,
His surcoat was in cloth of Tartary,
Studded with great white pearls; beneath its fold
A saddle of new-beaten, burnished, gold.
He had a mantle hanging from his shoulders,
Which, crammed with rubies, dazzled all beholders.
His hair was crisped in ringlets, as if spun
Of yellow gold, and glittered like the sun.
Aquiline nose and eyes with lemon light
And rounded lips he had, his colour bright,
With a few freckles sprinkled here and there,
Some yellow and some black. He bore an air
As of a lion when he cast a glance.
He was some twenty-five years old, to chance
A guess at it; a healthy beard was springing.
His voice resounded like a trumpet ringing.
He had a wreath of laurel on his head
For he was freshly, greenly garlanded.
And on his hand he bore for his delight
An eagle; it was tame and lily-white.
He had a hundred lords beside him there,
In all their armour (though their heads were bare)
And sumptuously decked with furnishings.
For take my word for it that dukes and kings
Were gathered in this noble company
For love and for the spread of chivalry.
Many a lion tame and spotted pard
Gambolled about this king of stern regard.
And in this manner in their fine adorning
These lords came to the city on Sunday morning,
Round about nine o'clock, and lighted down.
The noble Theseus led them through his town
(So it became him as a duke and knight),
And housed them each according to his right.

Many of the events surrounding the tournament have a stately quality that would have appealed to a courtly audience. The feast shows Theseus to be noble in his hospitality, 'as became him as a duke and knight'.

He feasted them and took great pains to please,
To honour and to set them all at ease,
And to this day it's said no human wit
However lofty could have bettered it.
What minstrelsy, what service at the feast,
What gifts bestowed on greatest as on least,
How richly decked the palace, what the place
Ordained for first and last upon the dais,
What ladies loveliest in the dancing throng,
And which most exquisite in dance and song
And which to speak most feelingly of love,
Or what the falcons that were perched above,
And what the hounds that couched upon the floor –
Of all such questions I shall say no more
Than the result of it; I will not tease you,
Here comes the point, so listen if it please you
That Sunday night ere day began to spring
There was a lark which Palamon heard sing
(Although two hours before the day came on,
Yet the lark sang, and so did Palamon).
With holy heart and in a lofty mood
He rose on pilgrimage and he pursued
His path to Citherea, the benign
And blissful Venus, to her honoured shrine.

Venus and her lover Adonis. Palamon chose to pray at the shrine dedicated to Venus where his prayers echo the language of Christian devotion: 'O Venus, Lady mine',/Consort of Vulcan, Daughter of Jove Divine ... take my humble prayer into thy heart.'

And in her hour, among the early mists,
He stepped towards her Temple in the lists
And down he knelt in humbleness and fear
With aching heart, and said as you shall hear:
Fairest of Fair, O Venus, Lady mine,
Consort of Vulcan, Daughter of Jove Divine,
Giver of joy upon the heights above
The Mount of Citherea, by that love
Thou gavest to Adonis, heal my smart
And take my humble prayer into thy heart.
Alas! I have no language that can tell
The ravages and torments of my hell,

Which heart is all unable to convey,
And I am so confused I cannot say
More than: "O Lady bright, that art aware
Of all my thought and seest my despair,
Consider this, have pity on my pain
As I shall ever struggle to maintain
Thy service, in so far as it shall be
Within my power to combat chastity."
This is my vow, if only thou wilt help!
I am not one of those who brag and yelp
Of victory, nor ask for it tomorrow,
Or for renown; I neither beg nor borrow
Vainglorious praise, nor do I make profession
Of prowess – but would fully have possession
Of Emily, and die thy worshipper.
Choose Thou the means for this, administer
The ways, I care not how, whether it be
By my defeat of them, or theirs of me,
So that I have my lady in my arms.
Though Mars be god of battles and alarms
Thy power is so great in Heaven above
That if thou please I well may have my love.
And I will worship at thy shrine for ever;
Ride where I may, to thee my whole endeavour
Shall be in sacrifice and kindling fires
Upon thy altars. Yet if my desires,
Sweet lady, cannot please thee, end my sorrow
With death upon Arcita's spear to-morrow.
I shall not care when I have lost my life
Though he should win my Emily to wife.
This is the sum and purpose of my prayer,
Give me my love, sweet Goddess ever fair!'

When Palamon had done his orison
He then did sacrifice with woe-begone
Devotion and with ceremonial rite
More than I now have leisure to recite.
And in the end the statue of Venus shook
And made a sign; and by that sign he took
His prayer had been accepted on that day,
For though the sign had hinted a delay
He knew for certain that his boon was granted,
And home he went at once, his soul enchanted.

In the third hour after Palamon
Had sought out Venus for his orison,
Up rose the sun, and up rose Emily
And hastened to Diana's sanctuary,
Taking such maidens as she might require,
And they were ready furnished with the fire,
The incense and the vestments and a throng
Of other necessaries that belong
To sacrifices, horns of brimming mead,
As was the custom, all that they could need.
The Temple smoked and the adornments there
Glittered in beauty. Emily the fair
Joyfully washed her body in a well,
But how she did her rite I dare not tell
Save in a general way, though I for one
Think that to hear the detail would be fun.

If one means well why bother to feel queasy?
It's good for people to be free and easy.
Her shining hair untressed upon her cloak
They combed and set a crown of cerrial oak
Green on her golden head with fitting grace.
Two fires she kindled in the proper place
And did her rites, as he will find who looks
In Statius' *Book of Thebes* and other books,
And when the fires were kindled she drew near
With piteous heart, and prayed as you shall hear:

'O Goddess Chaste of all the woodlands green,
That seest earth and heaven and sea, O Queen
Of Pluto's kingdom, dark and deep below,
Goddess of virgins that from long ago
Hast known my heart, and knowest my desire,
As I may shun the vengeance of thine ire
Such as upon Actaeon once was spent,
Thou knowest well, O chaste omnipotent,
That I would be a virgin all my life
And would be neither mistress, no, nor wife.
I am, thou knowest, of thy company,
A huntress, still in my virginity,
And only ask to walk the woodlands wild,
And not to be a wife or be with child,
Nor would I know the company of man.
O help me, Goddess, for none other can,
By the three Forms that ever dwell in thee,
And as for Palamon who longs for me
And for Arcita's passion, I implore
This favour of thy grace and nothing more;
Set them in amity and let them be
At peace, and turn their hearts away from me.
Let all their violent loves and hot desires,
Their ceaseless torments and consuming fires,
Be quenched, or turned towards another place.
Yet if thou wilt not do me so much grace,
Of if my destiny ordains it so
That one shall have me whether I will or no,
Then send me him that shall desire me most.
Clean Goddess of the chaste and virgin host,
Look down upon the bitter tears that fall
Upon my cheeks, O keeper of us all,
Keep thou my maidhood, prosper my endeavour,
And while I live a maid I'll serve thee ever.'

The fires flamed up upon the altar fair
And clear while Emily was thus in prayer;
But all at once she saw a curious sight,
For suddenly one fire quenched its light
And then rekindled; as she gazed in doubt
The other fire as suddenly went right out;
As it was quenched it made a whistling sound
As of wet branches burning on the ground.
Then, from the faggot's tip, there ran a flood
Of many drops that had the look of blood.

Now at the sight she was so terrified
It almost drove her from her wits, she cried,
Not knowing what it was to signify,
For it was her fear alone that made her cry,

She wept and it was pitiful to hear.
And then began Diana to appear,
With bow in hand, garbed as a Huntress,
And said, 'My daughter, cease your heaviness.
For thee the Gods on high have set their term,
And by eternal word and writ confirm
That thou shalt be espoused to one of those
That have for thee endured so many woes.
But unto which of them I may not tell.
Longer I cannot tarry, fare thee well.
And yet the fires of sacrifice that glow
Upon my altar shall, before thou go,
Make plain thy destiny in this for ever.'
And on the word the arrows in her quiver
Clattered together and began to ring
And forth she went and made a vanishing.
Wholly amazed at what had come to pass,
Emily thought, 'What can this mean? Alas!
O take me, take me under thy protection,
Diana, for I yield to thy direction!'
Then she went homeward by the shortest way
And that was all, there is no more to say.
Now in the hour of Mars next after this
Arcite rose up and sought the edifice
Of fiery Mars, to do beneath his banner
His sacrifice, as was the pagan manner,
In high devotion with a piteous heart,
And thus he said his orison apart:
O thou strong God of War that art adored
In the cold realms of Thrace and held for Lord,
That hast of every monarchy and land
Of warlike men the bridle in thine hand,
And dealest them their fortunes by thy choice,
Accept my sacrifice and hear my voice.
And if my youth be such as to deserve
Thy favour, if my strength be fit to serve
Thy godhead, if I may be one of thine,
I pray thee then, pity this pain of mine.

Arcite opts for the god of war, but he reminds Mars of the episode when Mars loved Venus and begs, 'Pity me too that suffer the same smart!'

By that same suffering and burning fire
That long ago consumed thee with desire,
Having in use the incomparable flesh
Of fair free-hearted Venus, young and fresh,
Holding her in thine arms and at thy will,
– Albeit that once the time was chosen ill,
Seeing that Vulcan caught thee in his net
And found thee lying with his wife – but yet
By all the pain and passion of thy heart
Pity me too that suffer the same smart!
Thou knowest I am ignorant and young
And, as I think, more passionately stung
By love than any creature dead or living;
Little she thinks, in all the grief she's giving,
Of me, or cares whether I swim or sink,
And well I know ere she can learn to think
Kindly of me that force must have its place,
And well I know without thy help or grace
The little strength I have is all too slight;
Then help me, Lord, tomorrow, in the fight,
Not only for the flames that burnt in thee
Bur for the fire that now is burning me.
Grant victory tomorrow to my sword!
Mine be the labour, thing the glory, Lord;
Thy sovereign temple I will honour above
All other places, it shall be my love
To work for thy delight, to use thy arts,
And hang my banner, yea, my heart of hearts
Above thy altar. All my Company
Shall do the same for ever, there shall be
Eternal fires burning before thy Shrine.
Nay, further to this binding vow of mine,
My beard and hair, whose length and excellence
Has never suffered yet from the offence
Of razor or of shear, to Thee I give,
And I'll be thy true servant while I live.
Now, Lord, have pity on a heart so sore;
And give me victory, I ask no more.'
His prayer was over, and the rings that hung
Upon the portals of the Temple swung;
So did the doors and clattered far and near,
At which Arcita felt the touch of fear.
The fires blazed, the altar glistened bright,
So that the Temple was suffused with light,
A scented air rose upward from the ground.
Arcita lifted up his hand and found
More incense and he cast it on the flame
With other rituals. At last the frame
Of mighty Mars began to shake and ring
Its hauberk, and he heard a murmuring,
Low-voiced and dim, that answered *'Victory';*
And giving thanks and glorifying he,
Filled with the joyful hope that he would win,
Returned at once and went to seek his inn,
As happy as a bird is of the sun.
Immediately an uproar was begun
Over this granted boon in Heaven above
As between Venus, fairest Queen of Love,

The goddess Venus sits in her chariot drawn by doves in this Flemish illumination. Doves, who are notoriously promiscuous in their mating habits, were one of the traditional attributes of Venus.

In wisdom and by custom, that's the truth.
The old may be out-run but not out-reasoned.
And Saturn stopped their argument and seasoned
Their fears, although it's not his nature to,
And found a remedy for this to-do.
'My dearest daughter Venus,' said old Saturn,
'My heavenly orbit marks so wide a pattern
It has more power than anyone can know;
In the wan sea I drown and overthrow,
Mine is the prisoner in the darkling pit,
Mine are both neck and noose that strangles it,
Mine the rebellion of the serfs astir,
The murmurings, the privy poisoner;
And I do vengeance, I send punishment,
And when I am in *Leo* it is sent.
Mine is the ruin of the lofty hall,
The falling down of tower and of wall
On carpenter and mason, I their killer.
Twas I slew Samson when he shook the pillar;
Mine are the maladies that kill with cold,
The dark deceits, the stratagems of old;
A look from me will father pestilence.
Then weep no more, for by my diligence
This Palamon, your dedicated knight,
Shall have his lady, as you swore he might.
Though Mars should help his champion, none the less
Peace must be made between you soon, I guess,
Although you do not share the same complexions;
That is what brings these daily insurrections.
I am your grandfather and, as before,
I'll do my best to please you; weep no more.'
Now I shall cease to speak of Gods above,
Of angry Mars and Venus Queen of Love,
And tell you all, as plainly as I can,
The grand result for which I first began.

And the armipotent Mars; it did not cease,
Though Jupiter was busy making peace,
Until their father Saturn, pale and cold,
Who knew so many stratagems of old,
Searched his experience and found an art
To please the disputants on either part.
Age has a great advantage over youth

PART IV

GREAT was the festival they held that day
In Athens, and the lusty time of May
Put everyone so well in countenance
They spent all Monday at a joust and dance
And the high services of Venus. Yet
Because they knew that up they'd have to get,
And early too, to witness the great fight,
They went to bed betimes on Monday night.
Next morning when the day began to spring
Clattering horse and noise of harnessing
Echoed through all the hostelries about.
Up to the palace cantered rout on rout
Of lords on palfreys, stallions, many a steed;
And what device of harness too indeed,
So rich and so outlandish, what a deal

Of goldsmith work, embroidery and steel!
Bright shields and trappings, headpieces and charms,
Great golden helmets, hauberks, coats of arms,
Lords on apparelled coursers, squires too
And knights belonging to their retinue,
Spears being nailed and helmets buckled strong,
Strapping of shields and lacing up of thong,
The work was urgent, not a man was idle.
The foamy steeds gnawing the golden bridle,
The armourers up and down and round about
Racing with file and hammer through the rout,
Yeomen on foot and commonalty come
With pipe and clarion, trump and kettle-drum,
Armed with short sticks and making such a rattle
It sounded like the blast of bloody battle.

A battle scene from Marco Polo's 'Livre de Graunt Cam'. The vivid description of the hectic preparations for battle is completely medieval and could easily be paralleled in any contemporary chronicler, such as Chaucer's contemporary, Froissart.

The palace full of people up and down,
Here three, there ten, in all the talk of town
And making bets about the Theban knights.
Says one, 'He'll win'; another, 'Not by rights';
Some backed the man whose beard was black and squared,
Some backed the skin-heads, some the shaggy-haired;
Said one, 'There's a grim fellow, I'll be bound
He'll fight, his battle-axe weighs twenty pound!'
And prophecy went seething round the hall
Long after day had risen on them all.
Great Theseus was awoken out of sleep
By minstrelsy and noise about the keep,
But kept his chamber – a resplendent room -
Till the two Theban knights, to both of whom
An equal honour was done, were brought in presence.
Throned in a window giving on a pleasance
Sat Theseus like a god in panoply,
And all the people crowded there to see
The Duke and offer him their reverence
And hear what orders he might issue thence.
A herald on a scaffold shouted 'Ho!'
Till all the noise was quieted below;
Seeing at last the people hushed and still
He thus declared the mighty Theseus' will:
Our Lord the Duke has in his high discretion
Considered the destruction and suppression
Of gentle blood, were he to jeopardize
The lives of those engaging under guise
Of mortal battle. Wishing none to die,
His Grace now purposes to modify
His ordinance. On forfeit of your lives
No cross-bow darts, no poleaxes or knives
May pass into the lists or be conveyed
Thither, no stabbing-sword with pointed blade
Be drawn or even carried at the side.

Further, no pair of combatants shall ride
More than one course with spears, descending thence
To thrust on foot only in self-defence.
If any man be injured, none shall take
His life; he shall be carried to the stake
That is to be ordained on either side,
And there conveyed by force he shall abide.
And should the principal of either faction
Be taken to the stake, or killed in action,
All fighting shall determine thereupon.
God speed you all, go forward and lay on!
With mace and long-sword you may fight your fill.
Now go your ways. This is his Grace's will.'
The people rifted heaven with a shout
Of merriest good humour, crying out,
'God bless our Duke for doing what he can
To save the blood of many a gentleman!'
Up go the trumpets and the melody,
Forth to the lists canter the company,
As they were bidden, to the city verge;
The streets were hung in cloth-of-gold, not serge.
And like a lord the Duke began to ride
With him a Theban knight, on either side.
Behind them rode the Queen and Emily,
And behind them another company
Of one or other according to their rank,
Threading through the city with the clank

The great tournament is not only the dramatic climax of 'The Knight's Tale', but also the moment when the destiny of Arcite and Palamon is relinquished to Fortune and the pagan gods.

Of hoof and armour to the lists that lay
Beyond. It was not fully prime of day
When Theseus took his seat in majesty.
Hippolyta the Queen and Emily
Were with him, other ladies ranked about,
And round the scaffoldage a seething rout.
And westward, look! Under the Martian Gate
Arcita and his hundred knights await,
And now, under a banner of red, march on.
And at the self-same moment Palamon
Enters by Venus' Gate and takes his place
Under a banner of white, with cheerful face.
You had not found, though you had searched the earth,
Two companies so equal in their worth.
Never were two so splendidly arrayed
And there was none so wise as to have weighed
Which of them had the advantage of his foe
In valiance, age, degree or strength of show;
They were so equal one could only guess.
In two formations they began to dress
And when the roll was called that all might see
Their number was not swelled by treachery,
The gates were shut, and then the herald cried:
'Young knights, now do your duty, show your pride!'
The heralds then withdrew, their work was done;
Out blared the trumpet and the clarion.
There is no more to say, but east and west
In go the spears in readiness, at the 'rest',
In go the spurs into the horse's side.
It's easy seeing which can joust and ride.
There the shafts shiver on the shields so thick;
One through his breast-bone feels the thrust and prick.
Up spring the spears to twenty foot in height,
Out go the long-swords flashing silver-bright,
Hewing the helmets as they shear and shred;
Out bursts the blood in streams of sternest red,
The mighty maces swing, the bones are bashed,
One thrusting through the thickest throng has crashed,
There the strong steeds have stumbled, down goes all,
Man under foot and rolling like a ball.
Another on his feet with truncheon pound
Hurtles a rider and his horse to ground;
One's wounded in the body, whom they take,
Spite of his teeth, and bear him to the stake
As was ordained, and there he has to stay;
One more is carried off the other way.
From time to time the Duke decrees a rest
To drink and be refreshed as they think best
Many a time our Thebans in the flow
Of battle met and did each other woe,
And each unhorsed the other. There could be
No tiger in the vale of Galgophy
Raging in search after a stolen cub
So cruel as Arcite with spear and club
For jealousy of heart to Palamon.
No lion is so fierce to look upon
In all Benamarin, and none so savage
Being hunted, nor so hunger-mad in ravage

To be knocked off your horse in heavy armour could well be fatal.

For blood of prey as Palamon for Arcite.
The blows upon their helmets bite and beat
And the red blood runs out on man and steed.
There comes at last an end to every deed,
And ere into the west the sun had gone
Strong King Emetrius took Palamon
As he was fighting with Arcite, still fresh,
And made his sword bite deeply in his flesh;
It asked the strength of twenty men to take
The yet-unyielded Palamon to stake.
Seeking a rescue, King Lycurgus coursed
Towards Palamon but was himself unhorsed,
And King Emetrius for all his strength
Was flung out of the saddle a sword's length
By Palamon's last stroke in sweeping rake.
But all for nought, they brought him to the stake;
Nothing could help, however hard he fought,
His hardy heart must stay there, he was caught
By force and by the rules decided on.
Who clamours now in grief but Palamon
That may no more go in again and fight?
And when the noble Theseus saw this sight
He rose and thundered forth to every one,
'Ho! Stop the fight! No more, for it is done!
I will be true judge and no partisan.
The Theban Prince Arcita is the man
And shall have Emily, won by Fortune's grace.'

Arcite and Palamon each had to find one hundred knights to fight for them in the tournament. Medieval armies were often raised in a similar way, with powerful magnates raising a band of knights and others, and then acting as their commander within a larger army.

A tumult of rejoicing filled tall space
From every throat in such a caterwaul
It seemed as if the very lists would fall.

W hat now can lovely Venus do above?
What is she saying, hapless Queen of Love?
Wanting her will her eyes were filled with mists
And shining tears fell down upon the lists.

S he cried, 'I am disgraced and put to shame!'
But Saturn said, 'Peace, daughter, watch the game.
Mars has his will, his knight has had his boon,
But, by my head, it shall be your turn soon.'

T he trumpeters with loudest minstrelsy
And the shrill heralds shouting frenziedly
Were in high joy for honour of Arcite.
But listen quietly and keep your seat,
See what a miracle happened thereupon!

T he fierce Arcita, with no helmet on,
Riding his courser round to show his face
Cantered the whole length of the jousting-place,
Fixing his eye on Emily aloft;
And her returning gaze was sweet and soft,
For women, speaking generally, are prone
To follow Fortune's favours, once they're known.
She was his whole delight, his joy of heart.

O ut of the ground behold a fury start,
By Pluto sent at the request of Saturn.
Arcita's horse in terror danced a pattern
And leapt aside and foundered as he leapt,
And ere he was aware Arcite was swept
Out of the saddle and pitched upon his head
Onto the ground, and there he lay for dead;
His breast was shattered by the saddle-bow.
As black he lay as any coal or crow
For all the blood had run into his face.
Immediately they bore him from the place

Sadly to Theseus' palace. What avail
Though he was carved out of his coat of mail
And put to bed with every care and skill?
Yet he was still alive, and conscious still,
And calling ceaselessly for Emily.

T heseus, attended by his company,
Came slowly home to Athens in full state
Of joyous festival, no less elate
For this misfortune, wishing not to cast
A gloom upon them all for what had passed.
Besides they said Arcita would not die,
He would recover from his injury.
And then there was another thing that filled
All hearts with pleasure, no one had been killed,
Though some were badly hurt among the rest,
Especially the man with stoven breast.
As for the other wounds and broken arms
Some produced salves and some relied on charms,
Herb pharmacies and sage to make them trim;
They drank them off, hoping to save a limb.

F or such as these Duke Theseus did his best,
He comforted and honoured every guest
And ordered revelry to last the night
For all the foreign princes, as was right.
None were discouraged or in discontent;
It was a jousting, just a tournament.

Like Emily and Queen Hippolyta, courtly ladies would join the spectators at a tournament. They would grant their favours to the knights but would also witness the often fatal injuries, like that to poor Arcite when 'his breast was shattered by the saddle bow'.

A detail from a fifteenth-century manuscript. By the end of the fourteenth century the art of heraldry had become a symbol of the status and magnificence of the war-loving aristocracy.

Why should they be discouraged? After all,
It's only an accident to have a fall.
There is no shame in being borne by force,
Unyielded, to the stake by twenty horse,
Alone, with none to help – it must be so,
Harried away by arm and foot and toe,
And on a horse maddened by sticks and noise,
By men on foot, by yeomen and their boys -
There's nothing despicable in all this;
No one could ever call it cowardice.
And therefore Theseus made proclamation
To stop all rancour, grudge and emulation,
That each side was as valorous as the other
And both as like as brother is to brother.
He gave them gifts, to each in his degree,
And for three days they held festivity.
Then he conveyed the Kings in solemn state
Out of his city, far beyond the gate,
And home went everyone by various ways
With no more than 'Good-bye!' and 'Happy days!'

he battle done with, I may now go on
To speak of poor Arcite and Palamon.
Up swells Arcita's breast, the grievous sore

About his heart increases more and more;
The clotting blood, for all the doctor's skill,
Corrupts and festers in his body still,
That neither cupping, bleeding at a vein
Or herbal drink can make him well again.
The expulsive forces, known as 'animal',
Had lost their power to cleanse the 'natural'
Of poison, and it could not be expelled.
His lungs began to choke, the vessels swelled.
Clotted was every muscle of his chest
By poison and corruption in his breast.
Nor could he profit, in his will to live,
By upward vomit or by laxative.
All, all was shattered and beyond repair,
Nature no longer had dominion there,
And certainly, where nature will not work,
Physic, farewell! Go, bear the man to kirk!
This is the sum of all, Arcite must die.

And so he sent for Emily to be by,
And Palamon, the cousin of his heart,
And thus he spoke, preparing to depart:
Nothing of all the sorrows in my breast
Can now declare itself or be expressed
To you, O lady that I love the most;

53

But I bequeath the service of my ghost
To you, above all creatures in the world,
Now that my life is done, and banner furled.
Alas the woe! Alas the pain, so strong,
That I have suffered for you, and so long!
Alas, O Death! Alas, my Emily!
Alas the parting of our company!
Alas, my heart's own queen, alas, my wife,
O lady of my heart that ends my life!
What is this world? What does man ask to have?
Now with his love, now in his cold, cold grave,
Alone, alone, with none for company!
Farewell, my sweetest foe, my Emily!
O softly take me in your arms, I pray.
For love of God, and hearken what I say.

'I have here, with my cousin Palamon,
Had strife and rancour many a day now gone,
For love of you, and for my jealousy.
And may Jove's wisdom touch the soul in me,
To speak of love and what its service means
Through all the circumstances and the scenes
Of life, namely good faith and knightly deed,
Wisdom, humility and noble breed,
Honour and truth and openness of heart,
For, as I hope my soul may have its part
With Jove, in all the world I know of none
So worthy to be loved as Palamon,
Who serves you and will serve you all his life.
And should you ever choose to be a wife,
Forget not Palamon, that great-hearted man.'

Speech failed in him, the cold of death began
Its upward creeping from his feet to numb
The breast, and he was slowly overcome,
And further still as from his arms there went
The vital power; all was lost and spent.
Only the intellect, and nothing more,
That dwelt within his heart, so sick and sore,
Began to falter when the heart felt death.
Dusked his two eyes at last and failed his breath,
And yet he gazed at her while he could see
And his last word was 'Mercy . . . Emily!'
His spirit changed its house and went away
Where I came never – where I cannot say,
And so am silent. I am no divine.
Souls are not mentioned in this tale of mine,
I offer no opinion, I can tell
You nothing, though some have written where they
  dwell.
Arcite is cold. Mars guide him on his way!
Something of Emily I have to say.

Palamon howls and Emily is shrieking,
And Theseus leads away his sister, seeking
To bear her from the corpse; she faints away.
Why tarry on her tears or spend the day
Telling you how she wept both eve and morrow?
For in these cases women feel such sorrow
When it befalls their husbands to be taken
The greater part seem utterly forsaken

And fall into a sickness so extreme
That many of them perish, it would seem.

Infinite were the sorrows and the tears
Of older folk and those of tender years
Throughout the town, all for this Theban's
  death.
Wept man and boy, and sure a wilder breath
Of lamentation never had been heard
Since Hector, freshly slaughtered, was interred
In Troy. Alas to see the mourning there,
The scrabbled faces, the dishevelled hair!
'Must you have died?' the women wailed. 'For see,
Had you not gold enough – and Emily?'

No one could lighten Theseus of his care
Except his father, old Aegeus, there.
He knew the transmutations of the world
And he had seen its changes as it whirled
Bliss upon sorrow, sorrow upon bliss,
And gave his son instruction upon this:

'Just as there never died a man,' said he,
'But had in life some station or degree,
Just so there never lived a man,' he said,
'In all the world but in the end was dead.
This world is but a thoroughfare of woe
And we are pilgrims passing to and fro.
Death is the end of every worldly sore.'
On top of this he said a great deal more
To this effect, with wisest exhortation,
Heartening the people in their tribulation.

In time the thoughts of Theseus were astir
To find a site and build a sepulchre
For good Arcite, and how it best might be
Ordained to fit his honour and degree.
And in the end the place decided on
Was where Arcite first met with Palamon
In battle for their love, and there between
The branches in that very grove of green
Where he had sung his amorous desire
In sad complaint, and felt love hot as fire,
He planned a fire to make, in funeral
Observances, and so accomplish all.
So he commanded them to hack and fell
The ancient oak-trees and to lay them well
In rows and bundles faggoted to burn.

Forth ride his officers and soon return
On swiftest foot with his commandments done.
And after this, Theseus appointed one
To fetch a bier and had it fitly clad
In cloth-of-gold, the finest that he had.
And in the self-same cloth he clad Arcite
And on his hands white gauntlets, as was meet,
He placed, and on his head a laurel crown
And in his hand the sword of his renown.
He laid him, bare his face, upon the bier,
And wept upon him, pity was to hear.
And that his body might be seen by all,
When it was day he bore him to the hall
That roared with mourning sounds in unison.

hen came that woeful Theban, Palamon,
With fluttering beard and ash-besprinkled hair,
In sable garments stained with many a tear.
Yet, passing all in weeping, Emily
Was the most sorrowful of the company.
And that the service to be held might be
The nobler, more befitting his degree,
Duke Theseus commanded them to bring
Three steeds, all trapped in steel and glittering,
And mantled with the arms of Prince Arcite.
Upon these huge white steeds that paced the street
On these rode one who bore Arcita's shield,
A second bore the spear he used to wield;
His Turkish bow and quiver of burnished gold
Was given to the third of them to hold;
Slowly they paced, their countenances drear,
Towards the destined grove, as you shall hear.
Upon the shoulders of the noblest men
Among the Greeks there came the coffin then.
Their eyes were red with tears, their slackened feet
Paced through the city by the master-street;
The way was spread with black, and far on high
Black draperies hung downwards from the sky.

he old Aegeus to the right was placed
With Theseus on his left, and so they paced
Bearing gold vessels of a rare design
Brimming with honey and milk, with blood and wine;
And then came Palamon with his company,
And after that came woeful Emily
With fire in her hand, the custom then
Used in the obsequies of famous men.

igh was the labour, rich was the attire
And service, at the making of the fire
That reached to heaven in a cone of green.
The arms were twenty fathoms broad – I mean
The boughs and branches heaped upon the ground -
And straw in piles had first been loaded round.

ut how they made the funeral fires flame,
Or what the trees by number or by name
– Oak, fir-tree, birch, aspen and poplar too,
Ilex and alder, willow, elm and yew,
Box, chestnut, plane, ash, laurel, thorn and lime,
Beech, hazel, whipple-tree – I lack the time
To tell you, or who felled them, nor can tell
How their poor gods ran up and down the dell
All disinherited of habitation,
Robbed of their quiet and in desolation,
The nymph and dryad of the forest lawn,
The hamadryad and the subtle faun,
These I pass over, birds and beasts as well
That fled in terror when the forest fell;
Nor shall I say how in the sudden light
Of the unwonted sun the dell took fright,
Nor how the fire first was couched in straw,
Then in dry sticks thrice severed with a saw,
Then in green wood with spice among the stems
And then in cloth-of-gold with precious gems
And many a flower-garland in the stir

'Prince Arcita burnt to ashes cold.' Cremation was regarded as an exotic and unchristian ritual. This illustration of a shrouded corpse being burned is from Marco Polo's 'Livre du Graunt Cam'.

Of breathing incense and the scent of myrrh;
Nor how Arcita lay among it all,
Nor of the wealth and splendour of his pall,
Nor yet how Emily thrust in the fire
As custom was and lit the funeral pyre,
Nor how she fainted when they fed the flame,
Nor what she said or thought; and I shall name
None of the jewels that they took and cast
Into the fire when it flamed at last,
Nor shall I tell how some threw shield and spear,
Or what their garments, by the burning bier,
Nor of the cups of wine and milk and blood
That others poured upon the fiery flood,
Nor tell you how the Greeks in mighty rout
Left-handedly went thrice and thrice about
The flaming pyre, and shouted as they drove,
And thrice they clashed their spears about the grove;
Nor yet relate how thrice the ladies wept
Nor who supported Emily and kept
Pace with her homeward, nor shall it be told
How Prince Arcita burnt to ashes cold;
Nor how the wake was held in the delight
Of funeral games that lasted all the night.
What naked wrestler, glistening with oil,
Made the best showing in his dangerous toil
I will not say, nor say how one by one
They all went home after the games were done;
But shortly to the point; for I intend
To bring my long narration to an end.

n course of time, and after certain years,
Mourning had been accomplished and their tears
Were shed no more, by general consent.
And then it seems they held a parliament
At Athens touching certain points and cases;
And among these they dealt with certain places

With which to form alliances abroad
To keep the Thebans fully overawed,
And noble Theseus ordered thereupon
That summons should be sent for Palamon.

Not knowing for what reason ordered back,
And still in melancholy suit of black,
Palamon came on this authority
In haste. Then Theseus sent for Emily.

When all were seated there and hushed the place,
The noble Duke kept silent for a space
And ere he spoke the wisdom in his breast
He let his eyes fall where it pleased him best.
Then with a sober visage and the still
Sound of a sigh, he thus expressed his will:

'The First Great Cause and Mover of all above
When first He made that fairest chain of love,
Great was the consequence and high the intent.
He well knew why He did, and what He meant.
For in that fairest chain of love He bound
Fire and air and water and the ground
Of earth in certain limits they may not flee.
And that same Prince and Mover then,' said he,
'Stablished this wretched world, appointing ways,
Seasons, durations, certain length of days,
To all that is engendered here below,
Past which predestined hour none may go,
Though they have power to abridge those days.
I need not quote authority or raise
More proof than what experience can show,
But give opinion here from what I know.

Since we discern this order, we are able
To know that Prince is infinite and stable.
Anyone but a fool knows, in his soul,
That every part derives from this great whole.
For nature cannot be supposed to start
From some particular portion or mere part,
But from a whole and undisturbed perfection
Descending thence to what is in subjection
To change, and will corrupt. And therefore He
In wise foreknowledge stablished the decree
That species of all things and the progression
Of seed and growth continue by succession
And not eternally. This is no lie,
As any man can see who has an eye.

Look at the oak; how slow a tree to nourish
From when it springs until it comes to flourish!
It has so long a life, and yet we see
That in the end it falls, a wasted tree.

Consider too how hard the stone we tread
Under our feet! That very rock and bed
On which we walk is wasting as it lies.
Time will be when the broadest river dries
And the great cities wane and last descend
Into the dust, for all things have an end.

For man and woman we can plainly see
Two terms appointed; so it needs must be
– That is to say, the terms of youth and age.
For every man will perish, king and page,

Some in their beds and some in the deep sea,
And some upon the battle-field, maybe.
There is no help for it, all take the track,
For all must die and there is none comes back.

Who orders this but Jupiter the King,
The Prince and Cause of all and everything,
Converting all things back into the source
From which they were derived, to which they course?
And against this no creature here alive
Whatever his degree may hope to strive.

Then hold it wise, for so it seems to me,
To make a virtue of necessity,
Take in good part what we may not eschew,
Especially whatever things are due
To all of us; his is a foolish soul
That's rebel against Him who guides the whole,
And it is honour to a man whose hour
Strikes in his day of excellence and flower,
When he is certain of his own good name
And never known in any act of shame.
And gladder should a friend be of his death
Where there is honour in the yielded breath,
Gladder than for a name by age made pale,
And all forgotten the heroic tale.
Then is the time, if you would win a name,
To die, upon the moment of your fame.

The contrary of this is wilfulness;
Why do we murmur? Where is the distress
If good Arcite, the flower of chivalry,
Is gone in honour and in duty, free
Of the foul prison of this life?
Shall those he loved, his cousin and his wife,
Murmur against his welfare, or suppose
He can return them thanks? Not he, God knows.
Offending so against him, they offend
Themselves, and are no happier in the end.

In one of the last illustrations from the copy of the 'Roman de la Rose' made for Louise of Savoy, the mother of the French king, Francis I, the lover finally approaches the sanctuary where the lady is seated. So at last Palamon has suffered and persevered sufficiently to win the hand of Emily.

'One perfect joy.' The marriage of Palamon and Emily, true to aristocratic reality, was a very public union, arranged by Duke Theseus in the presence of all his peerage.

'So what conclusion can I draw from this
Except that after grief there should be bliss
And praise to Jupiter for all his grace?
So, ere we make departure from this place,
I rule that of two sorrows we endeavour
To make one perfect joy, to last for ever.

Then let us look, and where we find herein
The greatest grief let happiness begin.
'Sister,' he said, 'it has my full assent,
And is confirmed by this my parliament,
That gentle Palamon, your own true knight,
Who loves and serves you, heart and soul and might,
And always has since first he saw your face,
Shall move you to feel pity, gain your grace
And so become your husband and your lord.
Give me your hand, for this is our award.
Let us now see your womanly compassion.
By God, he's a king's nephew! Were his fashion
No more than that of a knight-bachelor,
What with the years he served and suffered for
Your love (unless his sufferings deceive me)
He would be worth considering, believe me.
A noble mercy should surpass a right.'
And then he said to Palamon the knight,
'I think there needs but little sermoning
To gain your own assent to such a thing.
Come near, and take your lady by the hand.'
And they were joined together by the band
That is called matrimony, also marriage,
By counsel of the Duke and all his peerage.
And thus with every bliss and melody
Palamon was espoused to Emily,
And God that all this wide, wide world has
  wrought,
Send them his love, for it was dearly bought!
Now Palamon's in joy, amid a wealth
Of bliss and splendour, happiness and health.
He's tenderly beloved of Emily
And serves her with a gentle constancy,
And never a jealous word between them spoken
Or other sorrow in a love unbroken.
Thus ended Palamon and Emily,
And God save all this happy company!
                                                    Amen.

'The Miller's Tale', bawdy and comic, tells of a gullible carpenter and his unfaithful young wife. It offers a complete contrast to the courtly Knight's Tale and Chaucer jokingly apologizes for its inclusion.

THE MILLER'S TALE

Words between the Host and the Miller

WHEN we had heard the tale the Knight had
    told,
Not one among the pilgrims, young or old,
But said it was indeed a noble story
Worthy to be remembered for its glory,
And it especially pleased the gentlefolk.
Our Host began to laugh and swore in joke:
It's going well, we've opened up the bale;
Now, let me see. Who'll tell another tale?
Upon my soul the game has begun well!
Come on, Sir Monk, if you've a tale to tell,
Repay the Knight a little for his tale!'
The Miller, very drunk and rather pale,
Was straddled on his horse half-on half-off
And in no mood for manners or to doff
His hood or hat, or wait on any man,
But in a voice like Pilate's he began
To huff and swear. 'By blood and bones and belly,
I've got a noble story I can tell 'ee,
I'll pay the Knight his wages, not the Monk.'
Our Host perceived at once that he was drunk
And said, 'Now hold on, Robin, dear old brother;
We'll get some better man to tell another;
You wait a bit. Let's have some common sense.'
'God's soul, I won't!' said he. 'At all events
I mean to talk, or else I'll go my way.'
Our Host replied, 'Well, blast you then, you may.
You fool! Your wits have gone beyond recall.'
Now listen,' said the Miller, tone and all,
To what I have to say. But first I'm bound
To say I'm drunk, I know it by my sound.
And if the words get muddled in my tale
Just put it down to too much Southwark ale.
I will relate a legend and a life
Of an old carpenter and of his wife,
And how a student came and set his cap . . . '
The Reeve looked up and shouted, 'Shut your
    trap!
Give over with your drunken harlotry.
It is a sin and foolishness,' said he,

'To slander any man or bring a scandal
On wives in general. Why can't you handle
Some other tale? There's other things beside.'
To this the drunken Miller then replied,
'My dear old brother Oswald, such is life.
A man's no cuckold if he has no wife.
For all that, I'm not saying you are one;
There's many virtuous wives, all said and done,
Ever a thousand good for one that's bad,
As well you know yourself, unless you're mad.
Why are you angry? What is this to-do?
I have a wife, God knows, as well as you,
Yet not for all the oxen in my plough
Would I engage to take it on me now
To think myself a cuckold, just because . . .
I'm pretty sure I'm not and never was.
One shouldn't be too inquisitive in life
Either about God's secrets or one's wife.
You'll find God's plenty all you could desire;
Of the remainder, better not enquire.'
What can I add? The Miller had begun,
He would not hold his peace for anyone,
But told his churl's tale his own way, I fear.
And I regret I must repeat it here,
And so I beg of all who are refined
For God's love not to think me ill-inclined
Or evil in my purpose. I rehearse
Their tales as told, for better or for worse,
For else I should be false to what occurred.
So if this tale had better not be heard,
Just turn the page and choose another sort;
You'll find them here in plenty, long and short;
Many historical, that will profess
Morality, good breeding, saintliness.
Do not blame me if you should choose amiss.
The Miller was a churl, I've told you this,
So was the Reeve, and other some as well,
And harlotry was all they had to tell.
Consider then and hold me free of blame;
And why be serious about a game?

The Miller's Tale

SOME time ago there was a rich old codger
Who lived in Oxford and who took a lodger.
The fellow was a carpenter by trade,
His lodger a poor student who had made
Some studies in the arts, but all his fancy
Turned to astrology and geomancy,
And he could deal with certain propositions
And make a forecast under some conditions
About the likelihood of drought or showers
For those who asked at favourable hours,
Or put a question how their luck would fall
In this or that, I can't describe them all.

Astrology gave its practitioners considerable authority well beyond medieval times and this woodcut illustrates the superstitious flavour of an age in which the clever young student Nicholas could dupe the poor Carpenter all too easily.

This lad was known as Nicholas the Gallant,
And making love in secret was his talent,
For he was very close and sly, and took
Advantage of his meek and girlish look.
He rented a small chamber in the kip
All by himself without companionship.
He decked it charmingly with herbs and fruit
And he himself was sweeter than the root
Of liquorice, or any fragrant herb.
His astronomic text-books were superb,
He had an astrolabe to match his art
And calculating counters laid apart
On handy shelves that stood above his bed.
His press was curtained coarsely and in red;
Above there lay a gallant harp in sight
On which he played melodiously at night
With such a touch that all the chamber rang;
It was *The Virgin's Angelus* he sang,
And after that he sang *King William's Note*,
And people often blessed his merry throat.

The husband as cuckold was a common Chaucerian theme. This illustration from the 'Roman de la Rose' shows a jealous husband on guard. The Carpenter should have been as vigilant....

And that was how this charming scholar spent
His time and money, which his friends had sent.
This carpenter had married a new wife
Not long before, and loved her more than life.
She was a girl of eighteen years of age.
Jealous he was and kept her in a cage,
For he was old and she was wild and young;
He thought himself quite likely to be stung.
He might have known, were Cato on his shelf,
A man should marry someone like himself;
A man should pick an equal for his mate.
Youth and old age are often in debate.
However, he had fallen in the snare,
And had to bear his cross as others bear.
She was a fair young wife, her body as slender
As any weasel's, and as soft and tender;
She used to wear a girdle of striped silk;
Her apron was as white as morning milk
Over her loins, all gusseted and pleated.
White was her smock; embroidery repeated
Its pattern on the collar, front and back,
Inside and out; it was of silk, and black.
The tapes and ribbons of her milky mutch
Were made to match her collar to a touch;
She wore a broad silk fillet, rather high,
And certainly she had a lecherous eye.
And she had plucked her eyebrows into bows,
Slenderly arched they were, and black as sloes;
And a more truly blissful sight to see
She was than blossom on a cherry-tree,
And softer than the wool upon a wether;
And by her girdle hung a purse of leather,

Tasselled with silk and silver droplets, pearled;
If you went seeking up and down the world,
The wisest man you met would have to wrench
His fancy to imagine such a wench;
And her complexion had a brighter tint
Than a new florin from the Royal Mint.
As to her song, it was as loud and quick
As any swallow's chirping on a rick;
And she would skip or play some game or other
Like any kid or calf behind its mother.
Her mouth was sweet as mead or honey – say
A hoard of apples lying in the hay.
Skittish she was, and jolly as a colt,
Tall as a mast and upright as a bolt
Out of a bow. Her collaret revealed
A brooch as big as boss upon a shield.
High shoes she wore, and laced them to the top.
She was a daisy, O a lollypop
For any nobleman to take to bed
Or some good man of yeoman stock to wed.

Now, gentlemen, this Gallant Nicholas
One day began to romp and make a pass
At this young woman, in a mood of play,
Her husband being out, down Osney way.
Students are sly, and giving way to whim,
He made a grab and caught her by the quim
And said, 'Unless I have my will of you
I'll die of secret love – O, darling, do!'
Then held her haunches hard and gave a cry
'O love-me-all-at-once or I shall die!'
She gave a spring, just like a skittish colt
Boxed in a frame for shoeing, and with a jolt
Managed in time to wrench her head away,
And said, 'Give over, Nicholas, I say!
No, I won't kiss you! Stop it! Let me go
Or I shall scream! I'll let the neighbours know!
Where are your manners? Take away your paws!'

*In an illustration from the 'Roman de la Rose', the errant wife is
punished and, although Alison avoids this, Nicholas is rewarded for
their adultery by being 'branded on the bum'.*

Then Nicholas began to plead his cause
And spoke so fair in proffering what he could
That in the end she promised him she would,
Swearing she'd love him, with a solemn promise
To be at his disposal, by St Thomas,
When she could spy an opportunity.
'My husband is so full of jealousy,
Unless you watch your step and hold your breath
I know for certain it will be my death,'
She said, 'So keep it well under your hat.'
'Oh, never mind about a thing like that.'
Said he; 'A scholar doesn't have to stir
His wits so much to trick a carpenter.'

And so they both agreed to it, and swore
To watch their chance, as I have said before.
When things were settled thus as they thought fit,
And Nicholas had stroked her loins a bit
And kissed her sweetly, he took down his harp
And played away, a merry tune and sharp.

It happened later she went off to church,
This worthy wife, one holiday, to search
Her conscience and to do the works of Christ.
She put her work aside and she enticed
The colour to her face to make her mark;
Her forehead shone. There was a parish clerk
Serving the church, whose name was Absalon.
His hair was all in golden curls and shone;
Just like a fan it strutted outwards, starting
To left and right from an accomplished parting.
Ruddy his face, his eyes as grey as goose,
His shoes cut out in tracery, as in use
In old St Paul's. The hose upon his feet
Showed scarlet through, and all his clothes were neat
And proper. In a jacket of light blue,
Flounced at the waist and tagged with laces too,
He went, and wore a surplice just as gay
And white as any blossom on the spray.
God bless my soul, he was a merry knave!
He knew how to let blood, cut hair and shave,
And draw up legal deeds; at other whiles
He used to dance in twenty different styles
(After the current school at Oxford though,
Casting his legs about him to and fro).
He played a two-stringed fiddle, did it proud,
And sang a high falsetto, rather loud;
And he was just as good on the guitar.
There was no public-house in town, or bar,
He didn't visit with his merry face
If there were saucy barmaids round the place.
He was a little squeamish in the matter
Of farting, and satirical in chatter.
This Absalon, so jolly in his ways,
Would bear the censer round on holy days
And cense the parish women. He would cast
Many a love-lorn look before he passed,
Especially at this carpenter's young wife;
Looking at her would make a happy life
She was so neat, so sweet, so lecherous!

And I dare say if she had been a mouse
And he a cat, she'd have been pounced upon.

In taking the collection Absalon
Would find his heart was set in such a whirl
Of love, he would take nothing from a girl,
For courtesy, he said, it wasn't right.

That evening, when the moon was shining bright
He ups with his guitar and off he tours
On the look-out for any paramours.
Larky and amorous, away he strode
Until he reached the carpenter's abode
A little after cock-crow, took his stand
Beside the casement window close at hand
(It was set low upon the cottage-face)
And started singing softly and with grace,

Now dearest lady, if thy pleasure be
In thoughts of love, think tenderly of me!'
On his guitar he plucked a tuneful string.

This carpenter awoke and heard him sing
And turning to his wife said, 'Alison!
Wife! Do you hear him? There goes Absalon
Chanting away under our chamber wall.'
And she, 'Yes, John, God knows I hear it all.'
If she thought more of it she didn't tell.

So things went on. What's better than 'All's well'?
From day to day this jolly Absalon,
Wooing away, became quite woe-begone;
He lay awake all night, and all the day,
Combed his thick locks and tried to pass for gay,
Wooed her by go-between and wooed by proxy,
Swore to be page and servant to his doxy,
Trilled and rouladed like a nightingale,
Sent her sweet wine and mead and spicy ale,
And wafers piping hot and jars of honey,
And, as she lived in town, he offered money.
For there are some a money-bag provokes
And some are won by kindness, some by strokes.

Once, in the hope his talent might engage,
He played the part of Herod on the stage.
What was the good? Were he as bold as brass,
She was in love with gallant Nicholas;
However Absalon might blow his horn
His labour won him nothing but her scorn.
She looked upon him as her private ape
And held his earnest wooing all a jape.
There is a proverb, true, as you may find,
That *Out-of-Sight is also Out-of-Mind.*
For Nigh-and-Sly has the advantage there;
And, much as Absalon might tear his hair,
And rage at being seldom in her sight,
Nicholas, nigh and sly, stood in his light.
Now, show your paces, Nicholas you spark!
And leave lamenting to the parish clerk.

And so it happened that one Saturday
When the old carpenter was safe away
At Osney, Nicholas and Alison
Agreed at last in what was to be done.
Nicholas was to exercise his wits

On her suspicious husband's foolish fits,
And, if so be the trick worked out all right,
She then would sleep with Nicholas all night,
For such was his desire and hers as well;
And even quicker than it takes to tell,
Young Nicholas, who simply couldn't wait,
Went to his room on tip-toe with a plate
Of food and drink, enough to last a day
Or two, and Alison was told to say,
In case her husband asked for Nicholas,
That she had no idea where he was,
And that she hadn't set eyes on him all day
And thought he must be ill, she couldn't say;
And more than once the maid had given a call
And shouted but no answer came at all.

So it continued, all that Saturday
Without a sound from Nicholas, who lay
Upstairs, and ate or slept as pleased him best
Till Sunday when the sun went down to rest.

This foolish carpenter was lost in wonder
At Nicholas; what could have got him under?
He said, 'I can't help thinking, by the Mass,
Things can't be going right with Nicholas.
What if he took and died? God guard his ways!
A ticklish place the world is, nowadays.
I saw a corpse this morning borne to kirk
That only Monday last I saw at work.
Run up,' he told the serving-lad, 'be quick,
Shout at his door, or knock it with a brick.
Take a good look and tell me how he fares.'

The serving-boy went sturdily upstairs,
Stopped at the door and, standing there, the lad
Shouted away and, hammering like mad,
Cried, 'Ho! What's up? Hi! Master Nicholay!
How can you lie up there asleep all day?'

But all for nought, he didn't hear a soul.
He found a broken panel with a hole
Right at the bottom, useful to the cat
For creeping in by: so he looked through that,
And, in the end, he saw him through the crack.
This Nicholas lay gaping on his back
As if he'd caught a glimpse of the new moon.
Down went the boy and told his master soon
About the state in which he found the man.

On hearing this the carpenter began
To cross himself and said, 'St Frideswide bless us!
We little know what's coming to distress us.
The man has fallen, with this here 'astromy',
Into a fit, or lunacy maybe.
I always thought that was how it would go.
God has some secrets that we shouldn't know.
How blessed are the simple, aye, indeed,
That only know enough to say their creed!
Happened just so with such another student
Of astromy and he was so imprudent
As to stare upwards while he crossed a field,
Busy foreseeing what the stars revealed;
And what should happen but he fell down flat

Into a marl-pit. He didn't foresee that!
But by the Saints we've reached a sorry pass;
I can't help worrying for Nicholas.
He shall be scolded for his studying
If I know how to scold, by Christ the King!
Get me a staff to prise against the floor.
Robin, you put your shoulder to the door.
We'll shake the study out of him, I guess!'

The pair of them began to heave and press
Against the door. Happened the lad was strong
And so it didn't take them very long
To heave it off its hinges; down it came.
Still as a stone lay Nicholas, with the same
Expression, gaping upwards into air.
The carpenter supposed it was despair
And caught him by the shoulders mightily,
Shook him and shouted with asperity:
'What, Nicholas! Hey! Look down! Is that a fashion
To act? Wake up and think upon Christ's passion.
I sign you with the cross from elves and sprites!'
And he began the spell for use at nights
In all four corners of the room and out
Across the threshold too and round about:

Jesu Christ and Benedict Sainted
Bless this house from creature tainted,
Drive away night-hags, white Pater-noster,
Where did you go, St Peter's soster?

And in the end the dandy Nicholas
Began to sigh, 'And must it come to pass?'
He said, 'Must all the world be cast away?'
The carpenter replied, 'What's that you say?
Put trust in God as we do, working men.'
Nicholas answered, 'Fetch some liquor then,
And afterwards, in strictest secrecy,
I'll speak of something touching you and me,
But not another soul must know, that's plain.'

This carpenter went down and came again
Bringing some powerful ale – a largish quart.
When each had had his share of this support
Young Nicholas got up and shut the door
And, sitting down beside him on the floor,
Said to the carpenter, 'Now, John, my dear,
My excellent host, swear on your honour here
Not to repeat a syllable I say,
For here are Christ's intentions, to betray
Which to a soul puts you among the lost,
And vengeance for it at a bitter cost
Shall fall upon you. You'll be driven mad!'
'Christ and His holy blood forbid it, lad!'
The silly fellow answered, 'I'm no blab,
Though I should say it. I'm not given to gab.
Say what you like, for I shall never tell
Man, woman or child by Him that harrowed Hell!'

'Now, John,' said Nicholas, 'believe you me,
I have found out by my astrology,
And looking at the moon when it was bright,
That Monday next, a quarter way through night,
Rain is to fall in torrents, such a scud

God warns Noah of the coming Flood. Such images were
powerfully ingrained, making Nicholas's warning of a new Flood
sufficiently credible for the carpenter to rush off to prepare himself.

It will be twice as bad as Noah's Flood.
This world,' he said, 'in just about an hour,
Shall all be drowned, it's such a hideous shower,
And all mankind, with total loss of life.'

The carpenter exclaimed, 'Alas, my wife!
My little Alison! Is she to drown?'
And in his grief he very near fell down.
'Is there no remedy,' he said, 'for this?'
'Thanks be to God,' said Nicholas, 'there is,
If you will do exactly what I say
And don't start thinking up some other way.
In wise old Solomon you'll find the verse
"Who takes advice shall never fare the worse,"
And so if good advice is to prevail
I undertake with neither mast nor sail
To save her yet, and save myself and you.
Haven't you heard how Noah was saved too
When God forewarned him and his sons and daughters
That all the world should sink beneath the waters?'
'Yes,' said the carpenter, 'a long time back.'
'Haven't you heard,' said Nicholas, 'what a black
Business it was, when Noah tried to whip
His wife (who wouldn't come) on board the ship?
He'd have been better pleased, I'll undertake,
With all that weather just about to break,
If she had had a vessel of her own.
Now, what are we to do? We can't postpone
The thing; it's coming soon, as I was saying,
It calls for haste, not preaching or delaying.

I want you, now, at once, to hurry off
And fetch a shallow tub or kneading-trough
For each of us, but see that they are large
And such as we can float in, like a barge.

And have them loaded with sufficient victual
To last a day – we only need a little.
The waters will abate and flow away
Round nine o'clock upon the following day.
Robin the lad mayn't know of this, poor knave,
Nor Jill the maid, those two I cannot save.
Don't ask me why; and even if you do
I can't disclose God's secret thoughts to you.
You should be satisfied, unless you're mad,
To find as great a grace as Noah had.
And I shall save your wife, you needn't doubt it,
Now off you go, and hurry up about it.

'And when the tubs have been collected, three,
That's one for her and for yourself and me,
Then hang them in the roof below the thatching
That no one may discover what we're hatching.
When you have finished doing what I said
And stowed the victuals in them overhead,
Also an axe to hack the ropes apart,
So, when the water rises, we can start,
And, lastly, when you've broken out the gable,
The garden one that's just above the stable,
So that we may cast free without delay
After the mighty shower has gone away,
You'll float as merrily, I undertake,
As any lily-white duck behind her drake.
And I'll call out, "Hey, Alison! Hey, John!
Cheer yourselves up! The flood will soon be gone."
And you'll shout back, "Hail, Master Nicholay!
Good morning! I can see you well. It's day!"
We shall be lords for all the rest of life
Of all the world, like Noah and his wife.

'One thing I warn you of; it's only right.
We must be very careful on the night,
Once we have safely managed to embark,
To hold our tongues, to utter no remark,
No cry or call, for we must fall to prayer.
This is the Lord's dear will, so have a care.

'Your wife and you must hang some way apart,
For there must be no sin before we start,
No more in longing looks than in the deed.
Those are your orders. Off with you! God speed!
To-morrow night when everyone's asleep
We'll all go quietly upstairs and creep
Into our tubs, awaiting Heaven's grace.
And now be off. No time to put the case
At greater length, no time to sermonize;
The proverb says, "Say nothing, send the wise."
You're wise enough, I do not have to teach you.
Go, save our lives for us, as I beseech you.'

This silly carpenter then went his way
Muttering to himself, 'Alas the day!'
And told his wife in strictest secrecy.
She was aware, far more indeed than he,
What this quaint stratagem might have in sight,
But she pretended to be dead with fright.
'Alas!' she said. 'Whatever it may cost,
Hurry and help, or we shall all be lost.

There was a medieval tradition, unsupported by any biblical text, that Noah's wife was disobedient. She is supposed to have refused to embark in the Ark until she had finished her spinning. Nicholas recalls this story to justify his proposal for separate tubs.

I am your honest, true and wedded wife,
Go, dearest husband, help to save my life!'

How fancy throws us into perturbation!
People can die of mere imagination,
So deep is the impression one can take.
This silly carpenter began to quake,
Before his eyes there verily seemed to be
The floods of Noah, wallowing like the sea
And drowning Alison his honey-pet.
He wept and wailed, his features were all set
In grief, he sighed with many a doleful grunt.
He went and got a tub, began to hunt
For kneading-troughs, found two, and had them sent
Home to his house in secret; then he went
And, unbeknowns, he hung them from a rafter.
With his own hands he made three ladders after,
Uprights and rungs, to help them in their scheme
Of climbing where they hung upon the beam.
He victualled tub and trough, and made all snug
With bread and cheese, and ale in a large jug,
Enough for three of them to last the day,
And, just before completing this array,
Packed off the maid and his apprentice too
To London on a job they had to do.
And on the Monday when it drew to night
He shut his door and dowsed the candle-light
And made quite sure all was as it should be.
And shortly, up they clambered, all the three,
Silent and separate. They began to pray
And '*Pater Noster* mum', said Nicholay,
And 'mum' said John, and 'mum' said Alison.
The carpenter's devotions being done,

He sat quite still, then fell to prayer again
With one ear rocked, however, for the rain.
   he carpenter, with all the work he'd seen,
     Fell dead asleep – round curfew, must have been,
     Maybe a little later on the whole.
He groaned in sleep for travail of his soul
And snored because his head was turned awry.
   own by their ladders, stalking from on high
     Came Nicholas and Alison, and sped
     Softly downstairs, without a word, to bed,
And where this carpenter was wont to be
The revels started and the melody.
And thus lay Nicholas and Alison
Busy in solace and the quest of fun,
Until the bell for lauds had started ringing
And in the chancel friars began their singing.
   his parish clerk, this amorous Absalon,
     Love-stricken still and very woe-begone,
     Upon the Monday was in company
At Osney with his friends for jollity,
And chanced to ask a resident cloisterer
What had become of John the carpenter.
The fellow drew him out of church to say,
'Don't know; not been at work since Saturday.
I can't say where he is; I think he went
To fetch the Abbot timber. He is sent
Often enough for timber, has to go
Out to the Grange and stop a day or so;
If not, he's certainly at home to-day,
But where he is I can't exactly say.'
   bsalon was a jolly lad and light
     Of heart; he thought, 'I'll stay awake to-night;
     I'm certain that I haven't seen him stirring
About his door since dawn; it's safe inferring
That he's away. As I'm alive I'll go
And tap his window softly at the crow
Of cock – the sill is low-set on the wall.
I shall see Alison and tell her all
My love-longing, and I can hardly miss
Some favour from her, at the least a kiss.

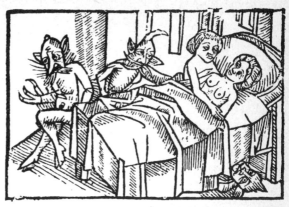

*A woodcut from an early printed book, 'Robert the Devyll',
showing disconsolate demons in the presence of matrimonial fidelity.
They would have had a happier time with Alison whose marriage
vows were readily vulnerable to temptation. . . .*

I'll get some satisfaction anyway;
There's been an itching in my mouth all day
And that's a sign of kissing at the least.
And all last night I dreamt about a feast.
I think I'll go and sleep an hour or two,
Then wake and have some fun, that's what I'll do.'
   he first cock crew at last, and thereupon
     Up rose this jolly lover Absalon
     In gayest clothes, garnished with that and this;
But first he chewed a grain of liquorice
To charm his breath before he combed his hair.
Under his tongue the comfit nestling there
Would make him gracious. He began to roam
Towards the carpenter's; he reached their home
And by the casement window took his stand.
Breast-high it stood, no higher than his hand.
He gave a cough, it was a semi-sound;
'Alison, honey-comb, are you around?
Sweet cinnamon, my little pretty bird,
Sweetheart, wake up and say a little word!

*A Flemish illustration of woodcutters at work and prayer. John
'was sent often enough for timber', and once too often for his own
good when the lecherous Nicholas and nubile Alison hatched their
plot. A lively interest in the people and goings-on of the workaday
world dominated Chaucer's poetry during the final phase of his
writing career, to which 'The Miller's Tale' belongs.*

You seldom think of me in all my woe,
I sweat for love of you wherever I go!
No wonder if I do, I pine and bleat
As any lambkin hungering for the teat,
Believe me, darling, I'm so deep in love
I croon with longing like a turtle-dove,
I eat as little as a girl at school.'
'You go away,' she answered, 'you Tom-fool!
There's no come-up-and-kiss-me here for you.
I love another and why shouldn't I too?
Better than you, by Jesu, Absalon!
Take yourself off or I shall throw a stone.
I want to get some sleep. You go to Hell!'
'Alas!' said Absalon. 'I knew it well;
True love is always mocked and girded at;
So kiss me, if you can't do more than that,
For Jesu's love and for the love of me!'
'And if I do, will you be off?' said she.
'Promise you, darling,' answered Absalon.
'Get ready then; wait, I'll put something on,'
She said and then she added under breath
To Nicholas, 'Hush . . . we shall laugh to death!'

This Absalon went down upon his knees;
'I am a lord!' he thought, 'And by degrees
There may be more to come; the plot may
  thicken.'
'Mercy, my love!' he said, 'Your mouth, my chicken!'

She flung the window open then in haste
And said, 'Have done, come on, no time to waste,
The neighbours here are always on the spy.'

Absalon started wiping his mouth dry.
Dark was the night as pitch, as black as coal,
And at the window out she put her hole,
And Absalon, so fortune framed the farce,
Put up his mouth and kissed her naked arse
Most savorously before he knew of this.

And back he started. Something was amiss;
He knew quite well a woman has no beard,
Yet something rough and hairy had appeared.
'What have I done?' he said. 'Can that be you?'
'Teehee!' she cried and clapped the window to.
Off went poor Absalon sadly through the dark.
'A beard! a beard! cried Nicholas the Spark.
'God's body, that was something like a joke!'
And Absalon, overhearing what he spoke,
Bit on his lips and nearly threw a fit
In rage and thought, 'I'll pay you back for it!'

Who's busy rubbing, scraping at his lips
With dust, with sand, with straw, with cloth,
  with chips,
But Absalon? He thought, 'I'll bring him down!
I wouldn't let this go for all the town.
I'd take my soul and sell it to the Devil
To be revenged upon him! I'll get level.
O God, why did I let myself be fooled?'

The fiery heat of love by now had cooled,
For from that time he kissed her hinder parts
He didn't give a tinker's curse for tarts;

His malady was cured by this endeavour
And he defied all paramours whatever.

So, weeping like a child that has been whipped,
He turned away; across the road he slipped
And called on Gervase. Gervase was a smith;
His forge was full of things for ploughing with
And he was busy sharpening a share.

Absalon knocked, and with an easy air
Called, 'Gervase! Open up the door, come on!'
'What's that? Who's there?' 'It's me, it's
  Abasalon.'
'What, Absalon? By Jesu's blessed tree
You're early up! Hey, *benedicite*,
What's wrong? Some jolly girl as like as not
Has coaxed you out and set you on the trot.
Blessed St Neot! You know the thing I mean.'

But Absalon, who didn't give a bean
For all his joking, offered no debate.
He had a good deal more upon his plate
Than Gervase knew and said, 'Would it be fair
To borrow that coulter in the chimney there,
The hot one, see it? I've a job to do;
It won't take long, I'll bring it back to you.'
Gervase replied, 'Why, if you asked for gold,
A bag of sovereigns or of wealth untold,
It should be yours, as I'm an honest smith.
But, Christ, why borrow that to do it with?'
'Let that,' said Absalon, 'be as it may;
You'll hear about it all some other day.'

He caught the coulter up – the haft was cool –
And left the smithy softly with the tool,
Crept to the little window in the wall
And coughed. He knocked and gave a little call
Under the window as he had before.

Alison said, 'There's someone at the door.
Who's knocking there? I'll warrant it's a thief.'
'Why, no,' said he, 'my little flower-leaf,
It's your own Absalon, my sweety-thing!
Look what I've brought you – it's a golden ring
My mother gave me, as I may be saved.
It's very fine, and prettily engraved;
I'll give it to you, darling, for a kiss.'

Now Nicholas had risen for a piss,
And thought he could improve upon the jape
And make him kiss his arse ere he escape,
And opening the window with a jerk,
Stuck out his arse, a handsome piece of work,
Buttocks and all, as far as to the haunch.

Said Absalon, all set to make a launch,
'Speak, pretty bird, I know not where thou are!'
This Nicholas at once let fly a fart
As loud as if it were a thunder-clap.
He was near blinded by the blast, poor chap,
But his hot iron was ready; with a thump
He smote him in the middle of the rump.

Off went the skin a hand's breadth round about
Where the hot coulter struck and burnt it out.
Such was the pain, he thought he must be dying

Before his comic genius could fulfil itself, Chaucer had to part company with the courtly world that had inspired his earlier work and move to the plane of humdrum actuality represented by such commonplace objects as ladders, coulters and tubs.

And, mad with agony, he started crying,
'Help! Water! Water! Help! For Heaven's love!'
he carpenter, startled from sleep above,
And hearing shouts for water and a thud,
Thought, 'Heaven help us! Here comes Nowel's Flood!'
And up he sat and with no more ado
He took his axe and smote the ropes in two

And down went everything. He didn't stop
To sell his bread and ale, but came down flop
Upon the floor and fainted right away.
p started Alison and Nicholay
And shouted, 'Help!' and 'Murder!' in the street.
The neighbours all came running up in heat
And stood there staring at the wretched man.
He lay there fainting, pale beneath his tan;
His arm in falling had been broken double.
But still he was obliged to face his trouble,
For when he spoke he was at once borne down
By Nicholas and his wife. They told the town
That he was mad, there'd got into his blood
Some sort of nonsense about 'Nowel's Flood',
That vain imaginings and fantasy
Had made him buy the kneading-tubs, that he
Had hung them in the rafters up above
And that he'd begged them both for heaven's love
To sit up in the roof for company.
ll started laughing at this lunacy
And streamed upstairs to gape and pry and poke,
And treated all his sufferings as a joke.
No matter what the carpenter asserted
It went for nothing, no one was converted;
With powerful oaths they swore the fellow down
And he was held for mad by all the town;
The students all ganged up with one another
Saying: 'The fellow's crazy, my dear brother!'
And every one among them laughed and joked.
And so the carpenter's wife was truly poked,
As if his jealousy to justify,
And Absalon has kissed her nether eye
And Nicholas is branded on the bum
And God bring all of us to Kingdom Come.

ioyeusement il fut apres anaise comme il
appert au . w . chappitre deser . Si mest
adine que cest vng pechie changent et mai
nent comme afaire plusems maulx .

¶ Comment abstinence est cause de
plusems biens . vi.e chappitre .

Gluttony contrasted with Abstinence. The Reeve was also a
carpenter 'of first-rate skill' and he took offence at the Miller's
story. He now makes a greedy miller the butt of his Tale.

THE REEVE'S TALE

The Reeve's Prologue

HEN all had laughed at the preposterous lark
Of Absalon and Nicholas the Spark,
Various folk made various comment after;
But the majority dissolved in laughter,
Nor did I see a soul it seemed to grieve
Unless it might be Oswald, the old Reeve,
For, as he was a carpenter by trade,
He was a little angry still and made
Grumbling remarks and scolded for a bit.
'As I'm a man I'd pay you back for it,'
He said, 'with how they bleared a Miller's eye,
If I liked dirt and wished to argufy.
But I am old. Dirt doesn't go with doddering,
Grass-time is done and I'm for winter foddering.
My hoary top-knot writes me down for old;
Same as my hair, my heart is full of mould,
Unless I be like them there medlar-fruit,
Them that gets rottener as they ripen to't,
Till they be rotted down in straw and dung.
That's how we get to be, no longer young.
Till we be rotten we can never ripe.
We hop along, as long as world will pipe;
Our will is always catching on the nail,
Wanting a hoary head and a green tail,
Like leeks have got; the strength to play that game
Is gone, though we love foolishness the same.
What we can't do no more we talk about
And rake the ashes when the fire is out.
'Yet we have four live coals, as I can show;
Lies, boasting, greed and rage will always glow.
Those are the sparks among the ancient embers
Though we be nigh unwelded in our members.
Desire never fails, and that's the truth,

For even now I have a coltish tooth,
Many as be the years now dead and done
Before my tap of life began to run.
Certain, when I was born, so long ago,
Death drew the tap of life and let it flow;
And ever since the tap has done its task,
And now there's little but an empty cask.
My stream of life's but drops upon the rim.
An old fool's tongue will run away with him
To chime and chatter of monkey-tricks that's past;
There's nothing left but dotage at the last!'
Our Host, on hearing all this sermoning,
Began to speak as lordly as a king,
And said, 'What does it come to, all this wit?
What! Spend the morning talking Holy Writ?
The devil that makes a preacher of a Reeve
Turns cobblers into doctors, I believe.
Give us your story, if you've one in stock.
Why, look! Here's Deptford and it's nine o'clock!
And Greenwich too, with many a blackguard in it.
High time to tell your story, so begin it.'
'Now, gentlemen,' Oswald the Reeve replied,
'I hope as none will be dissatisfied
Though I should tweak the Miller by the cap,
For lawful 'tis to give him tap for tap.
This drunken Miller we've had so much drool of,
Told how a carpenter was made a fool of,
Maybe to score off me, for I am one.
By y'r leave, I'll pay him back before I've done
In his own filthy words, you may expec'.
I hope to God he breaks his bloody neck.
He sees the mote in my eye, if there is un,
But cannot see the beam there is in his'n.'

The Reeve's Tale

AT Trumpington, not far from Cambridge town,
A bridge goes over where the brook runs down
And by that brook there stands a mill as well.
And it's God's truth that I am going to tell.
There was a miller lived there many a day
As proud as any peacock and as gay;
He could play bag-pipes too, fish, mend his gear,
And turn a lathe, and wrestle, and poach deer.
And at his belt he carried a long blade,
Trenchant it was as any sword that's made,
And in his pouch a jolly little knife.
No one dared touch him, peril of his life.
He had a Sheffield dagger in his hose.
Round was his face and puggish was his nose;
Bald as an ape he was. To speak more fully,
He was a thorough-going market bully
Whom none dared lay a hand on or come near
Without him swearing that they'd buy it dear.
He was a thief as well of corn and meal,
And sly at that; his habit was to steal.
Simpkin the Swagger he was called in scorn.
He had a wife and she was nobly born;
Her father was the parson of the town;
A dowry of brass dishes he put down
In order to have Simpkin his relation.
The nuns had given her an education.
Simpkin would take no woman, so he said,
Unless she were a virgin and well-bred,
To save the honour of his yeoman stock;
And she was proud, pert as a magpie cock.
It was a proper sight to see the pair
On holidays, what with him strutting there
In front of her, his hood about his head,
And she behind him all decked out in red,
Like Simpkin's hose, for scarlet-red he had 'em.
No one dared call her anything but 'Madam',
No one who passed was bold enough to try

A bit of fun with her or wink an eye,
Unless indeed he wanted Sim the Swagger
To murder him with cutlass, knife or dagger,
For jealous folk are dangerous, you know,
At least they want their wives to think them so.
And then her birth was smirched to say the least;
Being the daughter of a celibate priest
She must maintain her dignity, of which
She had as much as water in a ditch.
She was a sneering woman and she thought
That ladies should respect her, so they ought,
What with her well-connected family,
And education in a nunnery.
They had a daughter too between them both,
She was a girl of twenty summers' growth;
But that was all except a child they had
Still in the cradle, but a proper lad.
The wench was plump, well-grown enough to pass,
With a snub nose and eyes as grey as glass;
Her rump was broad, her breasts were round and high;
She'd very pretty hair, I will not lie.
The parson of the town, for she was fair,
Intended to appoint the girl as heir
To all his property in house and land
And he was stiff with suitors to her hand.
He purposed to bestow her if he could
Where blood and ancient lineage made it good.
For Holy Church's goods should be expended
On Holy Church's blood, so well-descended,
And holy blood should have what's proper to it
Though Holy Church should be devoured to do it.
This Miller levied toll beyond a doubt
On wheat and malt from the land about,
Particularly from a large-sized College

*A mill with its cottage. Five adults in the miller's tiny bedroom is
the setting for the farcical climax in 'The Reeve's Tale'.*

Both 'The Miller's Tale' and 'The Reeve's Tale' are set in university towns and in both students outwit tradesmen.

In Cambridge, Solar Hall. 'Twas common knowledge
They sent their wheat and malt to him to grind it.
Happened one day the man who ought to mind it,
The college manciple, lay sick in bed,
And some reported him as good as dead.
On hearing which the miller robbed him more
A hundred times than he had robbed before;
For up till then he'd only robbed politely,
But now he stole outrageously, forthrightly.

T he Warden scolded hard and made a scene,
  But there! The miller didn't give a bean,
  Blustered it out and swore it wasn't so.

T wo poor young Bible-clerks or students, though,
  Lived in this College (that of which I spoke).
  Headstrong they were and eager for a joke,
And simply for the chance of sport and play
They went and plagued the Warden night and day
Just for a little leave to spend the morn
Watching the miller grind their meal and corn,
And each was ready to engage his neck
The miller couldn't rob them half a peck
Of corn by trickery, nor yet by force;
And in the end he gave them leave, of course.

O ne was called John and Alan was the other,
  Both born in the same village, name of Strother,
  Far in the north, I cannot tell you where.

Alan collected all his gear with care,
  Loaded it on a horse the warden had,
  And off he went with John the other lad,
Each with his sword and buckler by his side.
John knew the way – he didn't need a guide -
Reaches the'mill and down the sack he flings.

Alan spoke first: 'Well, Simon, lad, how's things?
  And how's your canny daughter and your wife?'
  Says Simpkin, 'Welcome, Alan! Odds my life.
It's John as well! What, are you in the sequel?'
'By God,' said John, 'Needs-must has got no equal,
And it behoves a man that has nie servant
To work, as say the learned and observant.
Wor Manciple is like enough to dee,
Such aches and torments in his teeth has he;
So Alan here and I have brought wor sack
Of corn for grinding and to bring it back.
Help us get home as quickly as ye can.'
'It shall be done,' said he, 'as I'm a man.
What'll you do while I've the job in hand?'
'By God,' said John, 'I have a mind to stand
Right by the hopper here and watch the corn
As it gans in. Never since I was born
Saw I a hopper wagging to and fro.'

Alan spoke up: 'Eh, John, and will ye so?
  Then I shall stand below a short way off
  And watch the meal come down into the trough;
I need no more than that by way of sport,
For John, in faith, I'm one of the same sort
And diven't knaa nowt of milling, same as ye.'

T he miller smiled at their simplicity
  And thought, 'It's just a trick, what they're about,
  They think that nobody can catch them out,
But by the Lord I'll blear their eyes a bit
For all their fine philosophy and wit.
The more they try to do me on the deal,
When the time comes, the more I mean to steal.
Instead of flour I will give them bran;
"The greatest scholar is not the wisest man",
As the wolf said in answer to the mare.
Them and their precious learning! Much I care.'

A nd when he saw his chance he sidled out
  Into the yard behind and looked about
  Without their noticing until at last
He found their horse where they had made him fast
Under an arbour just behind the mill.

U p to the horse he goes with quiet skill
  And strips the bridle off him there and then.
  And when the horse was loose, off to the fen
Through thick and thin, and whinneying 'Weehee!'
He raced to join the wild mares running free.

T he miller then went back, and did not say
  A word of this, but passed the time of day
  With John and Alan till their corn was ground;
And when the meal was fairly sacked and bound,
John wandered out and found their horse was gone.
'Good Lord! Help! Help! Come quickly!' shouted John,
'Wor horse is lost, Alan! The devil's in it!

71

God's bones, man, use your legs! Come out this minute!
Lord save us all, the Warden's palfrey's lost.'
Alan forgot his meal and corn and cost,
   Abandoning frugality and care.
   'What's that?' he shouted. 'Palfrey? Which way?
   Where?'
The miller's wife ran clucking like a hen
   Towards them, saying, 'Gone off to the fen
   To the wild mares as fast as he can go.
Curse on the clumsy hand that tied him so!
Should have known better how to knit the reins.'
John said, 'Bad luck to it. Alan, for Christ's pains,
Put down your sword, man; so will I; let's gan!
We'll rin him like a roe together, man!
God's precious heart! He cannot scape us all!
Why didn't you put the palfrey in the stall?
You must be daft, bad luck to you! Haway!'
And off ran John and Alan in dismay,
Towards the fen as fast as they could go.

An illustration from 'The Grete Herbal' of a lady baking. In view of all his pilfering of his customers' corn, it is surprising that the miller's daughter has to buy bread as well as ale.

And when the miller saw that this was so,
   A good half-bushel of their flour he took
   And gave it over to his wife to cook.
'I think,' he said, 'these lads have had a fright.
I'll pluck their beards. Yes, let 'em read and write,
But none the less a miller is their match.
Look at them now! Like children playing catch.
Won't be an easy job to get him, though!'
These foolish Bible-clerks ran to and fro
   And shouted, 'Woa, lad, stand! . . . Look out
      behind!
Whistle him up . . . I've got him . . . watch it . . . *mind!*'

But to be brief, it wasn't until night
They caught the palfrey, hunt him as they might
Over the fens, he ran away so fast;
But in a ditch they captured him at last.
Weary and wet, like cattle in the rain,
   Came foolish John and Alan back again.
   Said John, 'Alas the day that I was born!
We've earned nowt here but mockery and scorn.
Wor corn is stolen and they'll call us fools,
Warden and all wor meäts in the Schools,
And most of all the miller. What a day!'
So back they went, John grousing all the way,
   Towards the mill and put the horse in byre.
   They found the miller sitting by the fire,
For it was night, too late for going home,
And, for the love of God, they begged a room
For shelter and they proffered him their penny.
'A room?' the miller said. 'There isn't any.
There's this, such as it is; we'll share it then.
My house is small, but you are learned men
And by your arguments can make a place
Twenty foot broad as infinite as space.
Take a look round and see if it will do,
Or make it bigger with your parley-voo.'
'Well, Simon, you must have your little joke
And, by St Cuthbert, that was fairly spoke!
Well, people have a proverb to remind them
To bring their own, or take things as they find them,'
Said John. 'Dear host, do get us out the cup;
A little meat and drink would cheer us up.
We'll give ye the full payment, on my word.
No empty-handed man can catch a bird;
See, here's the silver, ready to be spent.'
Down into Trumpington the daughter went
   For bread and ale; the miller cooked a goose,
   And tied their horse up lest it should get loose

'The House of Rest', a domestic scene from Pierre Gringore's 'Castell of Laboure', printed by Wynkyn de Worde. Alan and John found Simpkin's hospitality far from generous but they took from him and his family rather more than he intended. . . .

Again, and in his chamber made a bed
With clean white sheets and blankets fairly spread,
Ten foot from his, upon a sort of shelf.
His daughter had a bed all by herself
Quite close in the same room; they were to lie
All side by side, no help for it, and why?
Because there was no other in the house.

They supped and talked and had a fine carouse
And drank a lot of ale, the very best.
Midnight or thereabout they went to rest.
Properly pasted was the miller's head,
Pale-drunk he was, he'd passed the stage of red;
Hiccupping through his nose he talked and trolled
As if he'd asthma or a heavy cold.
To bed he goes, his wife and he together;
She was as jolly as a jay in feather,
Having well wet her whistle from the ladle.
And by her bed she planted down the cradle
To rock the baby or to give it sup.

When what was in the crock had been drunk up,
To bed went daughter too, and thereupon
To bed went Alan and to bed went John.
That was the lot; no sleeping-draught was needed.
The miller had taken so much booze unheeded,
He snorted like a cart-house in his sleep
And vented other noises, loud and deep.
His wife joined in the chorus hot and strong;
Two furlongs off you might have heard their song.
The wench was snoring too, for company.

Alan the clerk in all this melody
Gave John a poke and said, 'Are ye awake?
Did ye ever hear sich sang for guidness sake?
There's family prayers for ye among they noddies!
Wild fire come down and burn them up, the bodies!
Who ever heard a canny thing like that?
The devil take their souls for what they're at!
All this lang neet I shall na get nie rest.

But never ye mind, all shall be for the best;
I tell ye, John, as sure as I'm a man,
I'm going to have that wench there, if I can!
The law grants easement when things gan amiss,
For, John, there is a law that gans like this:
"If in one point a person be aggrieved,
Then in another he shall be relieved."

Wor corn is stolen, nivvor doubt of that;
Ill-luck has followed us in all we're at,
And since no compensation has been offered
Against wor loss, I'll take the easement proffered.
God's soul, it shall be so indeed, none other!'

John whispered back to him, 'Be careful, brother,
The miller is a torble man for slaughter;
If he should wake and find ye with his daughter
He might do injury to you and me.'
'Injury? Him! I coont him nat a flea!'

Alan rose up; towards the wench he crept.
The wench lay flat upon her back and slept,
And ere she saw him, he had drawn so nigh
It was too late for her to give a cry.

*The lover from the 'Roman de la Rose'. A traditional part of the
courtly romance was the parting exchange. Alan's departure from
Molly's bed is a parody in which his reluctance becomes weariness
and the lady's pledge the return of the flour!*

To put it briefly, they were soon at one.
Now, Alan, play! For I will speak of John.

John lay there still for quite a little while,
Complaining and lamenting in this style:
'A bloody joke . . . Lord, what a chance to miss!
I shall be made a monkey of for this!
My meät has got some comfort for his harms,
He has the miller's daughter in his arms;
He took his chance and now his needs are sped,
I'm but a sack of rubbish here in bed.
And when this jape is told in time to come
They'll say I was a softie and a bum!
I'll get up too and take what chance I may,
For God helps those that help theirsels, they say.'

He rises, steals towards the cradle, lifts it,
And stepping softly back again, he shifts it
And lays it by his bed upon the floor.

The miller's wife soon after ceased to snore,
Began to wake, rose up, and left the room,
And coming back she groped about in gloom,
Missing the cradle John had snatched away.
'Lord, Lord,' she said, 'I nearly went astray
And got into the student's bed . . . How dreadful!
There would have been foul doings. What a bed-ful!'

At last she gropes to where the cradle stands,
And so by fumbling upwards with her hand
She found the bed and thinking nought but good,
Since she was certain where the cradle stood,
Yet knew not where she was, for it was dark,
She well and fairly crept in with the clerk,
Then lay quite still and tried to go to sleep.
John waited for a while, then gave a leap
And thrust himself upon this worthy wife.
It was the merriest fit in all her life,
For John went deep and thrust away like mad.
It was a jolly life for either lad
Till the third morning cock began to sing.

Alan grew tired as dawn began to spring;
He had been hard at work the long, long night.
'Bye-bye,' he said, 'sweet Molly . . . Are ye
a'right?
The day has come, I cannot linger here,
But ever mair in life and death, my dear,
I am your own true clerk, or strike me deid!'
'Good-bye, my sweet,' she whispered, 'take good heed . . .
But first I'll tell you something, that I will!
When you are riding homewards past the mill

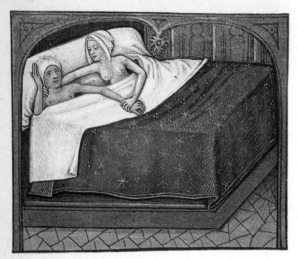

A couple in bed, from the 'Roman de la Rose'. When the miller
learns of his daughter's seduction he seems to be as much concerned
that Alan is not her social equal as about her lost virginity.
Simpkin's wife was well-connected, although her father was a priest.
The social aspirations of millers were a common topic of satire.

By the main entrance-door, a bit behind it,
There's the half-bushel cake – you're sure to find it –
And it was made out of the very meal
You brought to grind and I helped father steal . . . .
And, dearest heart, God have you in his keeping!'
And with that word she almost burst out weeping.
Alan got up and thought, 'Dawn's coming on.
Better get back and creep in beside John.'
But there he found the cradle in his way.
'By God,' he thought, 'I nearly went astray!
My heid is tottering with my work to-neet,
That'll be why I cannot gan areet!
This cradle tells me I have lost my tether;
Yon must be miller and his wife together.'
And back he went, groping his weary way
And reached the bed in which the miller lay,
And thinking it was John upon the bed
He slid in by the miller's side instead,
Grabbing his neck, and with no more ado
Said, 'Shake yourself, wake up, you pig's-head, you!
For Christ's soul, listen! O such noble games
As I have had! I tell you, by St James,
Three times the neet, from midnight into morn,

The miller's daughter helped me grind my corn
While you've been lying in your cowardly way . . . '
'You scoundrel!' said the miller. 'What d'you say?
You beast! You treacherous blackguard! Filthy rat!
God's dignity! I'll murder you for that!
How dare you be so bold as to fling mud
Upon my daughter, come of noble blood?'
He grabbed at Alan by his Adam's apple,
And Alan grabbed him back in furious grapple
And clenched his fist and bashed him on the nose.
Down miller's breast a bloody river flows
Onto the floor, his nose and mouth all broke;
They wallowed like two porkers in a poke,
And up and down and up again they go
Until the miller tripped and stubbed his toe,
Spun round and fell down backwards on his wife.
She had heard nothing of this foolish strife,
For she had fallen asleep with John the clerk,
Weary from all their labours in the dark.
The miller's fall started her out of sleep.
'Help!' she screamed. 'Holy cross of Bromeholme keep
Us! Lord! Into thy hands! To Thee I call!
Simon, wake up! The devil's among us all!
My heart is bursting, help! I'm nearly dead,
One's on my belly, and another's on my head.

'The Reeve's Tale' ends with an uproarious, slapstick free-for-all.
In the confusion the wife imagines that she has been attacked by an
incubus (a devil that was supposed to sleep with women and get
them pregnant). When she remembers the students, she assumes that
it is they who are fighting. The theme of mistaken identities is given
its final twist when she mistakes her husband's shining bald head
for one of their night-caps and smites it with her stick.

Help, Simpkin, help! These nasty clerks are fighting!'
Up started John, he needed no inciting,
And groped about the chamber to and fro
To find a stick; she too was on the go
And, knowing the corners better than them all,
Was first to find one leaning by the wall;
And by a little shaft of shimmering light
That shone in through a hole – the moon was bright –

Although the room was almost black as pitch
She saw them fight, not knowing which was which;
But there was something white that caught her eye
On seeing which she peered and gave a cry,
Thinking it was the night-cap of the clerk.
Raising her stick, she crept up in the dark
And, hoping to hit Alan, it was her fate
To smite the miller on his shining pate,
And down he went, shouting, 'O God, I'm dying!'
The clerks then beat him well and left him lying
And throwing on their clothes they took their horse
And their ground meal and off they went, of course,
And as they passed the mill they took the cake

Made of their meal the girl was told to bake.
And thus the bumptious miller was well beaten
And done out of the supper they had eaten,
And done out of the money that was due
For grinding Alan's corn, who beat him too.
His wife was plumbed, so was his daughter. Look!
That comes of being a miller and a crook!
I heard this proverb when I was a kid,
'Do evil and be done by as you did'.
Tricksters will get a tricking, so say I;
And God that sits in majesty on high
Bring all this company, great and small, to Glory!
Thus I've paid out the Miller with my story!

THE COOK'S TALE

The Cook's Prologue

THE Cook, in joy to hear the Miller pickled,
Laughed like a man whose back is being tickled;
'Haha!' he roared. 'Haha! Christ's blessed
    passion!
That miller was paid out in proper fashion
For trying to argue that his house was small!
"Be careful who you bring into the hall,"
Says Solomon in Ecclesiasticus,
For guests who stay the night are dangerous.
A man can't be too careful when he brings
A stranger in among his private things.
May the Lord send me misery and care
If ever, since they called me Hodge of Ware,
I heard a miller scored off so completely!
That jest of malice in the dark came neatly.
  But God forbid that we should stop at that,
So if you'll condescend to hear my chat,
    I'll tell a tale, though only a poor man;
But I will do the very best I can,
A little joke that happened in our city.'
    ell,' said our Host, 'let it be good and witty;
    Now tell on, Roger, for the word's with you.
    You've stolen gravy out of many a stew,
Many's the Jack of Dover you have sold
That has been twice warmed up and twice left cold;
Many a pilgrim's cursed you more than sparsely
When suffering the effects of your stale parsley
Which they had eaten with your stubble-fed goose;
Your shop is one where many a fly is loose.
Tell on, my gentle Roger, and I beg
You won't be angry if I pull your leg,
Many a true word has been said in jest.'
    hat's sure enough,' said Roger, 'for the rest,
    "True jest, bad jest" is what the Flemings say,
    And therefore, Harry Bailey, don't give way

A drinking den. Conflicts between masters and apprentices were frequent, and the description of Peterkin with his constant drinking, rioting and gambling reflects a common complaint.

To temper either if I have a plan
To tell a tale about a publican
Before we part. Still, I won't tell it yet,
I'll wait until we part to pay my debt.'
And then he laughted and brightened up a bit
And he began his story. This was it.

Left: Drunkenness, from an Italian treatise on the Seven Deadly Sins. 'The Cook's Tale' of an apprentice in the victualling trade is an example of a Tale in which subject and narrator are closely associated, for we know the Cook was a drunkard.

A marginal illustration from the Luttrell Psalter showing a cook at work. In the Prologue Chaucer gave a complimentary description of the Cook's skills and revealed a characteristic knowledge of culinary terminology.

The Cook's Tale

HERE was a prentice living in our town
    Worked in the victualling trade, and he was
        brown,
    Brown as a berry; spruce and short he stood,
As gallant as a goldfinch in the wood.
Black were his locks and combed with fetching skill;
He danced so merrily, with such a will,
That he was known as Revelling Peterkin.
He was as full of love, as full of sin
As hives are full of honey, and as sweet.
Lucky the wench that Peter chanced to meet.

At every wedding he would sing and hop,
And he preferred the tavern to the shop.
    henever any pageant or procession
        Came down Cheapside, goodbye to his
            profession!
He'd leap out of the shop to see the sight
And join the dance and not come back that night.
He gathered round him many of his sort
And made a gang for dancing, song and sport.
They used to make appointments where to meet
For playing dice in such and such a street,

Another marginal illustration from the Luttrell Psalter. Chaucer's Cook was probably based on a real character called Roger of Ware whom Chaucer seems to go out of his way to discredit.

78

And no apprentice had a touch so nice
As Peter when it came to casting dice.
Yet he was generous and freely spent
In certain secret places where he went.
Of this his master soon became aware;
Many a time he found the till was bare,
For an apprentice that's a reveller,
With music, riot, dice or paramour,
Will surely cost his shop and master dear;
Though little music will his master hear.
Riot and theft can interchange and are
Convertible by fiddle and guitar.
Revels and honesty among the poor
Are pretty soon at strife, you may be sure.
This jolly prentice – so the matter stood
Till nearly out of his apprenticehood –
Stayed in his job, was scolded without fail,
And sometimes led with minstrelsy to jail.
But in the end his master, taking thought
While casting up what he had sold and bought,
Hit on a proverb, as he sat and pored:

'Throw out a rotten apple from the hoard
Or it will rot the others': thus it ran.
So with a riotous servant; sack the man,
Or he'll corrupt all others in the place;
Far wiser to dismiss him in disgrace.
His master, then, gave Peterkin the sack
With curses, and forbade him to come back;
And so this jolly apprentice left his shop.
Now let him revel all the night, or stop.
As there's no thief but has a pal or plucker
To help him to lay waste, or milk the sucker
From whom he borrows cash, or steals instead,
Peter sent round his bundle and his bed
To a young fellow of the self-same sort
Equally fond of revelling, dice and sport,
Whose wife kept shop – to save her good repute;
But earned her living as a prostitute . . .

(Of the Cook's Tale Chaucer made no more)

A medieval painting of the court of the 'world ruler', Alexander the Great. This Tale ranges between Europe and the Orient.

THE MAN OF LAW'S TALE

Introduction to the Man of Law's Tale

OUR Host perceived the sun upon its arc
Of artificial day (from dawn to dark)
Quarter way up plus half an hour or more;
And though not deeply versed in heavenly
lore
He knew quite well it was the eighteenth day
Of April that is messenger to May,
And was aware the shadow of every tree
Was of the same extent and quantity
As the erected body casting it.
So, by the shadow cast, he had the wit
To judge that Phoebus, shining clear and bright,
Had climbed some forty-five degrees in height;
So for that day, and in these latitudes,
It must be ten o'clock, our Host concludes.
And suddenly he plucked his horse about;
'My lords,' he said, 'I would inform the rout
A quarter of the day's already gone.
Now, for the love of God and by St John,
Let us no longer waste the time, I say.
My lords, time wastes itself by night and day,
Steals from us secretly, sleep or waking,
If we are negligent. For time is making
Stealthy escape, a stream that never again
Turns to the hills, but glides on to the plain.
Seneca and philosophers of old
Bewail time's loss more than the loss of gold:
"Lost money is not lost beyond recall,
But loss of time brings on the loss of all."
It can return to us again, once sped,
No more than can poor Molly's maidenhead,
When she has lost it in her wantonness.
Let us not moulder here in idleness;
You, sir, the Man of Law, since you contracted
To tell a tale, that tale is now exacted.
You all submitted – your consent was free –
To put this case for judgement up to me.
Acquit yourself! You promised so for one,
And then at least your duty will be done.'

host,' he replied, 'I'm willing, make no doubt.
I never had a thought of backing out;
Promise is debt, and as I am your debtor
I'd like to keep my word, I can't say better.
Laws are for all, and he who seeks to lay them
On others should by rights himself obey them.
Our text demands it; but I make avow
I can't recall a pithy tale just now;
But Chaucer, clumsy as he is at times
In metre and the cunning use of rhymes,
Has told them in such English, I suppose,
As he commands; for everybody knows
That if he has not told them in another.
He has told more of lovers up and down
Than even Ovid honoured with renown
In his Epistles, which are very old.
Why tell them all again since they've been told?
In youth he wrote of Ceix and Halcyon,
And since has celebrated every one
Of all these noble women and their lovers
As who will seek his lengthy book discovers.
The work is called 'The Legend of Cupid's Saints',
And there you may perceive how Chaucer paints
Lucrece and her wide wounds, and Thisbe gored
In Babylon, and Dido's faithful sword
Because of false Aeneas, or may view
The fate of Phyllis that was hapless too,
Turned to a tree for love of Demophon.
There you may also listen to the moan
Of Deianira and Hermione,
Or Ariadne and Hypsipyle;
The barren island in the foaming sound
Is there to see, and brave Leander drowned
For Hero's love, and you may count the woes
Of Briseis or see the tear that flows,
Helen, from thee and thee, Laodamia!
There too the cruelty of Queen Medea,
Her little children hanging by the neck,
When the false Jason turned her love to wreck!

O Hypermnestra, true Penelope,
Faithful Alcestis, how he praises thee!
But certainly he never writes a word
Of Canace – that tale should not be heard,
She loved her brother in a sinful way,
Fie on such cursed tales as that, I say! –
Nor draws from Apollonius, him of Tyre,
How King Antiochus in mad desire
Bereft his daughter of her maidenhead.
The tale's too horrible, it can't be read.
He flung her on the pavement for his wooing!
But Chaucer knew quite well what he was doing

And would not soil his sermons with narration
Of such unnatural abomination.
No more will I; ignore them if we may.
What shall I do, then, for a tale to-day?
I'd rather not be likened, if you please,
To those old Muses called Pierides
– The *Metamorphoses* know what I mean –
Nevertheless I do not care a bean
Though I plod on behind him, somewhat dim;
I speak plain prose and leave the rhymes to him.'

And on the word, in sober-faced relation,
As you shall hear, he started this narration.

The Man of Law's Prologue

O HATEFUL grief to suffer indigence!
By hunger, thirst and cold to be confounded,
To feel heart's shame at asking a few pence,
Or, asking none, to know yourself surrounded
By such necessity your need is sounded
In every ear and you are left to creep
About and borrow, beg or steal your keep!

You lay the blame on Christ and bitterly
Reproach Him for misdealing wealth; the haul
Your neighbour has sets you at enmity;
You say, 'I have so little. He has all!'
'By God,' you say, 'a judgement's sure to fall
Upon him. He will feel the burning coals
Under his tail for scanting us poor souls!'

Then listen to the opinion of the wise:
'Better to die than live in indigence
Such as your next-door neighbours will despise.'
If you be poor, farewell to eminence!
Yet from the wise take this for common sense
That to the poor all times are out of joint
Therefore beware of reaching such a point.

If you are poor your very brother hates you
And all your friends avoid you, sad to say.
O, you rich merchant-men, how Fortune fêtes you!
Noble and prudent folk! You've won the day;
You throw no double-aces when you play,
But fives and sixes! Yours is the main chance
And Christmas-time for you's a time to dance!

You scour land and sea to fill your purses
And, like sagacious men, you bargain for
The fall and rise of kingdoms, you are sources
Of information, news of peace and war!
But for a merchant I should have no store
Of tales to tell you now, yet one I know,
Told to me by a merchant long ago.

A prosperous merchant dines in state. Chaucer had first-hand experience of the growing importance of trade and the mercantile classes, for in 1374 he was appointed Controller of the Customs.

The Man of Law's Tale

PART I

IN Syria once there dwelt a company
Of wealthy merchants, serious, straight and wise,
That had a far-flung trade in spicery
And cloth-of-gold and satins of rich dyes,
All serviceable stuff that could surprise
With novelty; and business was a pleasure
Dealing with them and bartering for their treasure.

It happened that some merchants of this sort
Made up their minds to venture out to Rome,
Whether for business dealings or for sport;
Nor were they satisfied to stay at home
And send a messenger, but crossed the foam
In person thither; and where their expectation
Of profit lay, they found accommodation.

And having made a sojourn in that town
At their good pleasure for a month or more,
It happened that the excellent renown
Of Constance, daughter of the Emperor,
Reached them with every detail answered for,
And fresh particulars from day to day
Came to these Syrians, as I shall say.

This was the common voice of every man:
'Our Emperor – God save his majesty! –
Has such a daughter, since the world began
There never was another such as she

Venice, the greatest trading city of Chaucer's age. In 'The Man of Law's Tale' Chaucer transplanted the activities of the prosperous Italian merchants of his own time into the beginning of a story that later strays into pre-Christian England and to Imperial Rome.

For beauty and for goodness; she could be
The Queen of Europe with all eyes upon her.
May God sustain her long in health and honour!

'Peerless in beauty, yet untouched by pride,
Young, but untainted by frivolity,
In all her dealings goodness is her guide,
And humbleness has vanquished tyranny.
She is the mirror of all courtesy,
Her heart the very chamber of holiness,
Her hand the minister to all distress.'

All this was true as God Himself is true;
But to our purpose: when their ships were laden
These Syrian merchants started off anew
For Syria, having seen this blissful maiden,
Happy in this as in the goods they trade in,
Pursued their business as they did before
And lived contented; I can say no more.

It happened that these merchants stood in grace
With the young Syrian Sultan. Their return
From Rome, or any other foreign place,
He met with a benevolent concern
And entertained them eagerly, to learn
The news from other kingdoms – any word
They had to tell of wonders seen and heard.

And, among other things, they made report
Of Lady Constance and with special mention
Of her nobility, in such a sort
As to entrap the Sultan's pleased attention.
Her features filled his fancy and invention
Till all the passion of his heart was cast
On loving her as long as life should last.

In that large book that overhangs the earth
And people call the heavens, it well may be
That it was written in his stars at birth
Love was to be his death; for certainly
The death of every man is there to see
Patterned in stars clearer than in a glass,
Could one but read how all will come to pass.

For in the stars, and many years before
His birth, the death of proud Achilles stood,
Hector's and Pompey's, Caesar's too; the War
Of Thebes, shorn Samson's death, the hardihood
Of Hercules, and Socrates the Good
And Turnus murdered, all was written plain.
Man cannot read it, he is dull of brain.

Papal letters being presented to the Khan. 'One Church One State'
was the medieval ideal of Christian unity. It needed the mediation
of the Pope to send Constance to the Infidel.

And thus it was the Sultan, to be brief,
Summoned the Privy Council of his land
And said that of his purposes the chief
Was to obtain the Lady Constance' hand,
And that at once; for they must understand
That he must perish, lacking her for wife;
Let them take thought in haste to save his life.

Various councillors said various things,
They argued and conjectured in profusion,
They brought forth many subtle reasonings
And spoke of charms and magical illusion,
But finally were drawn to the conclusion
There was no knowing how to save his life
Except by taking Constance for his wife.

They saw great difficulties in the case,
Reasoning thus (to make their feelings plain)
That there were such discrepancies to face
Between their laws and customs; it was vain
To ask a Christian prince to entertain
Thoughts of alliance under the dispensation
Mahomet blessedly had given their nation.

And he replied, 'Rather than that I lose
The Lady Constance, I will be baptized;
I must be hers, in this I cannot choose.
O leave your arguments and be advised,
Can you not see my life is jeopardized?
I have a sickness she alone can cure,
It is a grief I cannot long endure.'

What need is there for further dilatation?
I say by treaties and by embassy,
And by the Holy Father's mediation

Backed by the Church and the Nobility
To work destruction on Mahometry
And to enlarge the blessed law of Christ
All were agreed; the arguments sufficed.

The Sultan with his Peers in all their pride
And all his lieges were to undergo
Their christening; Constance was to be his bride,
And certain gold – how much I do not know -
Determined for the party to bestow
In surety; oaths were sworn on either side.
Fair Constance, God Almighty be your guide!

Now some of you expect, if I may guess
That I should tell you all the preparation
Made by the Emperor in his nobleness
For Lady Constance at the celebration;
But you must know that the elaboration
Ordained for an occasion such as this
Cannot be told in a parenthesis.

For bishops were appointed to attend,
Ladies and lords and knights of high renown
And many others; let me make an end.

'With solemn ceremonial, as was due,/The ship for this poor maid
was brought to shore;/She only said, "Christ Jesus be with you!"'

A messenger arrives at the court of Alexander. The ships in the background are typical trading vessels of the late fourteenth century.

And all were notified throughout the town
To pray with great devotion, calling down
Christ's blessing on the match, and to implore
A prosperous journey to the Syrian shore.

At last the day of her departure came,
I say there came that day of fatal woe.
No longer might she tarry or exclaim,
For each and all were ready decked to go.
Pale Constance rose in sorrow, for the glow
Of colour left her cheek as she prepared her,
Knowing too well that nothing would be spared her.

Alas, what wonder is it if she wept
At being sent into a stranger-nation
And parted from the friends that long had kept
Her tenderly, to suffer subjugation
To one she scarcely knew by reputation?
'All husbands are good husbands'; heretofore
Wives have established this, I say no more.

She said in tears, 'O father, your poor girl,
Your Constance, softly fostered in your love,
And O beloved mother, crown and pearl
Of all my joy, save only Christ above,
To your kind graces she that was your dove

Commends herself, and journeys to the shore
Of Syria and shall never see you more!

Alas, alas! Forth to a barbarous nation
At once to go! But since it is your will,
May Jesus Christ that died for our salvation
Give me the strength of purpose to fulfil
His wishes! Wretched girl, to fare so ill!
And yet what matter? Woman is a thrall
Disposed and ruled over by men in all!'

No, not in Troy, when Pyrrhus broke the wall
And burnt down Ilium, nor in Thebes destroyed,
Nor yet in Rome when it was ripe to fall
To conquering Hannibal that had thrice enjoyed
The victory, was grief so unalloyed
As in her chamber when she made to go.
But go she must, whether she wept or no.

First cause of motion, cruel firmament,
Driving the stars with thy diurnal sway
And hurling all from east to occident
That naturally would take another way,
Thy crowding force set heaven in such array
That this her first, fierce journey must miscarry
And Mars will slay this marriage, if she marry.

O thou unfortunate oblique degree
Of the Ecliptic, whence the cadent Mars,
Thrust from his proper angle, helplessly
Falls into *Scorpio*, darkest house of stars!
O lord of war, whose influence debars
All hope! O feeble Luna, vainly knit
To him, thrust forth from where thou shouldest sit!

And O imprudent Emperor of Rome,
Is one time like another in such case?
Haddest thou no astrologer at home
To choose the favourable time and place
For journeying? For one of such high race,
Whose hour of birth was known to thee? But O,
We are, alas, too ignorant, or too slow.

With solemn ceremonial, as was due,
The ship for this poor maid was brought to shore;
She only said, 'Christ Jesus be with you!'
And they, 'Farewell, fair Constance!' – nothing more.
How resolute a countenance she bore!
Forth in this manner then I let her sail
And turn to other matters in my tale.

The Sultan's mother was a well of vices;
She saw the course on which her son was bent
Of giving up their ancient sacrifices,
And so for certain councillors she sent
Who came to be apprised of her intent;
And when these men of mark were gathered near
She took her seat and said as you shall hear.

'My lords,' she said, 'you know it to a man
How that my son is purposed to abjure
The holy teaching of our *Alkoran*
And all Mahomet had from God the Pure.
And to that God I here make promise sure
Rather to die the death than to depart
From what that Faith has written in my heart.

'What could befall us from this newer Law
But thraldom of our bodies and remorse?
For to deny Mahomet can but draw
Our souls through everlasting Hell, perforce.
But, my good lords, will you pursue a course
I shall suggest and further my endeavour,
One that will surely make us safe for ever?'

They all assented, swearing to make good
Their oath to live and die with her and stand
In strength behind her; each as best he could,
Engaged to rally all his friends at hand.
This was the enterprise that she had planned
– I shall describe it to you if I may –
And thus addressing them went on to say:

'We first must make pretence to be baptized
– Cold water cannot hurt us very much –
And I shall have a banquet organized
To pay the Sultan out, if he should touch.
Though christened white, his wife and many such
Shall find there's blood to wash away! She'll want
More water than it takes to fill a font.'

O Sultaness! Root of iniquity!
Virago, second Queen Semiramis!
O serpent masked in femininity!
The Serpent bound in Hell was like to this
Pretended woman that can wreck the bliss
Of innocence and virtue, through the spite
Bred in thy devil's nest of foul delight!

O Satan, ever envious since the day
On which they chased you out of Paradise,
Our heritage! How soon you found the way
Through Eve to woman! Our bondage is the price.
And now this Christian match by your advice
Shall be undone. Of woman you have made
The instrument by which we are betrayed!

This Sultaness (on whom my imprecation!),
Having dismissed her court in secrecy
– Why spin things out into a long narration? –
Rode round to see the Sultan presently
And told him she'd renounce Mahometry
And be baptized in Christ. She had been wrong
(She said) to be a heathen for so long.

And after that she begged him for the honour
Of feasting him upon the wedding-day,
The Christians too; she'd take the work upon her
To please them all. He answered, 'As you say,'
And knelt to thank her. Having got her way
She kissed her son, and he, with gladdened heart
In speechless joy, allowed her to depart.

PART II

THE company of Christians reached the coast
Of Syria, a great and solemn rout;
Immediately the Sultan sent a post
First to his mother, then to all about,
To say his wife had come beyond a doubt
And beg her to take horse to meet his bride
And do her honour, for his kingdom's pride.

Great was the thong and splendid the array
Of Syrians and Romans in their meeting.
The mother of the Sultan, rich and gay,
Received his lady with as fond a greeting
As any mother would have shown in treating
A well-beloved daughter; so they ride
Solemnly to the city side by side.

Not Caesar threading a triumphal arch
(Whom Lucan celebrates with such a boast)
Was royaller than this exotic march

At the assembly of this blissful host.
But yet this scorpion, at her wicked post,
The Sultaness, for all her flattering,
Gathered herself most mortally to sting.

The Sultan came himself a little after,
So royal he was wonderful to see,
And welcomed her with joy and happy laughter
And in this merriment I let them be;
The fruit of it is what you'll get from me.
After a time they thought it for the best
To end their revelries and take their rest.

Right: An illumination from 'The Chronicles of Alfonso of Castile'.
Arabs and Christians in battle. The fourteenth century was still the
age of the Crusades; the enmity between heathen and Christian
underlies 'The Man of Law's Tale', and indeed gives Chaucer's
description of the conversion of the Sultan and its bloody aftermath
much of its impact.

A glittering picture of the exotic Court of the Great Khan, from Marco Polo's 'Livre du Graunt Cam'. Tales of the riches of the Islamic world were legendary to medieval Europeans; they inspired the greedier motives of the Crusaders and enabled Chaucer to write of the Sultan's journey to meet his bride: 'Not Caesar threading a triumphal arch/(Whom Lucan celebrates with such a boast)/Was royaller than this exotic march.'

The day appointed came, the Sultaness,
  Old harridan, fixed the feast of which I told;
  Thither the host of Christian people press
In general assembly, young and old.
What a display there was of kingly gold,
What dainties in the dishes! As for those
They bought them all too dear before they rose.

O sudden grief that ever art near neighbour
  To worldly bliss! Sprinkled with bitterness
  The ends of joy in all our earthly labour!
Grief occupies the goal to which we press.
For your own safety think it is no less,
And in your day of gladness bear in mind
The unknown evil forging on behind!

Briefly to tell my story as is fitting,
  Sultan and Christians all were overthrown,
  Hacked into pieces, stabbed where they were
    sitting,
All but the Lady Constance, spared alone.
The ancient Sultaness, accursed crone,
Helped by her friends, did all as she had planned,
Being resolved herself to rule the land.

For not a single one of those converted,
  Not one of them that knew the Sultan's mind,
  But he was hewn in pieces, ere alerted,
And Constance, as the Sultaness had designed,
Was hurried hot-foot off, and was confined
In an old rudderless vessel, and told to learn
Her way to Italy, and so return.

She had some store of treasure, let me add
  For sake of truth, and full supplies of food
  Were given her, with such garments as she had,
And forth she sailed the ocean salt and rude.
O Constance, full of sweet solicitude,
O Emperor's daughter of a mighty realm,
He that is Lord of Fortune guide thy helm!

She crossed herself and with a piteous falter
  Of voice, addressed the cross of Christ and said:
  'Holiest cross, O rich and shining altar
Bright with the blood of pity the Lamb bled
To wash the world's iniquity, O shed
Protection from the Fiend upon me! Keep
My soul the day I drown upon the deep!

Victorious Tree, protection of the true,
  Thou that wert only worthy to up-rear
  The King of Heaven in His wounds all new,
That whitest Lamb, hurt with the cruel spear,
O blessed cross, that puts the fiend in fear
Of man or woman that is signed with thee,
Help me amend my life, and succour me!'

For many a year and day this creature fled
  Upon the Grecian seas, and reached the strait
  Beyond Morocco, so her fortunes led.
Many a time in grief she must abate
Her sorry meals, expecting death, and wait
Till in the raging waves her vessel reach
What shore soever in the end, and beach.

It might be questioned why she was not slain?
  Who at that banquet could protect or save?
  To that demand I answer back again
Who succoured Daniel in the horrible cave
When everyone but he, master and slave,

This woodcut may be uncertain in its geography, but its theology is accurate. The Church and its teachings were central to life and thought. The story of Constance's conversion of a heathen Sultan was well known.

Fell to the lions and was torn apart?
No one but God, whom Daniel bore in heart.

God, to proclaim the wonders of His arm
By miracle through her, would have it so,
And Christ who is the honey to all harm
Has chosen instruments, as well we know,
To work his purposes, that darkly show
To human ignorance; our feeble sense
Grasps not the prudence of His providence.

And if not murdered at the feast, what law
Kept Constance then from drowning in the sea?
And who kept Jonah in the fish's maw
Till he was spouted up at Nineveh?
It was none other, certainly, than He
Who kept the Hebrew folk from being drowned,
Crossing the sea dry-footed, safe and sound.

And who commanded the tempestuous mouth
Of the four winds that trouble land and sea
Saying, "O west and east, O north and south,
Touch with no trouble ocean, land or tree!"?
There is no such commander if not He
That walked the water; He it was who kept
This woman safe, awake or when she slept.

Where, then, for some three years upon the wave,
Got she her food and drink? And who sufficed
To Mary the Egyptian in a cave
And fed her there? Certainly none but Christ.
Five loaves and two small fishes overpriced
The needs of the five thousand; so indeed
God's foison came to Constance in her need.

Forth over ocean then she drove and came
Safe through our stormy channel till at last,
Under a castle that I cannot name,
Far in Northumberland, the billows cast
Her vessel on the sands and held it fast
From ebb of tide to the returning crest;
There by the will of Christ she came to rest.

This castle had a Constable-in-Chief
Who came to see the wreck and, as he ought,
He searched it through and found in all her grief
This woman and the treasure she had brought.
Him, in her foreign language, she besought
For mercy, begging him to take her life
And so deliver her from earthly strife.

Latin she spoke, of a degenerate kind,
But all the same she made him understand;
And he, assured there was no more to find
Upon the vessel, brought her safe to land.
She knelt to thank him, seeing in him God's hand.
But who she was she would not utter breath,
For hope of favour or the fear of death.

She said the seas had blotted out her life
And she in truth had lost her memory.
The Constable, together with his wife,
Moved to compassion, wept in sympathy.
And Constance showed such sweet alacrity
To serve and please all people in that place
They loved her that but looked upon her face.

This Constable and Hermengild his wife
Were pagans like their neighbours everywhere;
Hermengild came to love her as her life
And Constance made so long a sojourn there,
Giving herself to weeping and to prayer,
That Jesus brought conversion, of His grace,
To Hermengild the lady of the place.

In all that land no Christians dared to meet
For worship, most had fled; for long before
A pagan army and a pagan fleet
Had made their conquest of this northern shore.
To Wales had therefore fled a Christian core
Of ancient Britons dwelling in our isle.
That was the refuge of the faith meanwhile.

Not wholly so, for there were some believed
And honoured Christ apart in secrecy,
So that their pagan rulers were deceived.
There happened, near the castle, to be three,
One among whom was blind and could not see,
Save with that inward eyesight of the mind
That still can shed its light upon the blind.

Bright was the sun when, on a summer's day,
The Constable suggested they might go,
He, Constance and his wife, along the way

An idealized illustration of pagan times from the 'Roman de la Rose'. Chaucer's story credits Constance with the conversion of Alla, King of Northumberland to Christianity and by implication with a main part in the creation of Christian England.

Towards the sea for half a mile or so,
Just for the pleasure of roaming to and fro.
And on their walk it chanced they met at last
This old and crooked man, with eyes shut fast.

The old, blind Briton cried, 'For Jesus' sake,
My Lady Hermengild, restore my sight!'
Now she on hearing him began to quake
For fear her husband, should it come to light
She was of Christ, would have her slain outright.
But Constance made her bold, bidding her search
And do Christ's will, as daughter of His Church.

The Constable, abashed at what he saw,
Said, 'What's all this about?' and stopped to stare.
And Constance answered, 'Sir, the power and law
Of Christ can save us from the devil's snare.'
Then she began so fully to declare
Our faith, that what she said to him sufficed
Ere evening fell to turn his heart to Christ.

This Constable was not the over-lord
Where Constance had been found upon the
strand,
But long had held the region with his sword
For Alla, king of all Northumberland.
He was a wise king with a powerful hand
Against the Scots, as everybody knows;
Let me turn back to how my story goes.

Now Satan who is ever on our track
To trick us, seeing Constance's perfection
And casting round how he might pay her back,
Filled a young knight who lived in that direction
With foul desires of such a fierce complexion
The fellow thought he'd die, so sharp the spur
Of lust, unless he had his will of her.

He wooed her fiercely; it availed him nought,
For she would yield to sin for no persuasion.
So, out of spite, he compassed in his thought
A shameful death for her by some evasion
Or stratagem, and when on some occasion
The Constable was absent, in he crept
Softly one night where Hermengilda slept.

Weary with prayer and holy meditation
She lay near Constance. Little did she note
How he, o'ermastered by the Fiend's temptation,
Had softly come upon her; then he smote
The Lady Hermengild and slit her throat,
Then laying the bloody knife beside the bed
Of Constance went his way. God strike him dead!

Next day the Constable returned again
With Alla too, king of the country round,
To find his wife was pitilessly slain.
Wringing his hands he wept and fell to ground,

And there by Constance in the bed he found
The bloody knife; alas, what could she say,
Out of her wits with terror and dismay?

They told the King of the unhappy deed
And also of the manner, time and place
In which they came on Constance in her need
Upon the ship, and brooding on the case
He felt a shock of pity; in her face
He saw benignity. Could such a glance
In one so lovely fall to such mischance?

And so, as when a lamb is brought to slaughter,
She stood, this innocent, before the king,
And the false knight, the villain that had sought
her
Destruction, swore that she had done the thing.
The rest stood weeping by, and clamouring
That it was unimaginable she
Had done so monstrous an iniquity.

For they had ever known her virtuous
And loving to her mistress Hermengild,
And the whole household gave its witness thus,
Except the knight by whom she had been killed.
Much moved by this the gentle King was filled
With a desire for stronger proof, to hit
By deeper questioning the truth of it.

Alas, my Constance! Champion hast thou none,
Nor canst defend thyself; what wilt thou say?
But He that died for our redemption, Son
Of God, who bound the fiend – and where he lay
There lies he still – shall champion thee this day!
Without an open miracle from on high
To save her she assuredly must die.

She fell upon her knees and thus she prayed:
'Immortal God, thou who didst save Susanna
Falsely accused, and thou, merciful maid
And mother, Mary, daughter of St Anna,
Before whose Child the angels sing Hosanna,
If I be innocent of this felony
Let me not die, support and succour me!'

Have you not some time seen the paler face
Among a crowd, of one that has been led
Towards his death, having obtained no grace,
With such a colour in his face, so dead,
As to be singled out, beset by dread,
Among all other faces in that rout?
So also Constance stood, and gazed about.

O Queens, abiding in prosperity,
You Duchesses and Ladies, hearts of stone
Would have compassion on her misery;
An Emperor's daughter, there she stands, alone,
Without a soul to whom she can make moan!

St Anne with her daughter the Virgin Mary from a fifteenth-century French Book of Hours. Constance prays: 'And mother, Mary, daughter of St Anna,/Before whose Child the angels sing Hosanna,/If I be innocent of this felony/Let me not die, support and succour me!' In her meekness and submissiveness, Constance represents the same image of Christian virtue as St Anne and the Virgin Mary. Even the conception of her son is described in such a way as to minimize the sexual side of her nature: 'For wives, albeit very holy things,/Are bound to suffer patiently at night.'

O royal blood, standing in greatest need
And deadly fear, far are they friends indeed!

King Alla felt compassion for her fears
  – Fine hearts feel pity quickly – at a look –
  And was unable to restrain his tears.
At last he said 'Let someone fetch a book
And if this knight will swear an oath she took
The knife and killed this woman, we shall confer
And name a man for executioner.'

They brought a British book in which were written
  The Gospels, and the knight stood forth alone
  And swore her guilt. And lo, the knight was smitten:
A hand appeared and struck him to the bone
Behind the neck and down he went like stone,

His eyes burst from their sockets in his face
In sight of all assembled in the place.

And as he fell a voice was heard to ring:
  'Thou has defamed the innocent and meek,
  A daughter of the Church, before the King;
Thus hast thou done, and yet I did not speak.'
Aghast at such a marvel, faces seek
Each other in amaze at the unknown,
Dreading a judgement, all but hers alone.

Great was their fear and great their penitence
  For having made a wrongful accusation
  And felt suspicion of her innocence.
And in the end the heavenly visitation,
With all that Constance spoke in mediation,
Converted Alla; many in that place
Were also turned to Christ, O blessed grace!

The treacherous knight was slain for his untruth
  By Alla's doom, there was no tarrying,
  Though Constance felt deep pity for his youth.
Then Jesus in his mercy caused the King
To wed this holy maiden. Belfries ring
In solemn joy, and Constance the serene
By ordinance of Christ is made a queen.

Who grieved at this? Who was it took no part
  In this rejoicing? Who but Donegild,
  The mother of the King? Her tyrant heart
Felt it would burst in two, for she was filled
With raging spite at what her son had willed.
She thought it gross dishonour to his state
To take this foreign creature for his mate.

I do not choose to stuff with chaff and straw
  My lengthy tale, I rather seek the corn.
  Why then relate the majesty and awe
Of course on course upon the marriage morn?
Who blew upon a trumpet or a horn?
But let me pluck the fruit of my story;
They ate, danced, drank, they sang and were in glory.

They went to bed, as reason was and right,
  For wives, albeit very holy things,
  Are bound to suffer patiently at night
Such necessary pleasures as the King's,
Or others' who have wedded them with rings.
Her holiness – well, she must do without it
Just for a little, and that's all about it.

He got a boy upon her then and there,
  And to the Constable, and a Bishop too,
  Entrusted Constance, being forced to fare
Once more to Scotland; there was work to do
Against his enemies. Constance, mild and true
And humble, heavy with her child, lay still
Within her chamber, waiting on Christ's will.

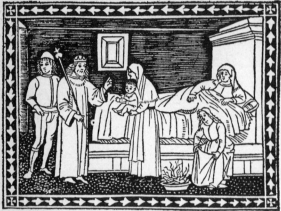

Constance '... lay still within her chamber, waiting on Christ's will./Time came to fullness and she bore a boy.' The birth of a prince and heir, depicted here in a late-medieval Italian manuscript, was an event of key political importance for the survival of a dynasty.

ime came to fullness and she bore a boy,
Maurice they christened him. In great content,
The Constable chose a man in his employ
And wrote the King a letter to be sent
By him with tidings of this glad event
And other news that brooked of no delay.
The envoy took the letter and went his way.

his man, upon a private calculation,
Rode quickly to the mother of the King
And proffered her a courteous salutation
In his own tongue: 'Madam, rejoice! I bring
You news enough to make the heavens ring
A hundred thousand times in thankful joy;
The Queen has been delivered of a boy!

ook, here are the sealed letters with the news
Which I must bear with all the speed I can
To greet your son the King, and should you choose
To write to him, I am your serving-man.'
'Not at the moment,' Donegild began,
'Stay here until to-morrow, take your rest.'
And added, 'Then I'll say as I think best.'

he messenger drank deep of ale and wine,
And all the letters secretly were cheated
Out of his box; he slept there like a swine.
Another letter then was counterfeited,
But with the utmost skill, and when completed,
Directed to King Alla, to appear
As from the Constable, as you shall hear

he letter said the Queen had been delivered,
But of some horrible fiend or creature lured
From Hell itself, and that the castle shivered
At sight of it, it could not be endured.
Its mother was an elf, they were assured,

A wandering witch of charms and sorcery.
None could abide her hateful company.

reat was King Alla's grief at what he read;
He spoke to no one of the woes he bore,
But wrote again in his own hand and said,
'Welcome the word of Christ for ever more
To me, that now am learned in His lore!
Lord, welcome be thy pleasure and thy will!
All mine I place at thy commandment still.

reserve this infant, be it foul or fair,
Until I come, and let my wife be nursed.
Christ, when He wills, can bless me with an heir,
One that can please me better than the first.'
And sealing this in private, his tears burst
Forth from his eyes. The messenger went away
Bearing the letter; there's no more to say.

messenger, sodden in drunkenness,
Strong is your breath, your limbs are all astray,
You blab the secrets that you should repress,
Your mind is gone, you chatter like a jay,
Your features are distorted, turned to clay!
Wherever there is drunkenness about
No secret can be hidden, make no doubt.

Donegild, I have no English worthy,
Tyrant, of thy malignity and spying,
And therefore to the Devil I refer thee;
Let him make poems on your treacherous prying,
You man-shaped monster! – No, by God, I'm lying! –
You are a very fiend and I can tell,
Wherever you are, your spirit is in Hell.

he envoy left the King and once again
Reached the Queen-Mother's court to pass the night;
And Donegild was quick to entertain
The man as hospitably as she might.
He underpinned his girdle pretty tight
Boozing away, and snored with gummy eyes
All night, until the sun began to rise.

gain they stole his letters, and the pith
Of what they forged instead of them was now:
'King Alla bids the Constable forthwith,
On pain of hanging and the royal vow,
For no consideration to allow
Constance within his kingdom; let her bide
No longer than three days and half a tide.

Right: The Nativity from a French Book of Hours. Constance beseeches Mary as one mother in distress to another: 'Thy Child thou sawest slain before thine eyes;/My little child lives still and seeks thy aid.' The domestic idealism projected on the Holy Family in this painting was characteristic of the high Middle Ages. Mary is depicted as the model of homely virtue.

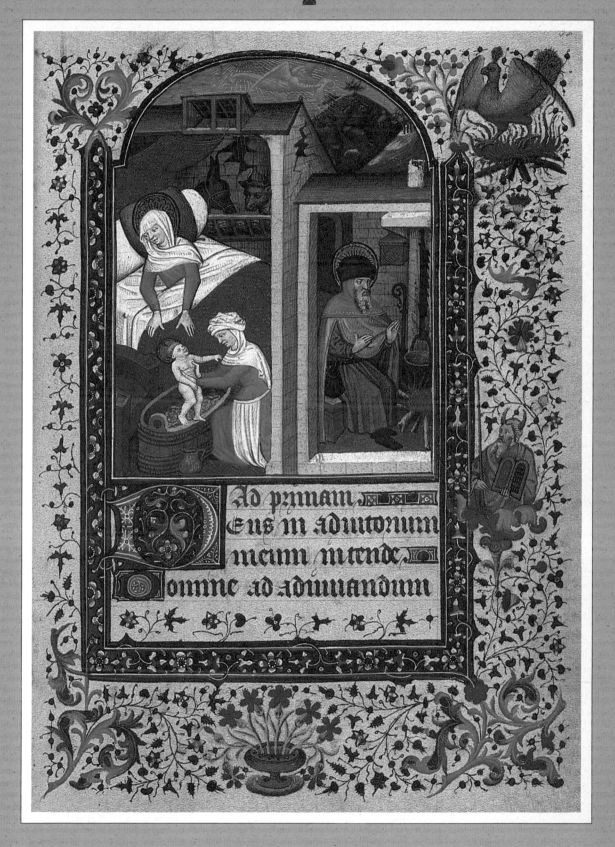

Ad primam.
Eus in adiutorium
meum intende.
omine ad adiuuandum

Into the very ship in which he found her
Let her be put and so thrust out to sea,
Her and her son, with all her gear around her,
And charge her never to return to me.'
O Constance, tremble at the harsh decree!
What dreams will haunt your troubled sleeping, filled
With dread! All this was planned by Donegild.

On the next morning when they day was full
The envoy woke and took the shortest way
Towards the castle. To the Constable
He gave the letter, who in great dismay
Cried out repeatedly, 'Alas, the day!
Lord Jesus Christ, how can the world go on
With such a mort of wickedness thereon?

'O mighty God! And can it be thy will?
Thou art a righteous Judge, how can it be
That Thou shouldst suffer innocence to spill
And leave the wicked in prosperity?
Ah kindest Constance! O the grief to me
To be thy executioner or pay
It with my life! There is no other way.'

They wept, both young and old, throughout the
place
At this accurst command the King had sent,
And Constance with a pale and deadly face
Arose the fourth day after; down she went
Towards the ship, fully obedient
To the will of Christ, and kneeling on the shore,
Said, 'Welcome, Lord, thy word, for evermore!

He that protected me from unjust blame,
When first I came among you will allow
No shame or harm, will shield me just the
same
In the salt sea, although I know not how.
As strong as ever He was, so is He now.
In Him I trust and in His mother dear,
My rudder and my sail! What need I fear?'

Her little child lay weeping in her arm,
And kneeling with him pityingly she said:
'Peace, little son, I will not do you harm!'

And then she took a kerchief from her head
And laid it on his little eyes instead;
She rocked him in her arms and lulled his cries
And up to Heaven's height she cast her eyes.

Mary,' she said, 'O maid and mother bright,
Truth is that by a woman's egging on
Mankind was lost, condemned to death and
night,
For which thy Son was rent and spit upon.
Thou sawest His torment; what comparison
Can ever be between thy sufferings there
And any other woe that man can bear?

Thy Child thou sawest slain before thine eyes;
My little child lives still and seeks thy aid.
Thou to whom every woeful spirit cries,
Bright lady, glory of womanhood, fair maid,
Haven of refuge, star that cannot fade,
Have pity on my child! Thy gentleness
Pities all sorrowful creatures in distress.

'O little child, alas, what is thy guilt
That never sinned as yet, and couldst not do?
Why would thy hard-heart father have thee spilt?
O Constable, is there no mercy in you?
Keep my sweet child . . . O, must he suffer too?
Let him but stay, or if you fear the blame,
Kiss him but once and in his father's name!'

And then she turned her gaze towards the land
And cried aloud, 'Hard husband, ah, good-bye!'
And she arose and went along the strand
Towards the vessel (and the crowd drew nigh)
And still she begged her baby not to cry,
And took her leave, and with a holy heart
Crossing herself, made ready to depart.

The ship was victualled well enough, indeed
Abundantly for her in such a case,
With necessaries to supply her need
Sufficiently. Thank God for all His grace!
May He send light to shine upon her face
And waft her home! What better can I say?
Over the open sea she drove her way.

PART III

Alla the King came home, his warfare done,
And reached the castle – that of which I told –
And asked at once to see his wife and son.
The Constable, who felt his heart turn cold,
Began to tell him plainly and unfold
What you have heard – I cannot tell it better –
Ending by shewing him his seal and letter,

Saying, 'My Lord, as you commanded me
On pain of death, I did. No less than that.'
The messenger was tortured until he
Acknowledged all, confessing full and flat
Where he had been, what places rested at
By night, and how; and so, by questioning,
They guessed the author of this dreadful thing.

he hand was recognized that wrote the letter
And mixed the venom for this cursed deed,
But how I know not, I can say no better
Than that the outcome was the King decreed
His mother should be killed, as you may read,
For false allegiance, treason and dishonour.
Thus ends old Donegild, my curse upon her!

he sorrows of King Alla night and day
Consumed him for his wife and little child;
How great his sufferings were no tongue can say,
And so I turn to Constance on the wild
Paths of the sea, five years and more exiled
In grief and misery, but in the hand
Of Christ's protecting angel; she neared land.

es, by a heathen castle at long last
– What name it had, alas I cannot find
In my authorities – the sea upcast
Her and the child. O Saviour of mankind,
Think upon Constance, have her child in mind!
She's fallen among heathens dwelling near,
On point of perishing as you shall hear.

own from the castle keep to see the sight
And stare at Constance many people came,
And from the castle also late that night
There came its steward, Heaven send him shame!
He was a thief that had renounced the name

Just as God gave David the strength to slay the Giant Goliath in the Old Testament story, so Constance, 'though a feeble woman', was granted the power to grapple with her lecherous assailant. Constance's punishment of being cast adrift (which she endures twice) was an actual penalty in medieval law for wives charged with infidelity, and also for illegitimate children.

Of Christ; he climbed the vessel, and made show
To lie with her, whether she would or no.

he wretched woman, overcome with grief,
Cried out for mercy, and her baby wept;
But Blessed Mary saved her from the thief,
For in the struggle, as the fellow leapt
In deadly grapple with her, he was swept
Over the side into the sea, and drowned;
And thus Christ kept her spotless, safe and sound.

oul lust of lechery, behold thy due!
Not only dost thou darken a man's mind,
But bringst destruction on his body too.
In their beginning all thy works are blind
And in their end are grief. How many find
That not the act alone, but even the will
To set about it can deprave and kill!

ow could this feeble woman have the strength
Against this scoundrel? Can you answer that?
Goliath, of immeasurable length,
How was it David came and knocked you flat,
So young and so unarmed and such a sprat?
How dared he look upon your dreadful face?
Only, one well can see, by Heaven's grace.

nd who gave Judith heart and hardiness
To slay King Holofernes in his tent,
And to deliver out of their distress
The people of the Lord? My argument
Is this, that just as God Almighty sent
A spirit of vigour to them in their woe
He could send strength to Constance, even so.

nwards her vessel through the narrow
mouth
Of Ceuta and Gibraltar forged her way,
Sometimes to westward, sometimes north and
south,
And sometimes east for many a weary day,
Until Christ's mother – blessed be she aye! –
Out of her endless goodness, to befriend
Poor Constance in her sorrow, made an end.

ow we turn to the Emperor of Rome
And say no more of Constance for a while;
From Syria the news had been brought home
About the Christians slaughtered, and the vile
Dishonour to his daughter by the guile
Of that foul Sultaness, accursed beast,
That had them murdered at the wedding-feast.

o take his vengeance then the Emperor chose
A Senator and many another lord
All royally appointed, and God knows
They took revenge upon that Syrian horde;
They smote and burnt and put them to the sword

For many a day, then, to be brief, turned home
– That was the end of it – and made for Rome.

And as this Senator returned in glory
Sailing in style, the laurel on his brow,
He met a vessel, driving, says the story,
With Constance, pale and piteous, at the prow.
Nothing he knew of who she was, or how
Brought down to such condition; nor would she
Tell, under threat of death, her history.

He brought her back to Rome, and to his wife
He gave her, with her little son, and so
Safe at the Senator's she lived her life.
Thus could Our Lady lift her out of woe
As she lifts many another here below.
There for a season Constance had her place
And lived in holy works, her gift of grace.

This Senator's wife, it happened, was her aunt;
But for all that she did not yet discern
Her niece, long-lost, in Constance. But I shan't
Delay my story longer; I return
To Alla. Long he felt his spirit yearn
And wept for Constance, who, for all his weeping,
Was safe enough in Rome, and in good keeping.

King Alla, who had doomed his mother's death,
One day was taken with a great remorse,
And, to relate the matter in a breath,

*Scythian ambassadors arrive at the court of Alexander. Although
pre-Christian, Alexander's epic conquests have an enduring echo in
'The Man of Law's Tale', not least in the swift revenge taken by
the Emperor on the Syrians: 'They smote and burnt and put them to
the sword.'*

Set sail to Rome for whatsoever course
Of penance that the Pope might there enforce,
Little or great, and as he sailed besought
Christ to forgive the evils he had wrought.

The news at once was bandied through the town:
'Alla the King has come on pilgrimage!'
His harbingers were going up and down
And, by a custom common in that age,
The Senator and all his lineage
Rode out, as much to show magnificence
As to receive a King with reverence.

Splendid the welcome that these noblemen
Gave to King Alla; he, no less than due,
Did honour to him in return, and then,
After their meeting, in a day or two,
King Alla bade the Senator renew
Their meeting at a feast. And, truth to tell,
The little son of Constance came as well.

Some say it was at Constance's request
The little child was taken to this feast;
– I can't know everything, I do my best –
But be that as it may, I know at least
That he was there, and, by her wish, released
To stand in front of Alla after grace.
The child stood looking at the kingly face.

Seeing the child, the King began to ponder
And made remark a little later on:
'Who is that pretty infant standing yonder?'
The Senator said, 'By God and by St John,
He has a mother, but his father's gone
For all I know....' He went on to expound
The circumstance in which the child was found.

God knows,' he then proceeded to declare,
'I never saw or heard in all my life
Of such a virtuous woman anywhere
As that boy's mother – woman, maid or wife.
And I'll be bound she'd rather have a knife
Thrust through her very heart than be impure;
No one could egg her on to that, for sure.'

In this child's face there was as great resemblance
To Constance as there possibly could be,
And Alla, bearing ever in remembrance
The beauty of his wife, bemusedly
Thought, 'Could the mother of the child be she
That once I had to wife?' And in his heart
He sighed, and sought occasion to depart,

Thinking, 'O Heaven! What phantoms in my head!
I should believe – unless all judgement's spent –
The seas have swallowed her and she is dead.'
And then there came the further argument,
'How do I know that Christ may not have sent

The scene in the top right corner shows the Pope in all his pomp.
Given the theoretical spiritual unity which was the Christian goal of
Chaucer's time, it was natural for King Alla to make his pilgrimage
to Rome.

My Constance hither safe, as once before,
He sent her safely to my northern shore?'

So, in the afternoon, the wondering King
Went with the Senator, upon the chance.
He took him home with honour, and made them bring
Constance in haste; he bade her to advance.
You may believe she had no thought to dance
When told the reason – whom she was to meet.
Faith, she could barely stand upon her feet.

When Alla saw his wife he greeted her
And wept. It was a moving thing to see
That first long look of recognition stir
Upon his face; he knew that it was she.
And she stood dumb in sorrow, like a tree;
Her heart was shut within its own distress
When she remembered his unnaturalness.

And twice she fell before him in a faint;
He wept and sought her pardon with the cry:
'As God above and every shining Saint
May show me mercy, dear, it was not I,
Who am as guiltless of the griefs that lie
On you as little Maurice here, whose look
Is so like yours – or blot me from God's book!'

Long was the sobbing, bitter was the pain
Before their troubled spirits came to peace,
And sad it was to hear them weep again
As if their weeping brought them an increase
Of sorrow, and I beg you to release
Me, for the task would take me till tomorrow
And I am weary now of so much sorrow.

But finally when all the truth was told
And when she knew him guiltless of her woes,
Their kisses fell, I think, a hundred-fold.
And such delight, such rapture then arose,
Save for the joys eternal, I suppose
Such joy as theirs has never been surpassed
Nor ever will be while the world may last.

Then, to repay her for her griefs, she pressed
Humbly upon her husband to agree
In sending a particular request
To beg her father, of his majesty,
To do him so much honour as to be
His guest one day at dinner, but to say
Nothing at all of her in any way.

Some men would have it that he sent his son,
Their little Maurice, to the Emperor;
But, as I think, King Alla was not one
To send a child as his ambassador
To greet the flower of Christian men, who bore
So sovereign an authority; I deem
He went himself, and so it well may seem.

The Emperor vouchsafed with courtesy
To come and dine with him as he besought.
I read he gazed at Maurice eagerly,
And Constance came at once into his thought.
Alla returned once more and, as he ought,
Made ready for the feast, and all his power
Was spent in preparation for the hour.

The morning came; King Alla and his Queen
Rose early and arrayed themselves to meet
The Emperor; they were of joyful mien.
And when she saw her father in the street
She lighted down and, falling at his feet,
Said, 'Father, Constance was your child! O Sir,
Have you no thought or memory of her?

I am your daughter Constance,' then said she,
'That once you sent to Syria as to slaughter,
And it is I that on the salty sea
Was thrust alone, to perish on the water.
Now, father dear, have mercy on your daughter!
Send me no more to lands in heathen blindness,
But thank my husband here for all his kindness.'

Who could describe the joys that seemed to rend
The hearts of all those three at such a meeting?
But I must bring my story to an end
And shall delay no more, the day is fleeting.
They then sat down to dine; I leave them eating,
These happy people, in their joyfulness
Greater a thousand times than you can guess.

A funeral procession, from the 'Croniques de France'. One of Chaucer's sources for this tale was an 'Anglo-Norman Chronicle' in which King Alla dies only nine months after his return to England.

Maurice in time became the Emperor,
Crowned by the Pope, and proved a very limb
Of Christ and lived to strive in honour for
His holy Church. My memories are dim;
This is a tale of Constance, not of him.
In ancient Roman histories you'll find
The life of Maurice – I have it not in mind.

His purpose ended, Alla chose the day
To bring his sweet and saintly wife and boy
To England, and they took the shortest way.
And there they lived in quietude and joy.
Not long it lasted; time, that can destroy
All happiness on earth, will never bide;
From day to night joy changes as the tide.

Who ever lived so happy for a day
As to have been unmoved by any sense
Of guilt or rage, unvexed by some affray,
By pride or envy, passion or offence?
And this I only say as evidence
That our felicities are of short life;
And so it was with Alla and his wife.

For death, that takes a rent from high and low,
After a year had passed, or even less,
Called for this king and Alla had to go;
He left his Constance full of heaviness.
God send a blessing on his soul, and bless
The Lady Constance, who returning home
Set sail on her last journey back to Rome.

To Rome she came, this holy soul, at last,
And found her friends again at home and well;
All her adventures now were safely past;
She found her father in the citadel
And weeping tears of tenderness she fell
Joyfully on her knees, pouring her praises
In thanks to God, a thousand eager phrases.

And so they lived in virtue and the giving
Of holy alms, never again to wend
Until by death divided from the living;
And so farewell! My tale is at an end.
May Jesus Christ, who in his might can send
Joy after sorrow, keep us in his grace,
Aye, every man and woman in this place!

Amen.

Epilogue to the Man of Law's Tale

OUR Host, after the Man of Law had done,
Rose in his stirrups. 'Listen, everyone,
Good value, that,' he said, 'to say the least,
A thrifty tale. God's bones, Sir Parish Priest,
Tell us a tale! You promised it before.
You learned men are full of ancient lore,
God's dignity! You know a lot, I see.'
The Parson answered, 'Benedicite!
What ails the man so sinfully to swear?'
Our Host retorted, 'Ho! Is Johnny there?
I smell a Lollard in the wind!' said he.
'Good men,' our Host went on, 'attend to me;
Don't run away! By Jesu's noble passion,
We're in for something done in sermon-fashion.

This Lollard here would like to preach, that's what.'
The Skipper said, 'By thunder, he shall not!
He shan't come here to vex us with his preaching,
His commentaries and his Gospel-teaching.
We all believe in God round here,' said he,
'And he'll go starting up some heresy
And sow his tares in our clean corn, perchance;
And therefore, Host, I warn you in advance
This little body has a tale to tell
That ought to set you ringing like a bell;
I shall be waking up the company.
It won't be much about philosophy
Or phislyas or curious terms in law.
There is but little Latin in my maw!'

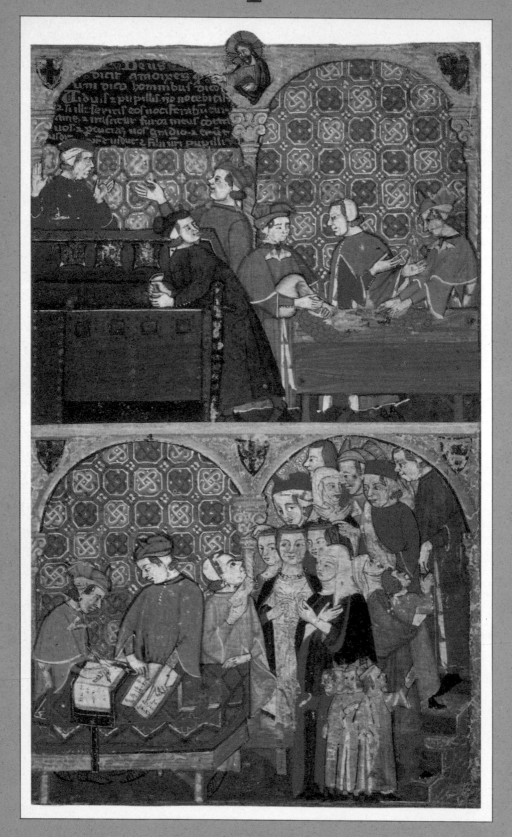

THE SHIPMAN'S TALE

HERE was a merchant in St Denys once
Who being rich was held to be no dunce.
He had a wife, unusually fair,
One of a gay, companionable air,
A thing which causes more pecunial dearth
Than all the foppish compliments are worth
That menfolk offer them at feasts and dances.
Such nods and becks and party countenances
Pass as a shadow passes on a wall.
But woe to him that has to pay for all!
The silly husband always has to pay,
He has to clothe us, he has to array
Our bodies to enhance his reputation,
While we dance round in all this decoration.
And if he cannot pay, as it may chance,
Or won't submit to such extravagance,
Thinking his money thrown away and lost,
Then someone else will have to bear the cost
Or lend us money, and that's dangerous.

This noble merchant kept a splendid house
And all day long so many guests there were
– For he was generous and his wife was fair –
You would have been surprised; but to my tale.

His guests from up and down the social scale
Included a young monk, well-made and bold;
I judge he was some thirty winters old,
And he was always visiting the place.

Now this young monk, with his delightful face,
Was on such friendly terms with this good man
Ever since their acquaintance first began
That he was welcomed as familiarly
As it is possible for a friend to be.

And for as much as this good-natured man,
He and the monk, of whom my tale began,
Were born in the same village, the monk stated

That they were cousins, very near related;
The claim was neither questioned nor withdrawn;
Both were as glad of it as bird of dawn.
It pleased the merchant's heart, and his compliance
Had furthered this unbreakable alliance,
And each was happy to assure the other
He always would regard him as a brother.

This monk, Sir John, was very free in spending
Whenever he stayed there, carefully attending
To what should please; he poured out tips like
wages,
Forgetting not the meanest of the pages
About the house; to each in his degree,
Master or man, he gave a gift or fee
Whenever he came – some honest kind of present –
And so, to them, his coming was as pleasant
As sunrise is to bird upon the nest.
I must have said enough, so let it rest.

The merchant, as it happened, one fine day,
Began to make arrangements for a stay
Somewhere near Bruges to further his affairs
And buy a fresh consignment of his wares.
And so he sent a message thereupon
To Paris, and invited good Sir John
Down to St Denys, so as to give pleasure
To him and to his wife, and spend his leisure
With them agreeably, a day or two,
Before he left – as he would have to do -
For Bruges. This noble monk I am describing
Was glad enough, and needed little bribing;
He saw his Abbot and he got permission,
Being a man of prudence and position,
In fact a superintendent, one to ride
Inspecting abbey granges far and wide.

Off to St Denys, then, the monk has gone.
Who was so welcome as my lord Sir John,
So full of courtesy and 'cousin mine'?
He brought with him a jug of Malmsey wine
And also one of sweet Italian juice,
With these a brace of birds as was his use.

Left: An illumination depicting Avarice from an Italian treatise on the seven deadly sins. Not averse to a bit of piracy at sea, the Shipman gives us a rollicking tale of an unfaithful wife who tries to justify her conduct on the grounds of her husband's avarice.

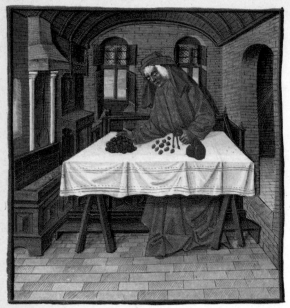

'Many a ledger and money-bag he got/And laid them out upon his counting-board.' In life as well as fiction, the line between thrift and prudence on the one hand and meanness and avarice on the other was hard to draw.

And thus I leave them at their meat and drink,
Merchant and monk, a day or two, I think.
On the third morning up the merchant gets
In serious thought about his needs and debts
And up into his counting house he goes
To reckon up, as you may well suppose,
All the past year and how things stood with him,
What he had spent, how the accounts would trim,
And whether his business had increased or not.
Many a ledger and money-bag he got
And laid them out upon his counting-board.
He had a deal of treasure in his hoard
And so he locked the door with an abrupt
Command that no one was to interrupt
His casting of accounts; he worked away
Sitting up there till past the prime of day.
Sir John had risen early too, to go
Into the garden. Walking to and fro
He said his office, courteous and devout.
This excellent wife then stealthily came out
Where he was walking softly in the sun
And greeted him, as she had often done.
A little girl was there for company
Beside her, under her authority,
Still subject to the rod; her mistress said:
'Ah, my dear cousin John! What, not in bed?
What's wrong with you that you are up so soon?'
'Niece,' he replied, 'a man can keep in tune
On five good hours of sleep, as I should judge,
Unless he is a poor old pallid drudge
Like all those married men who cower there

In bed, as in her form a weary hare
When she has had the hounds upon her tail.
But, my dear niece, why do you look so pale?
I cannot but imagine our good man
Has been at work with you since night began;
You really ought to go and take a rest.'
And he laughed merrily at this little jest,
And for his private thoughts his face turned red.
This pretty wife began to shake her head
And answered thus: 'Ah, God knows all!' said she.
'No, cousin mine, things aren't like that with me;
For, by the Lord that gave me soul and life,
In all the realm of France there is no wife
That has less pleasure in that sorry play.
For I may sing "Alas, and woe the day
That ever I was born!" I daren't,' said she,
'Tell anyone how matters go with me.
If only I could get away, or end
It all – Oh, I could kill myself, dear friend,
I am so terrified, so full of care. . . .'
On hearing this the monk began to stare
And said, 'Alas, dear cousin, God forbid
That fear or grief, whatever else they did,
Should make you kill yourself! Unfold your grief;
It may be I can give you some relief,
Advice or help, perhaps; and therefore, come,
Tell me about your trouble, I'll keep mum.

'The Shipman's Tale' reflects the low reputation of monks.

Look, on this prayer-book I will take a vow
Never by chance or choice, no matter how,
To give away what you may say to me.'
'I say the same again to you,' said she,
'By God and by this prayer-book I can swear,
Though I were torn in pieces, to play fair
And never breathe a syllable or tell
A living soul, not though I went to Hell;
Not on account of cousinship, but just
Out of affection for you, love the trust.'
And having sworn, they kissed to seal the oath
And then conversed as impulse prompted both.
'Cousin,' she said, 'if I had time and space
And I have none, especially in this place,
I could unfold a legend of my life
And what I've had to suffer as a wife.
As for my husband, though he's your relation . . .'
'No!' said the monk. 'By God and my salvation!
Cousin indeed! He's no more cousin to me
Than is this leaf, here hanging on the tree.
I call him so, but by the saints of France
I do so only for a better chance
Of seeing you – because I love you dearly,
Above all other women, most sincerely.
I swear it you on my profession, love!
Tell me your troubles while he's still above,
Quick, don't hang back! and then you can be gone.'
'O my dear love,' she answered, 'sweet Sir John,
I hate to tell you. . . . O if I were stronger!
But it must be out, I cannot bear it longer.
My husband is the very meanest man,
To me at any rate, since the world began.
It's unbecoming, since I am his wife,
To tell a soul about our private life,
Whether in bed or any other place,
And God forbid I sank to such disgrace!
I know a wife should only speak in honour
About her husband, or else fie upon her!
Only to you, the only one on earth,
This much I'll say. God help me, he's not worth
A fly upon the wall! In no respect.
But his worst fault is niggardly neglect.
For you must know that women naturally
Need to have sixty things, the same as me;
They want to have their husbands, to be candid,
Sturdy and prudent, rich and open-handed,
Obedient to their wives and fresh in bed.
But by the Lord that died for us and bled,
By Sunday next, if I am to look smart
And do my husband honour I must part
With – well, a hundred francs; or I'm undone.
Far better not be born than to be one
That people slander and say cheap things about.
Yet if my husband were to find it out
I were as good as lost – ah, don't deny!
Lend me this little sum or I shall die.
Sir John, I say, lend me these hundred francs!
Trust me I will not fail you in my thanks

'Usury', from a fifteenth-century French manuscript. The practice of money-lending at high rates of interest was condemned by the medieval Church. Many successful merchants found themselves suspected of usury.

If only you'll oblige me as I say.
I'll pay you back, and you shall name the day,
And if there's anything else – some little task
That I can do for you – well, only ask.
And if I don't, God send as foul mischance
To me as fell to Ganelon of France!'
The monk gave answer in his well-bred way:
'My own dear lady, I can truly say
I weep in sympathy for what I've heard,
And here I promise you and plight my word
That when your husband has gone off to Flanders
I will deliver you from fear of slanders
For I will bring you down a hundred francs.'
And on the word he caught her by the flanks
And clasped her closely, giving her a riot
Of kisses, saying softly, 'Keep things quiet . . .
And now let's have some dinner if we may,
My dial says it's past the prime of day;
You'd best be off. And be as true to me
As I to you.' 'God forbid else!' said she.
And off she went as jolly as a lark
And told the cooks to hurry off the mark
So that they all could dine without delay.
Up to her husband then she made her way
And boldly knocked upon the counter-door.
'Qui là'?' he said. 'It's me, dear. How much more
Have you to do up there,' she said, 'and fasting?
How long will you be reckoning up and casting
All those accounts of yours and books and things?
The devil run off with all such reckonings!
Heavens, you've had enough of it, my Own!
Come down and leave those money-bags alone.

Aren't you ashamed to leave that poor Sir John
Fasting all day while you go on and on?
What? . . . Let's hear Mass, and then go in to dine.'
'Dear wife,' he said, 'how little you divine
The complicated nature of affairs!
God save us all! Of such as deal in wares,
There's hardly two of us, as I'm alive,
Not two in twelve, I say, can hope to thrive
Till they retire, showing a steady clearance.
All very well to make a good appearance,
To drive about the world and make a mark,
But our affairs must always be kept dark
Till we are dead, unless we are to play
At pilgrimage and keep out of the way
Of creditors. It's vital to consider
This curious world and find the highest bidder;
There's always chance to fear, and many a slip
Makes for anxiety in salesmanship.
I have to go to Bruges at break of day;
I shall come home as quickly as I may.
Therefore, dear wife, I beg of you to be
Courteous and meek to all in place of me.
Look after all our property with care,
See to the house; here's plenty and to spare.
Govern it well. I'll see you have enough,
But still, be thrifty over household stuff.
You've all the clothes you need, and all the stores.
I'll put some silver in that purse of yours.'
And with that word he shut the counter-door
And came downstairs, he lingered there no more.
Quickly they all went off to Mass and prayed,
And quickly too the tables then were laid;
The merchant and his wife attacked the spread,
Sir John the monk was sumptuously fed.
Soon after dinner, soberly, Sir John
Took him aside – this merchant – and went on
To say as follows: 'Cousin, as I see,
You're off to Bruges for some commodity.
May God and St Augustine be your guide!
Now do be careful, cousin, how you ride,
And moderate in your diet; in this heat
You should be temperate in what you eat.
Well, don't let's stand on ceremony! Good-bye,
Dear cousin! God protect you from on high!
And if there's anything by night or day
That I can do to help you, only say.
Command me, and whatever be the task
It shall be done exactly as you ask.
'Oh . . . One thing. May I ask you as a friend
Before you go . . . Could you contrive to lend
A hundred francs? Just for a week or two?
I have to buy some cattle to renew
A farm of ours with animals and stores.
So help me God I wish the place were yours!
You may be sure I will not fail my day,
Not if it were a thousand francs, I say.
But please tell no one of this little debt.
– You see, I haven't bought the cattle yet.

And now, good-bye to you, my own dear cousin,
And for your kindness to me, thanks a dozen!'
This noble-hearted merchant thereupon
Replied, 'Good heavens, cousin! Dear Sir John,
This is indeed a very small request!
My gold is yours whenever you think best.
And not my gold alone, but all my stuff;
Take what you please, be sure you take enough.
Of course – I hardly need remind you now –
We merchants use our money like a plough.
We can get credit while our name will run,
But to be short of money is no fun;
So pay me back when you've the cash about.
Meanwhile I'm very glad to help you out.'
He fetched a hundred francs out of his trunk
And handed them in secret to the monk,
So secretly the deal was only known
To him – this merchant – and Sir John alone.
They drank and talked and loitered for a spell;
Sir John rode back then to his abbey cell.
Day came; the merchant started on his ride
To Flanders with a prentice as his guide
And came at last to Bruges in good condition.
Once there he worked in haste without remission
And did his business, borrowed, made advances,
And never turned aside for dice or dances,
But purely as a merchant, let me say,
He spent his time, and there I let him stay.
The very Sunday after he had gone,
Back to St Denys came the good Sir John
New-tonsured and with freshly-shaven face.
There was no little boy in all the place
Nor any other person, it was plain,
But was rejoiced to see Sir John again.
And to go shortly to the point indeed
This lovely woman readily agreed
To take his hundred francs and to requite
Sir John by lying in his arms all night.
And just as was agreed, so it was done.
All night they led a life of busy fun
Till dawn came up. Then with a kindly laugh
He left, wishing good luck to all the staff,
For not a soul, there or in town about,
Had formed the least suspicion or slightest doubt
Of what had happened. Homewards, or where whim
Directed, off he rode; no more of him.
This merchant, having finished his affairs,
Turned for St Denys; thither he repairs
And cheers his wife with fun and feast and such,
But said his merchandise had cost so much
That he must needs negotiate an advance
For he was bound by a recognisance

Right: The money markets of the European capitals were a growing feature of mercantile life and one with which Chaucer's career in the customs would have brought him into frequent contact. The Paris 'bourse' where the merchant borrows money was particularly flourishing.

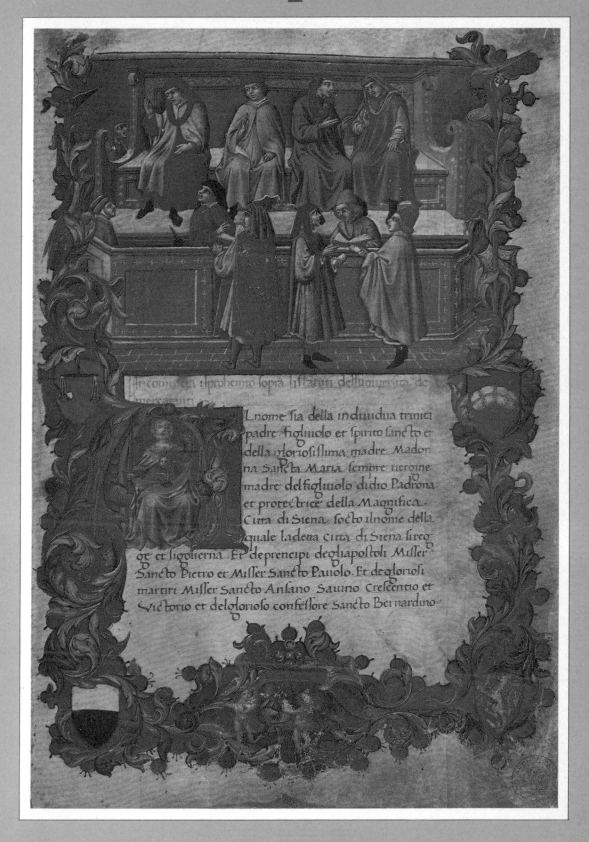

Incomincia ilprohemio sopra listatuti dellunuersita de mercatanti

L nome sia della induidua trinita padre figliuolo et spirito sancto et della gloriosissima madre Madonna Sancta Maria sempre uergine madre delfigliuolo didio Padrona et protectrice della Magnifica Citta di Siena socto ilnome della quale ladecta citta di Siena sireg ge et sigouerna. Et deprencipi deghapostoli Misser Sancto Pietro et Misser Sancto Pauolo. Et degloriosi martiri Misser Sancto Ansano. Sauino Crescentio et Victorio et delglorioso confessore Sancto Bernardino

But I returned the money to your wife
– The sum you lent – and put it in your till
At home. She'll know about it all, she will,
For it was all arranged by double entry.
Now I must go and leave you business gentry.
I have to join the Abbot here today,
He's going out of town – I cannot stay.
Best greetings to my pretty little niece,
Your wife! Good-bye, dear cousin, go in peace!
Let's hope it won't be long before we meet.'
T his merchant, who was wary and discreet,
    Soon managed to negotiate his loan;
    The bond that he had signed became his own
For he paid down the money to a franc
To certain Lombards at their Paris Bank.
He left as merry as a popinjay
For home, his business done in such a way
That he was bound to make, to the extent
Of fully a thousand francs, more than he'd spent.
H is wife was there and met him at the gate
    Just as she always did, and they sat late
    That night and had a feast. He did not fret,
Knowing that he was rich and out of debt.

The respectable citizens of Paris conducting their business. The jokes about the monk's repayments being made 'in double entry' echoes a sexual innuendo made in Chaucer's original text.

For twenty thousand crowns he had to pay.
He'd have to go to Paris the next day
To borrow certain sums among his friends
Which, with his ready cash, would meet his ends.
N o sooner had he come into the town
    Than, out of pure affection, he got down
    And called upon Sir John for simple pleasure
And not at all to claim the borrowed treasure,
But just to see him, ask how he was doing
And tell him what affairs he was pursuing
As friends will do on their occasional meetings.
Sir John was most effusive in his greetings
And he as blithely chatted back and told
How prosperously he had bought and sold,
Thanks be to God, in all his merchandise,
Save that it was incumbent to devise
The raising of a loan at interest;
That done, he could afford to take a rest.
S ir John replied, 'Indeed, I am delighted
    That you are safely back with matters righted;
    If I were rich – we all have ups and downs –
You should not lack for twenty thousand crowns,
You were so kind to me the other day
Lending me money; all I have to say
Is many, many thanks! God give you life!

An Abbot was the head of a monastery, in charge of large estates and with considerable funds to command, and would be even more vulnerable than ordinary monks to temptations of the flesh.

At dawn this merchant started to embrace
His wife afresh, and kissed her on the face,
And up he went and made it pretty tough.
'No more!' she said. 'By God, you've had enough!'
And wantonly she gambolled for a while,
Until at last the merchant with a smile
Said, 'I'm a little cross with you, my dear,
Though I am loth to be so, never fear.
Do you know why? By God, or so I guess,
You've brought about a sort of awkwardness
Between myself, I say, and Cousin John.
You should have warned me, dear, before I'd gone,
That he had paid you back my hundred francs
By double entry. It was little thanks
He gave me when I spoke of borrowing money.
His face showed plainly that it wasn't funny.
But all the same, by God our Heavenly King,
I had no thought to ask for anything!
I beg you not to do it any more.
When off on business I must know before
If any debtor has paid you back my pence
Unknown to me, in case your negligence
Should make me ask for what's been paid already.'

So far from being frightened or unsteady,
This wife retorted boldly thereupon:
'Then I defy that treacherous monk Sir John!
Him and his entries! I don't care a bit!
He gave me a sum of money, I admit.
So what? A curse upon his monkish snout!
God knows I had imagined, out of doubt,

That he had given it me because of you,
To spend on looking smart, on what is due
To your position and the friendly cheer
You've always shown him as a cousin here!
But now it seems that things are out of joint.
Well then! I'll answer briefly to the point;
You've many slacker debtors than myself!
I'll pay you readily, and as for pelf,
If that should fail, from sunset to revally
I am your wife, so score it on my tally.
I'll pay you back as promptly as I may.
I promise you I spent it in the way
Of pretty clothes; it didn't go in waste,
But, I assure you, in the best of taste
To honour you; for goodness' sake I say
Don't be so angry, dear, let's laugh and play.
My jolly body's pledged to you instead;
By God I'll never pay except in bed.
Forgive me, dearest husband, just this while;
Turn round again and let me see you smile!'

This merchant saw that there was no redress
And that to chide her was but foolishness
Since nothing could be done, and was content
To say, 'Well, I forgive you what you spent,
But don't be so extravagant again;
You must economize, let that be plain.'

And now my story's done, and may God send us
Plenty of entries until death shall end us!

Amen.

The Virgin panel from the Wilton Diptych, painted in about 1395.
The legend of the murdered boy restored to life by the power of the
Virgin existed in many different forms.

THE PRIORESS'S TALE

Words of the Host to the Shipman and the Prioress

'WELL said, by *Corpus Dominus*!' cried our Host.
      'Long life to you! And may you sail the coast
In safety, noble skipper! Don't get sunk.
A load of lousy luck upon that monk!
Hey, fellows, watch your step for such a jape!
He took the merchant's hood and put an ape
Inside, by St Augustine, and what's more
Into his wife's hood too! Well, shut your door

Against all monks! . . . What next? . . . Well, let me see;
Who else shall entertain the company?'
      And turning round, he checked himself, displayed
      A courtesy becoming to a maid,
      And said, 'My Lady Prioress, by your leave,
If I felt certain not to vex or grieve,
I'd judge it time for you to show your skill
By telling the next story, if you will.
Will you vouchsafe, dear lady, to comply?'
'Gladly,' the Prioress answered, 'I will try.'

The Prioress's Prologue
Domine, dominus noster
(Psalm viii)

'O LORD, our Lord, how marvellous Thy name,
      Spread through the reaches of the earth!' said she,
      'Nor only are Thy precious praise and fame
Found in the mouths of men of dignity,
For in the mouths of children, such maybe
As suck the breast, the bounty of Thy ways
Can be declared in worship and in praise.

      Therefore in honour of Thee, as best I can,
      Of Thee and of that whitest lily-flower
      That bare Thee, all without the touch of man,
I tell my tale and will put forth my power,
Though all unable to increase her dower
Of honour, who is honour itself, and root
Of bounty, next to Thee, her body's fruit.

'O mother-maid, maid-mother, chaste and free!
      O bush unburnt, burning in Moses' sight,
      Thou that didst ravish down from Deity

Upon thy humbleness the Spirit's flight
That lit upon thy heart, and in whose might
The Word took flesh, help me to tell my story
In reverence of thee and of thy glory!

      No tongue or knowledge can have confidence,
      Lady, to tell thy great humility,
      Thy bounty, virtue and magnificence;
For sometimes, lady, ere men pray to thee
Thou goest before in thy benignity
And through thy prayer thou gettest for each one
Light that may guide them to thy blessed Son.

      Weak is my skill in speech, O blissful Queen;
      How then shall I declare thy worthiness
      Or how sustain the weight of what I mean?
For as a child, a twelvemonth old, or less,
That hardly has a word it can express,
Just so am I, and therefore pity me!
Guide thou the song that I shall sing for thee!'

The Prioress's Tale

A late-medieval painting of Jewish elders, from a psalter. Jews had been banished from England by Edward I in 1290 but prejudice lingered on. The anti-Semitism of 'The Prioress's Tale' would not have shocked Chaucer's audience.

A happy child will always learn and hear.
When I remember this, the ever-near
Saint Nicholas stands in my presence, he
Who did Christ reverence in infancy.

This little child, while he was studying
His little primer, which he undertook,
Sitting at school, heard other children sing
O Alma redemptoris from their book.
Close as he dared he drew himself to look,
And listened carefully to work and part
Until he knew the opening verse by heart.

He had no notion what this Latin meant
Being so young, so tender too, so green;
But in the end, one morning there, he went
And asked a comrade what the song might mean
And why it was in use. He was so keen
To know that he went upon his knees
Begging the boy explain it if he please.

IN Asia once there was a Christian town
In which, long since, a Ghetto used to be
Where there were Jews, supported by the
Crown
For the foul lucre of their usury,
Hateful to Christ and all his company.
And through this Ghetto one might walk or ride
For it was free and open, either side.

A little school stood for the Christian flock
Down at the further end, and it was here
A heap of children come of Christian stock
Received their early schooling year by year
And the instruction suited to their ear,
That is to say in singing and in reading
– The simple things of childhood and good breeding.

Among these children was a widow's son,
A little chorister of seven years old,
And day by day to school he used to run
And had the custom (for he had been told
To do so) should he happen to behold
An image of Christ's mother, to kneel and say
Hail Mary as he went upon his way.

Thus had this widow taught her little boy
To reverence the mother of Christ, our dear
And blissful lady, and it was his joy;

A medieval schoolroom. Some scholars have argued that Chaucer was describing a school of choir-boys, but others have maintained that a regular village school was what he had in mind. The learning of anthems was certainly a regular part of the curriculum.

An illustration to another version of the legend. The idea that the Virgin might intervene and miraculously enable a murdered boy to sing would not have seemed as fanciful to a fourteenth-century audience as it does today.

his schoolfellow – an older boy than he –
Answered him thus: 'This song, I have heard say,
Is to salute Our Blessed Lady; she
Will hear us when we turn to her and pray
For help and comfort on our dying day.
I can explain no more – that's all I know;
I can learn singing, but my grammar's slow.'

And is this anthem made to reverence
Christ's mother?' said this innocent. 'If I may,
I certainly will show my diligence
To learn it off by heart for Christmas Day.
Though they should scold me when I cannot say
My primer, though they beat me thrice an hour,
I'll learn it in her honour, to my power.'

So every day his comrade secretly
As they went homewards taught it him by rote;
He sang it with a childlike clarity
And boldly, word by word and note by note;
And twice a day it filled his little throat,
Going to school and coming back again,
Praising Christ's mother with all his might and main.

As I have said, this child would go along
The Jewish street and, of his own accord,
Daily and merrily he sang his song
O Alma Redemptoris; as it soared,
The sweetness of the mother of our Lord
Would pierce his heart, he could not choose but pray
And sing as, to and fro, he went his way.

First of our foes, the Serpent Satan shook
Those Jewish hearts that are his waspish nest,
Swelled up and said. 'O Hebrew people look!
Is this not something that should be redressed?

Is such a boy to roam as he thinks best
Singing to spite you, canticles and saws
Against the reverence of your holy laws?'

From that time forward all these Jews conspired
To chase this innocent child from the earth's
        face.
Down a dark alley-way they found and hired
A murderer who owned that secret place;
And as the boy passed at his happy pace
This cursed Jew grabbed him and held him, slit
His little throat and cast him in a pit.

Cast him, I say, into a privy-drain,
Where they were wont to void their excrement.
O cursed folk of Herod come again,
Of what avail your villainous intent?
Murder will out, and nothing can prevent
God's honour spreading, even from such seed;
The blood cries out upon your cursed deed.

'O martyr wedded to virginity,
Now mayest thou sing and follow, on and on,
The white, celestial Lamb of Heaven,' said she,
'Of whom the great evangelist, St John,
In Patmos wrote, who says that there they don
White robes before that Lamb, and sing afresh
That never have known woman in the flesh.'

This wretched widow waited all that night,
She waited for her child, but all for nought;
And very early in the morning light,
All pale with sleepless dread and busy thought,
She searched his school, then up and down she sought
Elsewhere, and finally she got the news
That he was last seen in the street of Jews.

Within her breast her mother's pity closed,
She went about as one half out of mind
To every place in which, as she supposed,
There was some likelihood for her to find
Her child, and to Christ's mother, meek and kind,
She cried in heart, and in the end was brought
Among the accursed Jews, and there she sought.

She made enquiry with a piteous cry
Of every Jew inhabiting that place,
Asking if they had seen her child go by,
And they said, 'No.' But Jesus of His grace
Put in her thought, after a little space,
To come upon that alley as she cried,
Where, in a pit, he had been cast aside.

Great God, that to perform Thy praise hast called
The innocent of mouth, how great Thy might!
This gem of chastity, this emerald,
This jewel of martyrdom and ruby bright,
Lying with carven throat and out of sight,

The hostility of the Christian world towards the Jews in the middle ages was fully reciprocated. This illustration from the late fourteenth-century Vernon manuscript is of a Jew who threw his own child into an oven because he had been contaminated by entering a Christian Church. Christian hostility towards the Jews was, ironically, sharpened by the Crusades.

Began to sing *O Alma* from the ground
Till all the place was ringing with the sound.

The Christian people going through the street
   Came crowding up astonished at the thing,
   And sent to fetch the Provost to entreat
His presence, and he came and heard him sing.
The Provost, praising Christ our heavenly king
And His dear mother, honour of mankind,
Bade all the Jews be fettered and confined.

They took the child with piteous lamentation
   And he was brought, still singing out his song,
   In high solemnity and celebration
Towards the nearest abbey by the throng.

His mother, swooning as they went along
Beside the bier, could not be reconciled,
A second Rachel, weeping for her child.

The Provost then did judgement on the men
   Who did the murder, and he bid them serve
   A shameful death in torment there and then
On all those guilty Jews; he did not swerve.
'Evils shall meet the evils they deserve.'
And he condemned them to be drawn apart
By horses. Then he hanged them from a cart.

Still lay this innocent child upon his bier
   At the high altar while a Mass was said.
   The abbot and his convent then drew near

To hasten on his burial, and spread
A rain of holy water on his head;
And as they let the holy water spill
He sang *O Alma Redemptoris* still.

This abbot then, who was a holy man
As abbots are, or else they ought to be,
In invocation of the boy began
To say aloud, 'Dear child, I conjure thee
By virtue of the Holy Trinity
To say how singing is permitted thee
Although thy throat is cut, or seems to be.'

'Through to the bone my neck is cut, I know,'
Answered the child; 'and had I been confined
By natural law I should, and long ago,
Have died. But Christ, whose glory you may find
In books, wills it be also kept in mind.
So for the honour of his mother dear
I still may sing *O Alma* loud and clear.

'That well of mercy, sweetest mother of Christ,
I long have loved with all that I could bring;
This at the hour of my death sufficed
To draw her down to me. She bade me sing
This anthem till my time of burying
As you have heard; and when my song was sung
She seemed to lay a grain upon my tongue.

'And so I sing as I must sing again
For love of her, the blissful and the free,
Till from my tongue you take away the grain.

For after that, the Virgin said to me,
"My little child, behold I come for thee
When from thy tongue this grain of seed is taken.
And have no fear; thou shalt not be forsaken."'

This holy monk, this abbot, even he,
Touched the child's tongue and took away the
    grain;
And he gave up the ghost so peacefully,
So softly, and the marvel was so plain,
Salt fell the abbot's tears in trickling rain,
And down he fell, prostrate upon the ground,
And lay as still as one who had been bound.

And all the weeping convent also bent
To earth and praised Christ's mother with many
    a tear,
And after that they rose, and forth they went
Taking this little martyr from his bier,
And in a sepulchre of marble clear
Enclosed his little body, fair and sweet.
Where he now is, God grant we all may meet!

O Hugh of Lincoln, likewise murdered so
By cursed Jews, as is notorious
(For it was but a little time ago),
Pray mercy on our faltering steps, that thus
Merciful God may multiply on us
His mercy, though we be unstable and vary,
In love and reverence of His mother Mary.

                              Amen.

THE TALE OF SIR TOPAZ

Words of the Host to Chaucer

NOW when they heard this miracle every man
Was sobered; it was marvellous to see.
But in the end our Host again began
His jokes, and then he turned and looked at me,
And thus he spoke: 'What man are you?' said he,
'You look as if you were trying to find a hare,
Scanning the ground with such a steady stare!

'Come nearer, man, look up, look merrily!
Make room there, gentlemen, let this man have
     place!
He's shaped about the waist the same as me;

He'd be a likely poppet to embrace
For any woman, small and fair of face!
There's something elvish in his countenance;
He never speaks a word in dalliance.

'Say something now, as other folk have done;
And let it be a tale of mirth; at once!'
'Host,' I replied, 'I hope you are not one
To take it in bad part if I'm a dunce;
I only know a rhyme which, for the nonce,
I learnt.' 'That's good,' he said, 'well, take your place;
It should be dainty, judging by your face.'

Chaucer's Tale of Sir Topaz

THE FIRST FIT

LISTEN, lords, with all your might
And I will tell you, honour bright,
     A tale of mirth and game,
About a fair and gentle knight
In battle, tournament and fight,
     Sir Topaz was his name.

And he was born in far countree
In Flanders all beyond the sea,
     At Poperinghe in that place.
His father was of high degree
And lord of all the land was he,
     As God had given him grace.

Left: Noblemen hawking. Chaucer's 'Tale of Sir Topaz' is quite deliberately one of the most disappointing and the Host interrupts him with a roar of disapproval: 'No more of this for God's dear dignity! You're wearying me to death with your illiterate stuff.'

Sir Topaz grew a doughty swain,
With face like bread of whitest grain.
     His lips were red as rose,
And his complexion like a stain
Of scarlet red, and I maintain
     He had a seemly nose.

He'd saffron hair and beard as well
That down below his girdle fell,
     His shoe-leather was Spanish;
Rich brown his hose (it so befell)
From Bruges, and rich his robe as well,
     It made the money vanish.

And he was great at hunting deer
And hawking down along the mere
     With goshawk on his hand;
He was an archer, never fear,

115

A wrestler too that had no peer,
No peer in all the land.

Full many a maiden bright in bower
Lay longing for him hour by hour
    Who should have been asleep;
But he was chaste and fled the power
Of lechery, chaste as bramble-flower
    Where red the berries creep.

It so befell upon a day,
As I'll tell truly if I may,
    Sir Topaz went to ride.
He mounted on his steed of grey
And, lance in hand, he rode away,
    A long-sword by his side.

He spurred his way through forest fair
Where many a monster has its lair,
    Such as the hare and buck;
And as he went by east and north,
I tell you, and was riding forth
    He met with evil luck.

The herbs were springing in the vale;
Green ginger plants and liquorice pale
    And cloves their sweetness offered,
With nutmegs too, to put in ale
No matter whether fresh or stale,
    Or else to be kept coffered.

The birds were singing, let me say,
The sparrowhawk and popinjay,
    It was a joy to hear.
The throstlecock attuned his lay,
The turtle-dove upon the spray
    Sang very loud and clear.

Sir Topaz fell in love-longing
On hearing thus the throstle sing
    And spurred away like mad.
His steed was hot with galloping
And sweated so, a man could wring
    Him out, such sweat he had.

Sir Topaz, so it came to pass,
Wearied of spurring o'er the grass;
    So very fierce his courage
That down he lay as bold as brass
And eased his steed by a morass
    Where there was splendid forage.

'Saint Mary, *benedicite*!'
He said. 'What love has done to me!
    It binds my heart, no joke.
By God I dreamt all night,' said he,
'An Elf-Queen should my mistress be
    And sleep beneath my cloak.

I'll have an Elf-Queen, I declare!
In all the world there's none so fair
    Or worthy to be mine
        In town;
All other women I resign,
An Elf shall be my Valentine
    By dell and dale and down!'

He climbed his saddle like a throne
And galloped over stile and stone
    To spy an Elfin Queen.
And soon, as fast as if he'd flown,
He found a secret place and lone,
    Sweet Fairy-land, I mean,
        So wild;
For not a soul in all that zone
There was and not a face was shown,
    No woman, not a child,

Until a mighty Giant came
On him, Sir Elephant by name,
    A perilous man indeed,
Who said, 'Sir Knight, by fire and flame
Be off! By Termagent, I'll maim
    You and your sturdy steed
        With mace
Unless you go. The Queen of Faerie
With harp and pipe and music airy
    Has dwelling in this place.'

The Knight replied, 'By all that's blue,
To-morrow I will meet with you
    When I have got my armour;
And then I hope to make you dance
With this my slender little lance
    And you shall be the warmer.
        Your belly
Shall feel its prick as I advance
Ere prime of day, and it may chance
    That you'll be slain, I tell 'ee.'

Sir Topaz quickly then retired;
The Giant took a sling and fired
    Fell stones, but greatly daring
Sir Topaz swiftly left the place
And got away by God's good grace
    And by his noble bearing.

My lords, still hearken to my tale
That's merrier than the nightingale,
    And let me whisper plain
How good Sir Topaz, small and pale,
By spurring over hill and dale
    Got back to town again.

He ordered all his merry throng
To cheer him up with sport and song,
    For he would have to fight

A three-head giant, very strong,
To gain the transports that belong
  To love and lady bright.

'Come forth,' he said, 'my minstrels all,
  Your story tellers in my hall,
    And tell me while I arm
Romances such as may befall
To Prince and Pope and Cardinal
  And of a lover's charm.'

They fetched him first the sweetest wine,
  Then mead in mazers they combine
    With lots of royal spice,
And gingerbread, exceeding fine,
And liquorice and eglantyne
  And sugar, very nice.

They covered next his ivory flank
  With cloth spun of the finest hank,
    With breeches and a shirt,
And over that (in case it fail)
A tunic, then a coat of mail,
  For fear he might be hurt,

And over that contrived to jerk
  A hauberk (finest Jewish work
    And strong in every plate)
And over that his coat of arms,
White as a lily-flower's charms,
  In which he must debate.

His shield was of a golden red
  Emblazoned with a porker's head,
    Carbuncles at the side;
And there he swore by ale and bread
That he would kill the giant dead,
  Betide what might betide!

Chaucer's Sir Topaz is a satire on the knightly heroes of fashionable romances. It is also possible that he was poking fun at Flemish knights who were generally despised by their English counterparts.

Boiled leather on his shins had he,
  His sword was sheathed in ivory,
    His helm was copper bright.
His saddle was of narwhal bone,
His bridle shone like precious stone,
  Or sun, or moon at night.

Of cypress was the spear he bore,
  Not made for peace, but boding war,
    The head was sharply ground.
His palfrey was of dapple-grey
It wandered in an ambling way
  And softly trotted round
  About.
My lords, this is the opening fit!
If you want any more of it
  I'll tell you more, no doubt.

THE SECOND FIT

NOW hold your tongues for charity,
  My noble knights and ladies free,
    And listen to my spell,
    To battle and to chivalry
And making love in wantonry
  For such is what I tell.

Men tell romances such as this
  About Sir Horn, Sir Hypotis,
    Sir Bevis and Sir Guy,
Sir Libeus and Sir Pleyndamour,
But our Sir Topaz will endure
  Above the lesser fry.

His worthy steed he then bestrode
  And forth upon his way he glode
    Like sparkles from a flame.
And on his crest he bore a tower
And stuck thereon a lily-flower,
  God guard him from all shame!

And as he was a valiant knight
  He sought no house at evening light
    But laid him down on earth,
Wrapped in his hood, his helm a pillow,
And tied his palfrey to a willow;
  It grazed to keep its girth.

But he drank water from the well,
  As did the knight Sir Percivell,
    That worthy man-at-arms,
Till on a day . . .

The Host stops Chaucer's Tale of Sir Topaz

'NO more of this for God's dear dignity!'
  Our Host said suddenly. 'You're wearying me
  To death, I say, with your illiterate stuff.
  God bless my soul! I've had about enough.
My ears are aching from your frowsty story!
The devil take such rhymes! They're purgatory!
That must be what's called doggerel-rhyme,' said he.
'Why so?' said I, 'Why should you hinder me
  In telling my tale more than another man,
  Since I am giving you the best I can?'
'By God,' he said, 'put plainly in a word,
  Your dreary rhyming isn't worth a turd!
  You're doing nothing else but wasting time.
Sir, in a word, you shall no longer rhyme.
Let's see if you can tell us one of those
Old tales from history; and speak in prose.
Let it be gay or have a wholesome moral.'
'Gladly,' I said, 'Dear God, I hate a quarrel.
  So let me tell a little thing in prose
  That ought to give you pleasure, I suppose,
Or else it must be very hard to please you;
It has a virtuous moral to appease you;
It has been told again and yet again
By various writers; but I may explain

No one Evangelist would have sufficed
To tell us of the pains of Jesus Christ,
Nor does each tell it as the others do;
Nevertheless what each has said is true,
And all agree as to their general sense,
Though each with some degree of difference.
If some of them say more and some say less
About his piteous Passion, I should guess
– Speaking of Mark and Matthew, Luke and John –
Their meaning doubtless was agreed upon.
And therefore let me beg of you, my lords,
If you should think my story ill accords
With the original – if, for instance, more
Proverbial matter than you've heard before
Is thrust into my little treatise here
To enforce its meaning in the moral sphere,
Or if the words I use are not the same
As you have heard, I beg you not to blame
My variations; in my general sense
You won't find much by way of difference
Between the little treatise as it's known
And this, a merry story of my own.
So listen, please, to what I have to say,
And let me tell my tale as best I may.'

CHAUCER'S TALE OF MELIBEE

CHAUCER's prose Tale of Melibee (the tone of which is entirely serious throughout) here follows in the original. It is a dialectical homily or moral debate, exhibiting a learned store of ethical precept culled from many ancient authorities. It extends over a thousand lines or so. Among the authorities quoted are Job, Solomon, St Paul, Jesus son of Sirach, St Augustine, St Jerome, St Gregory, Pope Innocent, Ovid, Cato, Seneca, Cicero, Cassiodorus, and Petrus Alphonsus.

The principal character in the debate is Dame Prudence, the wife of Melibee, but we also hear the views of his acquaintances, doctors, lawyers, prudent old men and hot-headed young ones. Melibee himself offers some opinions, most of which are wisely and modestly refuted by his wife. He is, however, more talked against than talking, and is always won over, in the end, to the right view.

The principal subject of the debate is whether we should avenge a violent injury by violence, and the subject arises because during his absence from home Melibee's daughter, Sophia, has been assaulted and wounded by three miscreants who have made a burglarious entry. Should revenge be taken upon them?

In the course of the debate the following subjects arise and are dealt with learnedly and logically, for the most part by Dame Prudence:

how to purify one's heart of anger, covetousness, and impetuosity; how to keep one's opinions to oneself and distinguish true friends from false ones, fools, and flatterers; how to examine any advance profferred and when to change one's advisers;

whether women are to be trusted, and whether their advice can ever be good, and if so, whether husbands ought to submit themselves to their direction (Dame Prudence wins heavily on this);

whether to take a private revenge is (a) dangerous, (b) justifiable morally, (c) in this case expedient (in parentheses, why does God permit evil? No one knows): the outcome of violence is uncertain, one cannot be sure of success in vengeance. It is better to agree or compound with one's enemies. But would not this involve a loss of prestige? Prestige considered;

the importance of not making God your enemy, to whom vengeance belongs. If you reconcile yourself with Him, He will reconcile your enemies with you.

The enemies of Melibee are then sent for; Dame Prudence sees them privately and points out the superiority of a peaceful settlement. They are astonished and delighted.

Melibee decides to let them off with a fine. Dame Prudence persuades him to forgive them altogether.

His enemies then return before Melibee, who forgives them utterly, but not before he has rebuked them severely and pointed out his own magnanimity. This is perhaps the only point he scores.

Nothing is said of what happened to Sophia or whether she recovered from her injuries. The homily is immediately followed by

THE MONK'S TALE

Words of the Host to the Monk

WHEN I had done my tale of Melibee
And of Dame Prudence's benignity,
Our Host exclaimed, 'As I'm an honest man,
And by the precious bones of Madrian,
I'd rather have had my wife to hear this tale,
Good soul, than have a barrelful of ale!
She never shows such patience when with me
As Prudence showed in handling Melibee.
God's bones! Whenever I go to beat those knaves
My tapsters, out she comes with clubs and staves,
"Go on!" she screams – and it's a caterwaul –
"You kill those dogs! Break back and bones and all!"

If any of my neighbours when in church
Fails to acknowledge her, or gives a lurch
And bumps against her, as may be the case,
No sooner home, she's ramping in my face,
"You wretched coward," she cries, "avenge your wife!
By *corpus* bones," she says, "give me your knife
And you shall have my distaff and go spin!"

That's how the evenings end and days begin.
"My word!" she says. "Things are in pretty shape;
I've married a milksop or a cowardly ape
Who lets himself be downed by every sot
And daren't stand up to back his wife, that's what!"

Such is my daily life; unless I fight,
By God, she turns me out of doors at night
Lost, if I show the slightest sign of tardiness
Or seem less than a lion in fool-hardiness!
Sooner or later, thanks to all her labours,
I shall be driven to murdering the neighbours;
For, knives out, I'm an ugly customer,
Though I confess I can't stand up to her.
Her arm is pretty tough as, by St Victor,

*Left: Fortune's Wheel, an early fifteenth-century manuscript
painting from the 'Roman de la Rose'. 'The Monk's Tale' centres
around the medieval concept of Fortune. People in the middle ages
were keenly aware of the insecurity of human life, and the idea of
Fortune as a powerful but arbitrary force is a pervasive one in
medieval thought.*

You'd find were you to wound or contradict her!
But now let's drop the subject and pass on.

My lord the Monk, don't look so woe-begone,
For it's your turn to tell a story, sir.
Why, look! We've almost got to Rochester!
Forward, my lord, and don't hold up our game.
But, in my honour, I don't know your name;
Sir John, perhaps? Why have you kept it from us?
Or should I say Sir Alban, or Sir Thomas?
What monastery have they shut you in?
I vow to God you have a pretty skin!
There was fine pasturage where you were sent,
You're nothing like a ghost or penitent!
My! You must surely be some officer,
Some worthy Sexton, or some Cellarer.
For by my father's soul, in my opinion,
When you're at home, you're in your own dominion.
You are no novice, cloistered in retreat,
But in control, and wily as discreet.
Moreover when it comes to brawn and bone,
You seem to be well-cared-for, you must own.
God send confusion on the fellow who
First had the thought to make a monk of you!
You would have put a hen to pretty use,
Had you permission, as you have the juice,
To exercise your pleasure in procreation!
You could have done your part to build the nation.
Alas, who put you in so wide a cope?
Damnation take me, but if I were Pope,
Not only you but many a mighty man
Going about the world with tonsured pan
Should have a wife; for look, the world's forlorn!
Religion has got hold of all the corn
Of procreation, laymen are but shrimps.
Weak trees make sorry seedlings! That's what skimps
Our heirs and children, makes them all so slender
And feeble that they hardly can engender.
And that's what makes our wives so apt to cope
Religious people; there they have some hope
Of honest coin to pay the debts of Venus;

We laymen hardly have a groat between us!
ut don't be angry, sir, at what I say;
Many a true word has been said in play!'

his worthy Monk took all without offence
And said, 'Sir, I will do my diligence
To tell you all a tale or two, or three,
As far as may conform with decency.
And if you care to hear, as our assessor,
I'll tell the *Life of Edward the Confessor;*
Or else I have some tragedies to tell;
I have at least a hundred in my cell.
ragedy' means a certain kind of story,
As old books tell, of those who fell from glory,
People that stood in great prosperity

And were cast down out of their high degree
Into calamity, and so they died.
Such tales are usually versified
In six-foot lines they call *Hexameter.*
Many are told in prose, if you prefer,
And other metres suited to the stuff;
This explanation ought to be enough.
ow listen, therefore, if you care to hear.
But first I beg you not to be severe
If my chronology in all these things,
Be they of popes, of emperors or kings,
Forsakes the order in which they fell of yore
And I put some behind and some before;
They come to my remembrance but by chance;
Accept excuses for my ignorance.'

The Monk's Tale

N Tragic Manner I will now lament
The griefs of those who stood in high degree
And fell at last with no expedient
To bring them out of their adversity.
For sure it is, if Fortune wills to flee,
No man may stay her course or keep his hold;
Let no one trust a blind prosperity.
Be warned by these examples, true and old.

LUCIFER
ith Lucifer, although an angel he
And not a man, I purpose to begin.
For notwithstanding angels cannot be
The sport of Fortune, yet he fell through sin
Down into hell, and he is yet therein.
O Lucifer, brightest of angels all,
Now thou art Satan, and canst never win
Out of thy miseries; how great thy fall!

ADAM
onsider Adam, made by God's own finger,
And not begotten of man's unclean seed,
He that in Eden was allowed to linger
– Now called Damascus – and had power at need
Over all Paradise, save that decreed
And single tree prohibited. Than he
None ever on earth stood higher, till his deed
Drove him to labour, Hell and misery.

SAMSON
ong ere his birth, by an annunciation,
Samson was heralded by an angel bright
Who marked him out for God in consecration.
He stood forth nobly while he had his sight;

Adam and Eve in Paradise. The idea of illustrating the workings of Fortune from scriptural and classical legends was a common literary device. The Monk reminds his audience of the expulsion of Adam and Eve from the Garden of Eden, an event frequently referred to in medieval art and literature.

There never was another of such might,
Or hardihood of mind for might to borrow;
And yet he let his secret come to light,
He told his wife, and killed himself for sorrow.

Samson, this noble warrior of Zion,
    Having no weapon by him for the fray
    But his bare hands, yet slew and tore a lion
While walking to his wedding, on the way.
His treacherous wife so pleased him with her play,
She coaxed his secrets forth; with double face
She then betrayed them to his foes that lay
In wait, and took another in his place.

And Samson took, in his avenging ire,
    And lashed three hundred foxes in a band,
    Tying their tails, then set the tails on fire
(To every tail he bound a fiery brand)
And burnt up every cornfield in the land
And every vine and olive in a mass
Of flame, and slew a thousand with his hand,
No weapon but the jaw-bone of an ass;

But having slain them was so parched with thirst
    He was near lost, yet prayed the Lord on high
    To show that favour He had showed at first
And send His servant water lest he die:
Then from that very jaw-bone which was dry
Out of a molar-tooth there sprang a well,
And there he drank enough to satisfy
His thirst; God sent His help, as *Judges* tell.

And then at Gaza on a certain night
    By force he rent apart the city gate,
    Bore off the pieces on his back, in spite
Of what the Philistines in fierce debate
Could do, and then he set them up in state
High on a hill. O Samson, dear thy worth!
Hadst thou not blabbed thy secrets to thy mate
None ever could have matched thee upon earth!

This Samson never drank of mead or wine,
    His head no razor ever touched, or shear;
    This precept was enjoined by the divine
Messenger-angel – all his strength lay here,
Lodged in his locks. And fully twenty year
He was a Judge and ruler of Israel;
Yet the day came to him for many a tear
And it was by a woman that he fell.

It was to Dálila, his lover, she
    To whom he owned that all his power lay
    Within his hair, and to the enemy
She sold her lover sleeping, as he lay
Upon her breast, and bade them cut away
His locks, revealed his secret to those spies,
And so they found him there an easy prey.
They bound him fast and put out both his eyes.

*Samson was another figure who owed his downfall to his wife.
Dálila's (Delilah) name was frequently cited to warn men against
confiding in their wives, especially secrets 'touching the safety of
their limbs and lives'.*

But yet before his hair was clipped and shaved
    There was no thong or lashing that could bind
    His arm; and now they took him and encaved
Him in a prison, set him there to grind
A quern! O Samson, strongest of mankind,
O sometime Judge in glory and in power,
Now mayst thou weep although thine eyes are blind!
Fled is thy joy and come thy bitter hour.

Perished this captive wretch as I shall say;
    His foes prepared a feast, and for their jeers
    Made him their fool and bade him to display
Amidst a temple, thronged in crowded tiers,
His strength; and yet he set them by the ears.
He grasped two pillars, shook and made them fall,
And the whole temple, shaken from its piers,
Crashed down and slew him, and his foemen all.

That is to say, not Magistrates alone
    But some three thousand others also slain
    In the huge ruin of the their temple of stone.
Of Samson I will say no more; but gain
A warning from his story, old and plain:
Men should keep counsel and not tell their wives
Secrets that it concerns them to retain,
Touching the safety of their limbs and lives.

HERCULES

For Hercules, victor of sovereign power,
    His labours sing his praise and lasting fame,
    Who in his time was human strength in flower.
He slew a lion and he skinned the same;
He robbed the Centaurs of their boasted name;
He slew the Harpies, cruel birds and fell;
He robbed the golden apples, overcame
Their dragon-guard, drove Cerberus from Hell,

Hercules, the mighty hero of classical mythology, was another who lost his supernatural powers through his lover's actions, when Deianira gave him a poisoned shirt. The chief source for Chaucer's version of the story was probably Boethius, the fifth-century Roman philosopher whose 'De Consolatione Philosophiae' he translated.

And slew Busiris the tyrannical,
And made his horses eat him, flesh and bone;
He brought about the fiery serpent's fall,
Made one of Acheloüs' horns his own,
Killed the fierce Cacus in his cave of stone
And left Antaeus the Gigantic dead;
He met the grisly boar and laid it prone,
And last he shouldered heaven overhead.

Was never creature since the world began
That slew so many monsters as did he.
Throughout the world his reputation ran,
What with his strength and magnanimity.
All kingdoms of the earth he went to see,
None said him nay, none equalled him in worth,
And the Chaldean prophet named Trophee
Says he set pillars up to bound the earth.

He had a lover, this redoubted man,
Her name was Deianira, fresh as May;
And as the learned tell us, she began
To fashion him a shirt, to make him gay.
O fatal shirt! Alas, alas, I say!
Poison was subtly woven in its mesh;
Ere he had worn it scarcely half a day
From every bone there fell away his flesh.

But some authorities would thus excuse her,
Saying that Nessus made the shirt, not she;
Let that be as it may, I won't accuse her;
He wore it anyhow, and certainly
Blackness began to rot his flesh, and he
Raked burning coals upon himself and died,
Having perceived there was no remedy
And scorning death by poison, out of pride.

Thus fell the famous, mighty Hercules!
Who then may trust the dice, at Fortune's throw?
Who joins in worldly struggles such as these
Will be, when least prepared for it, laid low!
Wise is the man who well has learnt to know
Himself. Beware! When Fortune would elect
To trick a man, she plots his overthrow
By such a means as he would least expect.

NEBUCHADNEZZAR

The mighty throne, the precious stores of treasure,
The glorious sceptre and the diadem
That once belonged to King Nebuchadnezzar
Tongue cannot tell, hard to describe one gem
Among them! Twice he took Jerusalem
And, from the Temple, bore the vessels plighted
To God, and to his realm he carried them
In Babylon, where he gloried and delighted.

The fairest children of the royal line
Of Israel he gelded, and this done,
Made each of them a thrall and let them pine
In servitude. Daniel of these was one,
Wisest among them all, or under sun.
He could expound the dreams whose visitation
Troubled the King; Chaldean there was none
That could interpret their signification.

This proud king made an image out of gold;
Its height was sixty cubits and its frame
Seven in breadth. He ordered young and old

The seizure of Belshazzar's Jerusalem by the Medes and Persians is given a distinctly medieval flavour in this woodcut of the city printed by Wynkyn de Worde. Armoured knights confer opposite a turreted Jerusalem.

To bow before this idol and acclaim
Its glory; in a furnace of red flame
Any that disobeyed him should be flung.
But Daniel would not stoop to such a shame
Nor would his two companions. They were young.

This king of kings, so mighty and elate,
Supposed that God who sits in majesty
Could never rob him of his kingly state,
Yet he was cast from it, and suddenly.
Forth in the rain, thinking himself to be
An animal, he went and fed without
On hay as oxen do; and there dwelt he
Among the beasts till time had come about.

And like an eagle's feathers grew his hair,
His nails were like the talons of a bird,
Till God released him of his madness there
For certain years and the king's heart was stirred
In thanks to God; with many a tearful word
He swore to sin no more, until the hour
Of death when at the last he was interred,
He recognized God's mercy and his power.

BELSHAZZAR

He had a son, Belshazzar was his name,
Who held the throne after his father's day,
But took no warning from him all the same,
Proud in his heart and proud in his display,
And an idolater as well, I say.
His high estate on which he so had prided
Himself, by Fortune soon was snatched away,
His kingdom taken from him and divided.

He made a feast and summoned all his lords
A certain day in mirth and minstrelsy,
And called a servant, as the Book records,
'Go and fetch forth the vessels, those,' said he,
'My father took in his prosperity
Out of the Temple of Jerusalem,
That we may thank our gods for the degree
Of honour he and I have had of them.'

His wife, his lords and all his concubines
Drank on, as long as appetite would last,
Out of these vessels, filled with sundry wines.
The king glanced at the wall; a shadow passed
As of an armless hand, and writing fast.
He quaked for terror, gazing at the wall;
The hand that made Belshazzar so aghast
Wrote *Mene, Tekel, Peres*, that was all.

In all the land not one magician there
Who could interpret what the writing meant;
But Daniel soon expounded it, 'Beware,'
He said, 'O king! God to your father lent
Glory and honour, kingdom, treasure, rent;
But he was proud and did not fear the Lord.

God therefore punished that impenitent
And took away his kingdom, crown and sword.

He cast him from the company of men
To make his habitation in the dew
Among the beasts, eat grass and tread the fen
In rain and drought, until at last he knew
By grace and reason God alone is true
And has dominion over crowns and creatures.
Then God at last was minded to renew
His mercy and restored his realm and features.

But you, his son, are proud, though well you know
The truth of all these things that I have told;
You are a rebel before God, his foe,
Having defiled his vessels of pure gold;
Your wife and all your wenches have made bold
To do the like and drink of many a wine
In honour of false gods, accurst of old.
But God will punish you, and this his sign!

That hand was sent of God, that on the wall
Wrote *Mene, Tekel, Peres*, as you see;
Your reign is done, you have been weighed, and fall;
Your kingdom is divided and shall be
Given to Persians and to Medes,' said he.
They slew the King Belshazzar the same night,
Darius took his throne and majesty,
Though taking them neither by law nor right.

My lords, from this the moral may be taken
That there's no lordship but is insecure.
When Fortune flees a man is left forsaken
Of glory, wealth and kingdom; all's past cure.
Even the friends he has will not endure,
For if good fortune makes your friends for you
Ill fortune makes them enemies for sure,
A proverb very trite and very true.

ZENOBIA

Palmyra (say the Persians) had a queen,
Zenobia; one accounted to possess
A noble nature, and in arms so keen
And hardy, none could match her, they profess.
Her lineage and her breeding were no less
Than of a Persian royally descended;
I will not call her first in loveliness
But say her beauty could not be amended.

I find that from her childhood she had fled
The offices of women, for she went
Off to the wildness of the woods to shed
The blood of forest deer, her bow she bent
On them, still swift of foot when they were spent;
And as she grew to woman she would kill
Leopard and lion too, and once she rent
A bear apart; she ruled the beasts at will.

She dared them all, would thrust into a den,
Or course upon the mountains through the night,
Taking her sleep in bushes; as for men
She was a wrestler and could win a fight
Against a stripling of whatever might;
None could resist her arm and none elude.
And she had kept her maiden honour bright,
Not deigning to be vanquished or subdued.

At last her friends prevailed and she was married
To one Prince Odenathus of that land,
Albeit that she long refused and tarried;
And yet it is as well to understand
He was reluctant too to give his hand,
Having like fantasies. When knit together
Nevertheless their union proved a bland
And happy one, they came to love each other.

Save for one thing: she never would consent
To let him lie with her, except it be
Once only, when it was her clear intent
To have a child, to leave posterity;
And therefore when she knew that certainly
She had conceived no child from such an act,
She then permitted him his fantasy
Again, but only once; and that is fact.

And when she was with child by him at last
She suffered no more toying at that game
Until the fortieth week was fully past,
Then she permitted him to do the same;
And Odenathus, whether wild or tame,
Could get no more of her. She would aver
It was no more than lechery and shame
To woman for a man to play with her.

Two sons she had by Odenathus then,
Whom she brought up in virtue and in learning.
Now let us turn back to our tale again;
I say once more a creature so discerning,
So much esteemed, so lavish and so burning
In warlike zeal, so courteous by her birth,
You never could have found although returning
From search in all the corners of the earth.

Her splendour of array may not be told,
Whether in clothing or in store of treasure,
For she was clad in jewelry and gold.
In spite of all her hunting she found leisure
For languages and learnt them in full measure
And she applied herself to many, feeling
The study of a book to be a pleasure
That taught the way to power and high dealing.

And briefly to continue with my story,
Her husband was as powerful as she;
They conquered many kingdoms of great glory
Far in the Orient, they held in fee

Cities belonging to the majesty
Of Rome itself, and made their conquests thrive.
They never fled before an enemy
So long as Odenathus was alive.

As for her battles (should you wish for reading)
Against Shapur the King, and more as well,
With all the details of the whole proceeding,
What title won, what captured citadel,
And how at length she came to grief and fell
Besieged, made captive – all that she endured –
Study my master Petrarch, he can tell;
He wrote enough about her, be assured.

When Odenathus died, she mightily
Held all those kingdoms in her sovereign hand,
And was so cruel to her enemy
There was no king or prince in all the land
But felt that it was grace enough to stand
In safety and secured from war and riot,
And treated with her, that they might disband;
Let her make wars so long as they had quiet.

And neither Claudius the Emperor
Nor his successor Gallienus ran
The danger of provoking her to war;
No, nor Armenian or Egyptian,
No Syrian either or Arabian
Dared take the field against her in a fight
Lest she should slay them, or her conquering van
Put them in all its multitude to flight.

In royal robe her sons were wont to go,
Heirs of their father's kingdoms, one and all,
Their names Hermanno and Thymalaö,
Or such at least are what the Persians call
The pair. But Fortune's honey turns to gall;
Fortune withdrew her shining countenance
From this great queen and brought about her fall,
And she was plunged in sorrow and mischance.

For when Aurelian came upon the scene
With Rome beneath his government and sway,
He planned a mighty vengeance on the queen,
And, gathering his legions, took his way
Against Zenobia; to be brief, I say,
He routed her, enslaved and brought her home
In fetters with her children, there they lay!
And having conquered, he returned to Rome.

Amongst the other trophies of the war
There was her golden chariot, richly gemmed;
And great Aurelian, Roman emperor,
Returned with it in glory and condemned
The queen to walk before his Triumph, hemmed
By shouting crowds, gold chains about her throat,
And still, as rank allowed her, diademed,
And there were jewels crusted on her coat.

O alas, Fortune! She that once had been
Terror of kings and of imperial powers,
Jeered at and gaped upon! A noble queen
That oft had worn the helmet through long hours
Of battle, and had taken towns and towers,
Now wears a mob-cap on her royal head;
She that had held a sceptre wreathed with flowers
Carries a distaff in her hand instead!

KING PETER OF SPAIN

O noble, worthy Peter, glory of Spain,
Whom Fortune held so high in majesty,
How bitterly should we lament thy pain,
Who, by thy brother driven forth to flee,
After a siege wert caught by treachery,
And thus betrayed wert taken to his tent
Where with his own bare hands he murdered thee
And gained succession to thy throne and rent!

U pon an argent field an eagle sable
Caught on lime-rod gules (if you can read
This riddle) brewed the treason and was able
– O 'wicked nest'! – to do a wicked deed!

No Oliver of Charlemagne he, to heed
Honour and truth, but Brittany's mishap,
A Ganelon-Oliver corrupt in greed
It was that brought this King to such a trap!

KING PETER OF CYPRUS

O Peter King of Cyprus, fine and true,
That conqueredst Alexandria by the right
Of arms, and didest woe on heathens too,
Thy very liegemen envied thee, and spite
(No other cause) against thy chivalrous might
Moved them to murder thee upon the morrow
There, on thy bed! Thus Fortune with a light
Turn of her wheel brings men from joy to sorrow.

BERNABO VISCONTI OF LOMBARDY

G reat Bernabo Visconti of Milan,
God of indulgence, scourge of Lombardy,
Should I not tell of thee, unhappy man,
That scaled the summit of felicity?
Thy brother's son, so doubly bound to thee,
Being thy nephew and thy son-in-law,

Fortune was often conceived of as a woman with an ever-turning
wheel to whose relentless revolutions all humanity was subjected.

Yet in his prison wrought thy misery
And death, but how or why I never saw.

COUNT UGOLINO OF PISA

There is no tongue of pity that has power
To tell Count Ugolino's tragedy.
A little out of Pisa stands a tower;
There in that tower he was imprisoned, he
And all his little children. There were three,
Of whom the eldest-born was barely five.
O Fortune! It was grievous cruelty
To put such birds in such a cage, alive!

He was condemned to perish in that prison,
For Bishop Ruggieri had framed lies
Against him, and the city folk had risen,
Believing all the Bishop could devise,
And jailed him, as I said, without supplies
Save for some water and a little meat,
But these so scant and poor, you may surmise
That there was scarce enough for them to eat.

And on a certain day when came the hour
At which their food was usually brought,
The jailer shut the opening to the tower.
He heard it well enough, but he said nought;
There came into his heart at once the thought
That they were minded he should starve to death.
'Alas that I was born!' he said, and sought
In vain to check his tears and calm his breath.

His younger son – just three – ah, it is cruel
To think of him! – said, 'Father dear, why weep?
When will the prison-jailer bring our gruel?
Is there no bread, a morsel, in the keep?
I am so hungry that I cannot sleep.
If only I could sleep till I were dead!
Hunger no more would then have power to creep.
There's nothing I should like so much as bread.'

Thus day by day the little child would cry
Till on his father's bosom down he lay,
And said, 'Farewell, dear father, I must die!'
And kissed him; and he died that very day.
Seeing him dead his father could but say,
Biting his arm and crying 'Wretched me!
Bitterest Fortune, thou hast had thy way,
Thy false wheel turns against me, as I see!'

The other children thought it must be hunger
That made him bite upon his arm, not pain.
'Ah father, don't, don't do it!' cried the younger,
'But rather eat the flesh upon us twain;
Our flesh you gave us, take it back again
And eat enough!' Thus both the children cried,
But in a day or two, their grief in vain,
They crept into his lap and there they died.

He in despair sat on, and slowly starved.
Thus, mighty once, he met his end in jail;
Fortune foreclosed on his estate and carved
His greatness from him. Of this tragic tale,
Those who wish more, and on a noble scale,
Should turn and read the great Italian poet
Dante by name; they will not find him fail
In any point or syllable, I know it.

NERO

Though Nero was a vicious man who lusted
As fiercely as a fiend who treads the deep
(Says Suetonius, and he may be trusted),
He ruled the whole wide world; 'twas his to keep.
East, west, north, south, he scoured it o'er to reap
Its rubies, sapphires, pearls of orient white . . .
And his embroidered garments, heap on heap,
Blazed with them richly; gems were his delight.

A prouder, more fastidious ostentation
Of pomp no emperor has ever shown;
A dress once worn he had no inclination
To see again, would scarcely seem to own.
His many nets of golden mesh were thrown
To fish the Tiber with, just to amuse him.
His pleasures were his laws, he made it known
That there was nothing Fortune could refuse him.

And Rome, to please his palate for sensations,
He burnt; he killed his senators in play,
Just for the fun of hearing lamentations

Although Chaucer cites Suetonius as the source of his account of Nero's downfall, in fact the story is also related in the 'Roman de la Rose'. This gory illumination of Nero cutting 'his dreadful way into his mother's womb' comes from a Flemish manuscript of the poem.

For once Fortune seems to be reacting to immoral behaviour. Nero's murder of Seneca was his final crime before Fortune decided to turn against him, tired of his 'tide of vice'. More characteristic is the pleasure she takes in turning on him 'when he least expects'.

'Shuns tyranny and follow's virtue's path.'
So Nero cut his veins for him and bled
The man to death, he killed him in a bath.

It had been Nero's practice, I should judge,
When he was young, to mutiny and rise
Against his master; he could bear a grudge
And killed him for it, so we may surmise.
Nevertheless this Seneca the wise
Preferred to perish thus lest worse disaster
Should overtake him in another guise.
Thus Nero murdered his beloved master.

But as it happened Fortune cared no longer
To cherish Nero in his soaring pride.
Though he was strong enough yet she was
   stronger
And thus she thought: 'By God, I let him ride
Far too indulgently upon the tide
Of vice, and lend the title that protects
An emperor. By heaven, he shall slide
Out of his seat, and when he least expects.'

One night the citizens of Rome revolted
Against his tyrannies and mad ambition
And, when he heard them mutiny, he bolted
Alone and sought his friends for coalition.
The more he knocked and begged them for admission
The more they shut their doors and said him nay.
And then he saw that of his own perdition
He was sole author and he fled away.

The people yelled for him and rumbled round
So that their shouts were dinning in his ear:
'Where's Nero? Where's the tyrant? Treacherous
   hound!'
He almost went out of his mind for fear.
Pitifully he prayed the gods to hear
And succour him; in vain, they would not shield him.
Distraught, and knowing that his end was near,
He ran into a garden that concealed him.

He found two peasants in the garden there
Seated beside a bonfire glowing red
And he approached these peasants with a
   prayer
To kill him and by smiting off his head
To shield his body after he was dead
From mutilation or a shameful stroke.
And then he slew himself, for all was said.
And Fortune laughed, for she had had her joke.

HOLOFERNES

There never was a captain served a king
Who brought so many countries in subjection
Or one more famous then for everything
Touching the fields of war and insurrection,
Or more presumptuous by predilection

And shrieks of pain; with his own sister lay;
Murdered his brother; carved his dreadful way
Into his mother's womb, only to know
Where he had been conceived. Alas the day
That ever man should treat his mother so!

Yet at the sight of it he shed no tear
But 'A fine woman once, she was,' he said.
Wonder it is that he could so appear
To sit in judgement on her beauty dead.
And then he bade a table to be spread
And drank some wine but showed no other grief.
Where power and a cruel heart are wed
How deep the poison, challenging belief!

In youth they gave him an instructor; he
Taught him to read and taught him gentle
   breeding.
He was the flower of morality
At that far time, according to my reading.
And for a while he mastered him, succeeding
In putting his intelligence to use
With suppleness and wisdom. Tyranny
And vice in him were not as yet let loose.

This Seneca – the man of whom I speak –
Made Nero fear him, but he went in dread
Of Seneca because he chose to speak
In the rebuke of wickedness instead
Of punishing him. 'An emperor,' he said,

Than Holofernes. Fortune ever fair
Kissed him with such a lecherous affection
He lost his head before he was aware.

It was not only that he made a wraith
Of the world's wealth and plundered liberty,
He made his enemies renounce their faith:
'Nebuchadnezzar is your God,' said he,
'You shall adore none other that may be!'
There was no city dared stand up to him
Save one that proved a rebel to decree,
Bethulia, and her priest Eliachim.

But watch how Holofernes met his fate;
Drunken amid his host he lay one night
In his enormous barn-like tent of state.
For all his pomp, his majesty and might,
Judith, a woman, had the strength to smite.
Off went his sleepy head and from the tent
She crept away before the morning light
Bearing his head with her, and home she went.

KING ANTIOCHUS THE ILLUSTRIOUS

What need to tell of King Antiochus
Or to describe his royal panoply,
His overweening pride, his venomous
Ill-doing? There was never such as he.
Read what is said of him in *Maccabee*,
Read those proud words so arrogantly spoken
And why he fell from his felicity
Upon a hill-side, festering and broken.

Fortune indeed had so enhanced his pride
That verily he thought to take his stand
Among the stars themselves or turn aside
To life and weigh a mountain in his hand
Or warn the flood of ocean from the land.
But it was God's own people he most hated
And slew by torture, steel and firebrand.
He thought his pride could never be abated.

Because Nicanor once and Timothy
Had by the Jews been mightily defeated
His hatred swelled for Israel. Hastily
He made his chariot ready and when seated
He vowed and swore that they should all be treated
To something of his spite, that they should rue it;
Jerusalem he said should be deleted.
He was prevented ere he came to do it.

God smote him for these menacing recitals
With an invisible and cureless blain
That carved his guts and bit into his vitals.
Afflicted with intolerable pain
He yet had little reason to complain;
It was a just revenge, for he had often
Carved out the guts of other men to gain
His ends; their tortures did not make him soften.

He gave the word to summon all his hosts
When suddenly, before he was aware,
God daunted his presumption and his boasts,
And down he fell out of his chariot there.
It tore his limbs and flesh, the bone lay bare;
No longer could he either walk or ride
But only could be carried in a chair
All bruised and lacerated, back and side.

The vengeance of the Lord smote cruelly;
Pestilent worms within his body crept
So that he stank, and stank so horribly,
Not one of all the servants that he kept
To guard him when awake or when he slept
Could bear the stench or look upon his features.
And in this agony he wailed and wept
And knew that God was lord of all his creatures.

To all his host and to himself no less
The carrion stench that rose from every vent
Was unendurable in loathsomeness;
They could not carry him. In redolent
And agonizing pain within his tent
Upon a hill this thief and homicide
Who made so many suffer and lament
Wretchedly perished, the reward of pride.

ALEXANDER

The story of Alexander is so famous
That it is known to everyone at least
In part, unless he be an ignoramus.
He conquered the wide world from west to east
By force of arms, and as his fame increased
Men gladly sued to have him for their friend.
He brought to naught the pride of man and beast
Wherever he came, as far as the world's end.

And never can comparison be made
Of him with any other; at his face
Kingdoms would quake, the whole world was afraid.
He was the flower of knighthood and of grace,
The heir of Fortune and in nothing base;
Save wine and women there was naught could part
Him from his high designs or take their place,
He was a man so leonine of heart.

What praise were it to him though I should tell
Of great Darius and a thousand more
Kings, princes, generals, dukes and earls as well
Conquered by him and brought to grief in war?
As far as men may ride from shore to shore
Of the wide world, the world was his to hold.
Though I should speak for ever on the score
Of knightly honour, his could not be told.

Twelve years he reigned, so say the *Maccabees*,
And was King Philip's son, of Macedon,
First to be king over the land of Greece.

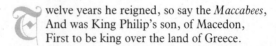

The story of the beautiful young Jewish widow, Judith, who saved the Israelites from their Assyrian enemies, comes in the Apocrypha. This magnificent stained glass window in the church of St John, Gouda, shows Judith and her maid holding Holofernes' head.

An illumination of Alexander the Great with two of his counsellors from the French manuscript of the 'Roman de la Rose' made for Louise of Savoy. Alexander's dazzling career, high intelligence and astounding magnanimity made him a legendary ideal of knightly soldiership in the Middle Ages. His sudden downfall only added to the drama of his story and several other medieval writers, including Boccaccio, the contemporary Italian poet whose work Chaucer translated into English, also cited Alexander as a victim of Fortune.

Alas that Alexander, such a son,
So gentle, so magnanimous, were one
To die by poison from the men he kept!
But Fortune threw him aces for the run
Of sixes thrown before. She little wept.

Who then will give me tears that I may plain
The death of greatness that was never rough,
Of generous feeling that had held domain
Over the world and thought it not enough?
His was a spirit brimming with the stuff
Of high design. Ah, help me to speak shame
Of poisoners and of the foul rebuff
Of fickle Fortune, whom alone I blame.

JULIUS CAESAR

By wisdom, manhood and the works of war
From humble bed to royal majesty
Arose great Julius Caesar, conqueror,
Who won the occident by land and sea
By strength of arms or by diplomacy
And made of each a Roman tributary
And last was emperor himself till he
Was picked by Fortune for her adversary.

O Caesar that in Thessaly excelled
Against your father-in-law great Pompey's sway,
The whole of orient chivalry was held
In whose command, far as the dawn of day!
Your valour was enough to take and slay
All but a few that fled with him, your spell

Held the whole east in terror and dismay.
Give thanks to Fortune for she served you well!

Yet for a little while I will bewail
This Pompey's fate, the noble governor
Of Rome who fled the battle, for the tale
Tells of a man of his, a perjurer,
Who smote his head off, for he hoped to stir
Some gratitude in Caesar, so he brought
The head to him. O Pompey, Justicer
Of all the east, alas that thou wert caught!

To Rome once more this Julius turned, to don
The laurel-wreath, triumphant and elate.
But Brutus Cassius as time went on,
One that had ever envied his estate,
Made a conspiracy in subtle hate
Against this Julius, gave the treacherous vow,
And chose the place where he should meet his fate
By dagger-thrust, and I shall tell you how.

Up to the Capitol this Julius went
A certain day as he was wont to do.
There he was taken by the malcontent
False-hearted Brutus and his scheming crew,
They stabbed him there with daggers through
   and through,
Many the wounds, and there they let him die.
After one dagger-stroke or maybe two
He never groaned, unless the stories lie.

He was a soldier with a manly heart;
So dear to him was honest decency
That deeply as he felt his gashes smart
He sought to shroud his person, casting free
His cloak about his hips and privity,
And in the trance of dying, though he knew
It was his death, he held in memory
The things of seemliness and order due.

I recommend you Lucan for this story
And Suetonius and Valerius too.
They write of these two conquerors in their glory
And in their end, how both of them once knew
Fortune to be their friend, and how she grew
To be their foe. No man may trust her long,
Beware of her in everything you do
And think of these great leaders, once so strong.

CROESUS

Rich Croesus, King of Lydia long ago,
Whom even Persian Cyrus held in dread
Was yet cut short in all his pride and show
And led out to be burnt; but as they led
Him to the stake such rain from overhead
Came down it quenched the fire and he escaped.
He failed to take the warning, be it said;
Fate kept him for the gallows, where he gaped.

For having thus evaded death by fire
Nothing would stop him making war again.
He thought that Fortune meant to raise him higher,
After his luck in being saved by rain,
And he presumed he never could be slain.
Moreover being favoured by a vision
That cockered up his heart, he felt so vain
He set himself to vengeance and derision.

He dreamt that he was perching in a tree
With Jupiter to wash him, back and side,
While Phoebus, with a towel fair to see,
Was drying him. This was what swelled his pride.
He told his daughter who was at his side,
Knowing her versed in mysteries, it would seem,
And asked her what the vision signified.
And thus she started to expound his dream:

'This tree,' she told him, 'signifies a gibbet
And Jupiter betokens snow and rain,
While Phoebus with his towel must exhibit
The streaming sun, to dry you off again.
You will be hanged, my father, that is plain;
The rain shall wash you and the sun shall bake.'
And thus his daughter warned him, but in vain;
Her name Phanýa, if I not mistake.

Hanged, then, was Croesus, this tremendous king;
His royal sceptre was of no avail.
Tragedy is no other kind of thing
Nor tunes her song save only to bewail
How Fortune, ever fickle, will assail
With sudden stroke the kingdoms of the proud,
And when men trust in her she then will fail
And cover her bright face as with a cloud . . .

Words of the Knight and the Host

'Ho, my good sir, no more!' exclaimed the Knight.
'What you have said so far no doubt is right,
And more than right, but still a little grief
Will do for most of us, in my belief.
As for myself, I take a great displeasure
In tales of those who once knew wealth and leisure
And then are felled by some unlucky hit.
But it's a joy to hear the opposite,
For instance tales of men of low estate
Who climb aloft and growing fortunate
Remain secure in their prosperity;
That is delightful as it seems to me
And is a proper sort of tale to tell.'

'That's certain, by St Paul's and by its bell!'
Our Host joined in. 'This Monk, he talks too loud;
All about "Fortune covered with a cloud"
– I don't know what – and as for "Tragedy",
You heard just now, what has to be must be.
It does no good to grumble and complain,
What's done is done. Moreover, it's a pain,
As you have said, to hear about disaster;
Let's have no more of it. God bless you, master,
It's an offence, you're boring us, that's why!
Such talk as that's not worth a butterfly,
Gives no enjoyment, doesn't help the game.
In short Sir Monk – Sir Peter – what's-your-name –

I heartily beg you'll talk of something else.
But for the clink and tinkle of those bells
That hang your bridle round on every side,
By my salvation, by the Lord that died,
I simply should have fallen down asleep
Into the mud below, however deep.
Your story then would have been told in vain,
For, quoting the authorities again,
"When lecturers find their audiences decrease
It does them little good to say their piece."
Give us a word or two on hunting, say.'
'No,' said the Monk, 'I'm in no mood today
For fun. Ask someone else, I've said enough.'

Our Host, whose language was a little rough,
Seeing a Priest beside the Nun, went on:
'Come here, you priest, step forward, you, Sir John,
And tell a tale to make our troubles pack.
Cheer yourself up although you ride a hack.
What if your ugly horse is poor and thin?
If it will serve you, never care a pin!
And always keep your heart up – that's the test!'
'Yes,' he replied, 'yes, Host, I'll do my best,
Not to be merry would deserve reproach.'
And he immediately began to broach
His story to us as we all rode on,
This charming priest and kindly man, Sir John.

An old woman personifies Poverty. 'The Nun's Priest's Tale' opens with a description of a poor but virtuous widow that is among the finest poetic passages that Chaucer ever wrote.

THE NUN'S PRIEST'S TALE

ONCE, long ago, there dwelt a poor old widow
In a small cottage, by a little meadow
Beside a grove and standing in a dale.
This widow-woman of whom I tell my tale
Since the sad day when last she was a wife
Had led a very patient, simple life.
Little she had in capital or rent,

But still, by making do with what God sent,
She kept herself and her two daughters going.
Three hefty sows – no more – were all her showing,
Three cows as well; there was a sheep called Molly.
Sooty her hall, her kitchen melancholy,
And there she ate full many a slender meal;
There was no *sauce piquante* to spice her veal,

A woman milking a cow, from an English bestiary dating from the second half of the fourteenth century. The humble widow and her daughters belong to the agricultural working class, counterparts of Chaucer's virtuous Ploughman. Her poverty and patience are characteristic of religious orders and she has transformed her poverty into moral excellence. She acts as a foil for Chanticleer whose vanity nearly costs him his life.

He may live in a humble farmyard, but Chanticleer is a prince among birds. The richness of the portrait of the cock contrasts sharply with that of his human mistress.

No dainty morsel ever passed her throat,
According to her cloth she cut her coat.
Repletion never left her in disquiet
And all her physic was a temperate diet,
Hard work for exercise and heart's content.
And rich man's gout did nothing to prevent
Her dancing, apoplexy struck her not;
She drank no wine, nor white, nor red had got.
Her board was mostly served with white and black,
Milk and brown bread, in which she found no lack;
Broiled bacon or an egg or two were common,
She was in fact a sort of dairy-woman.
She had a yard that was enclosed about
By a stockade and a dry ditch without,
In which she kept a cock called Chanticleer.
In all the land for crowing he'd no peer;
His voice was jollier than the organ blowing
In church on Sundays, he was great at crowing.
Far, far more regular than any clock
Or abbey bell the crowing of this cock.
The equinoctial wheel and its position
At each ascent he knew by intuition;
At every hour – fifteen degrees of movement –
He crowed so well there could be no improvement.
His comb was redder than fine coral, tall
And battlemented like a castle wall,
His bill was black and shone as bright as jet,
Like azure were his legs and they were set
On azure toes with nails of lily white,
Like burnished gold his feathers, flaming bright.
This gentlecock was master in some measure
Of seven hens, all there to do his pleasure.
They were his sisters and his paramours,

Coloured like him in all particulars;
She with the loveliest dyes upon her throat
Was known as gracious Lady Pertelote.
Courteous she was, discreet and debonair,
Companionable too, and took such care
In her deportment, since she was seven days old
She held the heart of Chanticleer controlled,
Locked up securely in her every limb;
O what a happiness his love to him!
And such a joy it was to hear them sing,
As when the glorious sun began to spring,
In sweet accord, *My Love is far from land*
– For in those far off days I understand
All birds and animals could speak and sing.
Now it befell, as dawn began to spring,
When Chanticleer and Pertelote and all
His wives were perched in this poor widow's hall
(Fair Pertelote was next him on the perch),
This Chanticleer began to groan and lurch
Like someone sorely troubled by a dream,
And Pertelote who heard him roar and scream
Was quite aghast and said, 'O dearest heart,
What's ailing you? Why do you groan and start?
Fie, what a sleeper! What a noise to make!'
'Madam,' he said, 'I beg you not to take
Offence, but by the Lord I had a dream
So terrible just now I had to scream;
I still can feel my heart racing from fear.
God turn my dream to good and guard all here,
And keep my body out of durance vile!

The interpretation of dreams was a constant medieval pre-occupation. Chanticleer's dream clearly fortells his doom, just as nightmares were feared to prophesy damnation. This horrific representation comes from a French painting of Hell.

I dreamt that roaming up and down a while
Within our yard I saw a kind of beast,
A sort of hound that tried or seemed at least
To try and seize me . . . would have killed me dead!
His colour was a blend of yellow and red,
His ears and tail were tipped with sable fur
Unlike the rest; he was a russet cur.
Small was his snout, his eyes were glowing bright.
It was enough to make one die of fright.
That was no doubt what made me groan and swoon.'

'For shame,' she said, 'you timorous poltroon!
Alas, what cowardice! By God above,
You've forfeited my heart and lost my love.
I cannot love a coward, come what may.
For certainly, whatever we may say,
All women long – and O that it might be! –
For husbands tough, dependable and free,
Secret, discreet, no niggard, not a fool
That boasts and then will find his courage cool
At every trifling thing. By God above,
How dare you say for shame, and to your love,
That there was anything at all you feared?
Have you no manly heart to match your beard?
And can a dream reduce you to such terror?
Dreams are a vanity, God knows, pure error.
Dreams are engendered in the too-replete
From vapours in the belly, which compete
With others, too abundant, swollen tight.

No doubt the redness in your dream to-night
Comes from the superfluity and force
Of the red choler in your blood. Of course.
That is what puts a dreamer in the dread
Of crimsoned arrows, fires flaming red,
Of great red monsters making as to fight him,
And big red whelps and little ones to bite him;
Just so the black and melancholy vapours
Will set a sleeper shrieking, cutting capers
And swearing that black bears, black bulls as well,
Or blackest fiends are haling him to Hell.
And there are other vapours that I know
That on a sleeping man will work their woe,
But I'll pass on as lightly as I can.

Take Cato now, that was so wise a man,
Did he not say, "Take no account of dreams"?
Now, sir,' she said, 'on flying from these beams,
For love of God do take some laxative;
Upon my soul that's the advice to give
For melancholy choler; let me urge
You free yourself from vapours with a purge.
And that you may have no excuse to tarry
By saying this town has no apothecary,
I shall myself instruct you and prescribe
Herbs that will cure all vapours of that tribe,
Herbs from our very farmyard! You will find
Their natural property is to unbind
And purge you well beneath and well above.
Now don't forget it, dear, for God's own love!
Your face is choleric and shows distension;

An illustration of centaury from a twelfth-century English herbal. Medieval physicians believed that dreams could be the result of a temporary imbalance in the humours of the body. The practical Pertelote suspects that her husband's dream is due to an excess of choler.

Be careful lest the sun in his ascension
Should catch you full of humours, hot and many.
And if he does, my dear, I'll lay a penny
It means a bout of fever or a breath
Of tertian ague. You may catch your death.
'Worms for a day or two I'll have to give
As a digestive, then your laxative.
Centaury, fumitory, caper-spurge
And hellebore will make a splendid purge;
And then there's laurel or the blackthorn berry,
Ground-ivy too that makes our yard so merry;
Peck them right up, my dear, and swallow whole.
Be happy, husband, by your father's soul!
Don't be afraid of dreams. I'll say no more.'
'Madam,' he said, 'I thank you for your lore,
But with regard to Cato all the same,
His wisdom has, no doubt, a certain fame,
But though he said that we should take no heed

A drawing of fumitory, another of the herbs Pertelote recommends as a laxative. Medieval medicine was governed by the Galenic theory of the four humours: blood, phlegm, choler and melancholy. These were associated with the four qualities – hot, wet, dry and cold, and their balance was considered essential for health.

Of dreams, by God, in ancient books I read
Of many a man of more authority
Than ever Cato was, believe you me,
Who say the very opposite is true
And prove their theories by experience too.
Dreams have quite often been significations
As well of triumphs as of tribulations
That people undergo in this our life.
This needs no argument at all, dear wife,
The proof is all too manifest indeed.

'One of the greatest authors one can read
Says thus: there were two comrades once who
went
On pilgrimage, sincere in their intent.
And as it happened they had reached a town
Where such a throng was milling up and down
And yet so scanty the accommodation,
They could not find themselves a habitation,
No, not a cottage that could lodge them both.
And so they separated, very loth,
Under constraint of this necessity
And each went off to find some hostelry,
And lodge whatever way his luck might fall.
'The first of them found refuge in a stall
Down in a yard with oxen and a plough.
His friend found lodging for himself somehow
Elsewhere, by accident or destiny,
Which governs all of us and equally.
'Now it so happened, long ere it was day,
This fellow had a dream, and as he lay
In bed it seemed he heard his comrade call,
"Help! I am lying in an ox's stall
And shall tonight be murdered as I lie.
Help me, dear brother, help or I shall die!
Come in all haste!" Such were the words he spoke;
The dreamer, lost in terror, then awoke.
But, once awake, he paid it no attention,
Turned over and dismissed it as invention,
It was a dream, he thought, a fantasy.
And twice he dreamt this dream successively.
'Yet a third time his comrade came again,
Or seemed to come, and said, "I have been slain!
Look, look! my wounds are bleeding wide and
deep.
Rise early in the morning, break your sleep
And go to the west gate. You there shall see
A cart all loaded up with dung," said he,
"And in that dung my body has been hidden.
Boldly arrest that cart as you are bidden.
It was my money that they killed me for."
'He told him every detail, sighing sore,
And pitiful in feature, pale of hue.
This dream, believe me, Madam, turned out
true;
For in the dawn, as soon as it was light,
He went to where his friend had spent the night
And when he came upon the cattle-stall
He looked about him and began to call.
'The innkeeper, appearing thereupon,
Quickly gave answer, "Sir, your friend has gone.
He left the town a little after dawn."
The man began to feel suspicious, drawn
By memories of his dream – the western gate,
The dung-cart – off he went, he would not wait,
Towards the western entry. There he found,
Seemingly on its way to dung some ground,
A dung-cart loaded on the very plan
Described so closely by the murdered man.

138

So he began to shout courageously
For right and vengeance on the felony,
"My friend's been killed! There's been a foul attack,
He's in that cart and gaping on his back!
Fetch the authorities, get the sheriff down
– Whosever job it is to run the town –
Help! My companion's murdered, sent to glory!"

What need I add to fnish off the story?
People ran out and cast the cart to ground,
And in the middle of the dung they found
The murdered man. The corpse was fresh and new.

O blessed God, that art so just and true,
Thus thou revealest murder! As we say,
"Murder will out." We see it day by day.
Murder's a foul, abominable treason,
So loathsome to God's justice, to God's reason,
He will not suffer its concealment. True,
Things may lie hidden for a year or two,
But still "Murder will out", that's my conclusion.

All the town officers in great confusion
Seized on the carter and they gave him hell,
And then they racked the innkeeper as well,
And both confessed. And then they took the wrecks
And there and then they hanged them by their necks.

By this we see that dreams are to be dreaded.
And in the self-same book I find embedded,
Right in the very chapter after this
(I'm not inventing, as I hope for bliss)
The story of two men who started out
To cross the sea – for merchandise no doubt –
But as the winds were contrary they waited.
It was a pleasant town, I should have stated,
Merrily grouped about the haven-side.
A few days later with the evening tide
The wind veered round so as to suit them best;
They were delighted and they went to rest
Meaning to sail next morning early. Well,
To one of them a miracle befell.

This man as he lay sleeping, it would seem,
Just before dawn had an astounding dream.
He thought a man was standing by his bed
Commanding him to wait, and thus he said:
"If you set sail to-morrow, as you intend,
You will be drowned. My tale is at an end."

He woke and told his friend what had occurred
And begged him that the journey be deferred
At least a day, implored him not to start.
But his companion, lying there apart,
Began to laugh and treat him to derision.
"I'm not afraid," he said, "of any vision,
To let it interfere with my affairs;
A straw for all your dreamings and your scares.
Dreams are just empty nonsense, merest japes;
Why, people dream all day of owls and apes,
All sorts of trash that can't be understood,
Things that have never happened and never could.
But as I see you mean to stay behind
And miss the tide for wilful sloth of mind

God knows I'm sorry for it, but good day!"
And so he took his leave and went his way.

And yet, before they'd covered half the trip
– I don't know what went wrong – there was a rip
And by some accident the ship went down,
Her bottom rent, all hands aboard to drown
In sight of all the vessels at her side,
That had put out upon the self-same tide.

So, my dear Pertelote, if you discern
The force of these examples, you may learn
One never should be careless about dreams,
For, undeniably, I say it seems
That many are a sign of trouble breeding.

Now, take St Kenelm's life which I've been
reading;
He was Kenulphus' son, the noble King
Of Mercia. Now, St Kenelm dreamt a thing
Shortly before they murdered him one day.
He saw his murder in a dream, I say.
His nurse expounded it and gave her reasons
On every point and warned him against treasons
But as the saint was only seven years old
All that she said about it left him cold.
He was so holy how could visions hurt?

By God, I willingly would give my shirt
To have you read his legend as I've read it;
And, Madam Pertelote, upon my credit,
Macrobius wrote of dreams and can explain us
The vision of young Scipio Africanus,
And he affirms that dreams can give a due
Warning of things that later on come true.

And then there's the Old Testament – a manual
Well worth your study; see the *Book of Daniel.*
Did Daniel think a dream was vanity?
Read about Joseph too and you will see
That many dreams – I do not say that all –
Give cognizance of what is to befall.

Look at Lord Pharaoh, king of Egypt! Look
At what befell his butler and his cook.
Did not their visions have a certain force?
But those who study history of course
Meet many dreams that set them wondering.

What about Croesus too, the Lydian king,
Who dreamt that he was sitting in a tree,
Meaning he would be hanged? It had to be.

Or take Andromache, great Hector's wife;
The day on which he was to lose his life
She dreamt about, the very night before,
And realized that if Hector went to war
He would be lost that very day in battle.
She warned him; he dismissed it all as prattle
And sallied forth to fight, being self-willed,
And there he met Achilles and was killed.
The tale is long and somewhat overdrawn,
And anyhow it's very nearly dawn,
So let me say in very brief conclusion
My dream undoubtedly foretells confusion,
It bodes me ill, I say. And, furthermore,

Upon your laxatives I set no store,
For they are venomous. I've suffered by them
Often enough before, and I defy them.

And now, let's talk of fun and stop all this.
Dear Madam, as I hope for Heaven's bliss,
Of one thing God has sent me plenteous grace,
For when I see the beauty of your face,
That scarlet loveliness about your eyes,
All thought of terror and confusion dies.
For it's as certain as the Creed, I know,
Mulier est hominis confusio
(A Latin tag, dear Madam, meaning this:
"Woman is man's delight and all his bliss"),
For when at night I feel your feathery side,
Although perforce I cannot take a ride
Because, alas, our perch was made too narrow,
Delight and solace fill me to the marrow
And I defy all visions and all dreams!'

And with that word he flew down from the
        beams,
For it was day, and down his hens flew all,
And with a chuck he gave the troupe a call
For he had found a seed upon the floor.
Royal he was, he was afraid no more.
He feathered Pertelote in wanton play
And trod her twenty times ere prime of day.
Grim as a lion's was his manly frown
As on his toes he sauntered up and down;
He scarcely deigned to set his foot to ground
And every time a seed of corn was found
He gave a chuck, and up his wives ran all.
Thus royal as a prince who strides his hall
Leave we this Chanticleer engaged on feeding
And pass to the adventure that was breeding.

Now when the month in which the world began,
March, the first month, when God created man,
Was over, and the thirty-second day
Thereafter ended, on the third of May
It happened that Chanticleer in all his pride,
His seven wives attendant at his side,
Cast his eyes upward to the blazing sun,
Which in the sign of *Taurus* then had run
His twenty-one degrees and somewhat more,
And knew by nature and no other lore
That it was nine o'clock. With blissful voice
He crew triumphantly and said, 'Rejoice,
Behold the sun! The sun is up, my seven.
Look, it has climbed forty degrees in heaven,
Forty degrees and one in fact, by this.
Dear Madam Pertelote, my earthly bliss,
Hark to those blissful birds and how they sing!
Look at those pretty flowers, how they spring!
Solace and revel fill my heart!' He laughed.

But in that moment Fate let fly her shaft;
Ever the latter end of joy is woe,
God knows that worldly joy is swift to go.
A rhetorician with a flair for style
Could chronicle this maxim in his file

Taurus, from a mid-twelfth-century English calendar. In Chaucer's time there was virtually no distinction between astrology and astronomy. The sign of Taurus, which the sun enters between 27 March and 12 April, is one of the houses of Venus – and thus appropriate for the lustful Chanticleer.

Of Notable Remarks with safe conviction.
Then let the wise give ear; this is no fiction.
My story is as true, I undertake,
As that of good Sir Lancelot du Lake
Who held all women in such high esteem.
Let me return full circle to my theme.

A coal-tipped fox of sly iniquity
That had been lurking round the grove for three
Long years, that very night burst through and
    passed
Stockade and hedge, as Providence forecast,
Into the yard where Chanticleer the Fair
Was wont, with all his ladies, to repair.
Still, in a bed of cabbages, he lay
Until about the middle of the day

A sly fox feigns death in order to catch birds. Fables of the fox and the birds were very popular in medieval Europe and can be traced back to Aesop.

Watching the cock and waiting for his cue,
As all these homicides so gladly do
That lie about in wait to murder men.
O false assassin, lurking in thy den!
O new Iscariot, new Ganelon!
And O Greek Sinon, thou whose treachery won
Troy town and brought it utterly to sorrow!
O Chanticleer, accursed be that morrow
That brought thee to the yard from thy high beams!
Thou hadst been warned, and truly, by thy dreams
That this would be a perilous day for thee.

But that which God's foreknowledge can foresee
Must needs occur, as certain men of learning
Have said. Ask any scholar of discerning;
He'll say the Schools are filled with altercation
On this vexed matter of predestination
Long bandied by a hundred thousand men.
How can I sift it to the bottom then?
The Holy Doctor St Augustine shines
In this, and there is Bishop Bradwardine's
Authority, Boethius' too, decreeing
Whether the fact of God's divine foreseeing
Constrains me to perform a certain act
– And by 'constraint' I mean the simple fact
Of mere compulsion by necessity –
Or whether a free choice is granted me
To do a given act or not to do it
Though, ere it was accomplished, God foreknew it,
Or whether Providence is not so stringent
And merely makes necessity contingent.

But I decline discussion of the matter;
My tale is of a cock and of the clatter
That came of following his wife's advice
To walk about his yard on the precise
Morning after the dream of which I told.
O woman's counsel is so often cold!
A woman's counsel brought us first to woe,
Made Adam out of Paradise to go
Where he had been so merry, so well at ease.
But, for I know not whom it may displease
If I suggest that women are to blame,
Pass over that; I only speak in game.
Read the authorities to know about
What has been said of women; you'll find out.
These are the cock's words, and not mine, I'm giving;
I think no harm of any woman living.

Merrily in her dust-bath in the sand
Lay Pertelote. Her sisters were at hand
Basking in sunlight. Chanticleer sang free,
More merrily than a mermaid in the sea
(For *Physiologus* reports the thing
And says how well and merrily they sing).
And so it happened as he cast his eye
Towards the cabbage at a butterfly
It fell upon the fox there, lying low.
Gone was all inclination then to crow.
'Cok cok,' he cried, giving a sudden start,
As one who feels a terror at his heart,

'Chanticleer sang free,/More merrily than a mermaid in the sea'/(For Physiologus reports the thing/And says how well and merrily they sing). According to the legend referred to by Chaucer, mermaids could sing so sweetly they lured sailors to sleep. Medieval bestiaries would often include such mythical creatures.

For natural instinct teaches beasts to flee
The moment they perceive an enemy,
Though they had never met with it before.
This Chanticleer was shaken to the core
And would have fled. The fox was quick to say
However, 'Sir! Whither so fast away?
Are you afraid of me, that am your friend?
A fiend, or worse, I should be, to intend
You harm, or practise villainy upon you;
Dear sir, I was not even spying on you!
Truly I came to do no other thing
Than just to lie and listen to you sing.
You have as merry a voice as God has given
To any angel in the courts of Heaven;
To that you add a musical sense as strong
As had Boethius who was skilled in song.
My Lord your Father (God receive his soul!),
Your mother too – how courtly, what control! –
Have honoured my poor house, to my great ease;
And you, sir, too, I should be glad to please.
For, when it comes to singing, I'll say this
(Else may these eyes of mine be barred from bliss),
There never was a singer I would rather
Have heard at dawn than your respected father.
All that he sang came welling from his soul
And how he put his voice under control!
The pains he took to keep his eyes tight shut
In concentration – then the tip-toe strut,
The slender neck stretched out, the delicate beak!
No singer could approach him in technique

Or rival him in song, still less surpass.
I've read the story in *Burnel the Ass*,
Among some other verses, of a cock
Whose leg in youth was broken by a knock
A clergyman's son had given him, and for this
He made the father lose his benefice.
But certainly there's no comparison
Between the subtlety of such a one
And the discretion of your father's art
And wisdom. Oh, for charity of heart,
Can you not emulate your sire and sing?'

This Chanticleer began to beat a wing
As one incapable of smelling treason,
So wholly had this flattery ravished reason.
Alas, my lords! there's many a sycophant
And flatterer that fill your courts with cant
And give more pleasure with their zeal forsooth
Than he who speaks in soberness and truth.
Read what *Ecclesiasticus* records
Of flatterers. 'Ware treachery, my lords!'

This Chanticleer stood high upon his toes,
He stretched his neck, his eyes began to close,
His beak to open; with his eyes shut tight
He then began to sing with all his might.

Sir Russel Fox leapt in to the attack,
Grabbing his gorge he flung him o'er his back
And off he bore him to the woods, the brute,
And for the moment there was no pursuit.

O Destiny that may not be evaded!
Alas that Chanticleer had so paraded!
Alas that he had flown down from the beams!

A woodcut from the Grete Herbal. 'Grabbing his gorge he flung him o'er his back/And off he bore him to the woods, the brute.' Medieval herbals would frequently include the habits and characteristics of a few animals.

O that his wife took no account of dreams!
And on a Friday too to risk their necks!
O Venus, goddess of the joys of sex,
Since Chanticleer thy mysteries professed
And in thy service always did his best,
And more for pleasure than to multiply
His kind, on thine own day, is he to die?

O Geoffrey, thou my dear and sovereign master
Who, when they brought King Richard to disaster
And shot him dead, lamented so his death,
Would that I had thy skill, thy gracious breath,
To chide a Friday half so well as you!
(For he was killed upon a Friday too.)
Then I could fashion you a rhapsody
For Chanticleer in dread and agony.

Sure never such a cry or lamentation
Was made by ladies of high Trojan station,
When Ilium fell and Pyrrhus with his sword
Grabbed Priam by the beard, their king and lord,
And slew him there as the *Aeneid* tells,
As what was uttered by those hens. Their yells
Surpassed them all in palpitating fear
When they beheld the rape of Chanticleer.
Dame Pertelote emitted sovereign shrieks
That echoed up in anguish to the peaks
Louder than those extorted from the wife
Of Hasdrubal, when he had lost his life
And Carthage all in flame and ashes lay.
She was so full of torment and dismay
That in the very flames she chose her part
And burnt to ashes with a steadfast heart.
O woeful hens, louder your shrieks and higher
Than those of Roman matrons when the fire
Consumed their husbands, senators of Rome,
When Nero burnt their city and their home;
Beyond a doubt that Nero was their bale!

Now let me turn again to tell my tale;
This blessed widow and her daughters two
Heard all these hens in clamour and halloo
And, rushing to the door at all this shrieking,
They saw the fox towards the covert streaking
And, on his shoulder, Chanticleer stretched flat.
'Look, look!' they cried, 'O mercy, look at that!
Ha! Ha! the fox!' and after him they ran,
And stick in hand ran many a serving man,
Ran Coll our dog, ran Talbot, Bran and Shaggy,
And with a distaff in her hand ran Maggie,
Ran cow and calf and ran the very hogs
In terror at the barking of the dogs;
The men and women shouted, ran and cursed,
They ran so hard they thought their hearts would burst,
They yelled like fiends in Hell, ducks left the water
Quacking and flapping as on point of slaughter,
Up flew the geese in terror over the trees,
Out of the hive came forth the swarm of bees;
So hideous was the noise – God bless us all,
Jack Straw and all his followers in their brawl
Were never half so shrill, for all their noise,

When they were murdering those Flemish boys,
As that day's hue and cry upon the fox.
They grabbed up trumpets made of brass and box,
Of horn and bone, on which they blew and pooped,
And therewithal they shouted and they whooped
So that it seemed the very heavens would fall.

And now, good people, pay attention all.
See how Dame Fortune quickly changes side
And robs her enemy of hope and pride!
This cock that lay upon the fox's back
In all his dread contrived to give a quack
And said, 'Sir Fox, if I were you, as God's
My witness, I would round upon these clods
And shout, "Turn back, you saucy bumpkins all!
A very pestilence upon you fall!
Now that I have in safety reached the wood
Do what you like, the cock is mine for good;
I'll eat him there in spite of every one."'

The fox replying, 'Faith, it shall be done!'
Opened his mouth and spoke. The nimble bird,
Breaking away upon the uttered word,
Flew high into the tree-tops on the spot.
And when the fox perceived where he had got,
'Alas,' he cried, 'alas, my Chanticleer,
I've done you grievous wrong, indeed I fear
I must have frightened you; I grabbed too hard
When I caught hold and took you from the yard.
But, sir, I meant no harm, don't be offended,
Come down and I'll explain what I intended;
So help me God I'll tell the truth – on oath!'
'No,' said the cock, 'and curses on us both,
And first on me if I were such a dunce
As let you fool me oftener than once.
Never again, for all your flattering lies,
You'll coax a song to make me blink my eyes;
And as for those who blink when they should look,
God blot them from his everlasting Book!'
'Nay, rather,' said the fox, 'his plagues be flung
On all who chatter that should hold their tongue.'

The twelfth-century French tale, 'Le Roman de Renard', is one oft-quoted source for Chaucer's tale and was one of the great animal stories in medieval European literature. There too the fox ends up being chased out of the farmyard by a woman with her distaff.

Lo, such it is not to be on your guard
Against the flatterers of the world, or yard,
And if you think my story is absurd,
A foolish trifle of a beast and bird,
A fable of a fox, a cock, a hen,
Take hold upon the moral, gentlemen.
St Paul himself, a saint of great discerning,
Says that all things are written for our learning;
So take the grain and let the chaff be still.
And, gracious Father, if it be thy will
As saith my Saviour, make us all good men,
And bring us to his heavenly bliss.

Amen.

Words of the Host to the Nun's Priest

'SIR Priest,' our Host remarked in merry tones,
'Blest be your breeches and your precious stones,
That was a merry tale of Chanticleer!
If you had only been a secular
You would have trodden a pretty fowl, no doubt.
Had you the heart, your muscles would hold out;
You look as if you needed hens, I mean,
Yes, more than seven. Seven times seventeen!
Just look what brawn he has, this gentle priest,
And what a neck! His chest's not of the least.
As for his eyes they're like a sparrow-hawk's,
And his complexion like a box of chalks;
He needs no dyes imported from the East
Or Portugal, Good luck to you, Sir Priest,
For telling a fine tale!' And saying thus
He turned, as you shall hear, to one of us.

Here follows the Physician's Tale.

143

THE PHYSICIAN'S TALE

LIVY has handed down a tale to us
About a knight surnamed Virginius.
He was a man of honourable birth,
Rich, well-befriended and of sterling worth.
This knight had had a daughter by his wife;
There were no other children in his life.
Of an excelling loveliness was she,
Above all others that a man might see.
Nature had shown a sovereign diligence
In forming her to such an excellence,
As if she wished to say, 'Look! I am Nature,
And this is how I form and paint a creature
When so I choose. Who dares a counterfeit?
No, not Pygmalion, though he forge and beat,
Colour and carve for ever; I maintain
That Zeuxis or Apelles would work in vain
To colour or to carve, to forge or beat,
If they presumed to make a counterfeit.
For He that is the Maker-Principal
Appointed me His vicar-general
To fashion creatures, all that ever were,
And paint them as I please; for in my care
Lies all that's under moon and, wax or wane,
I form them all. I do not work for gain;
My Lord and I are leagued in close accord.
I made her for the worship of my Lord,
And so I do with all my other creatures
Whatever be their colour or their features.'
This was, I think, what Nature meant to say.
The maiden was fourteen on whose array
Nature had spent her care with such delight.
For just as she can paint a lily white,
Redden a rose and teach it to unfurl
Her petals, so she touched this noble girl
Ere she was born; her limbs so lissom she

According to the legend referred to by Chaucer, the painter Xeuxis tried to vie with the goddess Nature and create five beautiful virgins. Nature was believed to pay special attention to the creation of beautiful women.

Left: An Italian miniature depicting the Triumph of Chastity. 'The Physician's Tale' about the chaste and virtuous daughter is another adaptation of an old story. Chaucer claims Livy as his source but there was a version of it in the 'Roman de la Rose'.

Had touched with colour where they ought to be.
Phoebus her mass of tresses with a gleam
Had dyed in burnish from his golden stream,
And if her beauty was beyond compare,
Her virtue was a thousand times more rare;
There lacked no quality in her to move
The praises sober wisdom would approve.
Chaste of her body and her soul was she,
And so she flowered in her virginity
With all humility and abstinence
In temperate and patient innocence,
With modesty of bearing and of dress
And showed in speech a modesty no less.
Though I dare say as wise as Pallas, she
Was simple in her words, and womanly;
She used no fancy terms in affectation
Of learning, but according to her station
She spoke; in all and everything she said

She showed that she was good and gently bred.
Shamefast she was, in maiden shamefastness,
And constant in her heart. She was express
In conquering sloth to fill the busy hour;
Over her mouth had never Bacchus power,
For wine and youth swell Venus and desire,
Much as when oil is cast upon the fire.
Indeed her native goodness unconstrained
So prompted her that she had often feigned
Some sickness to escape from company
Where there was likelihood of ribaldry,
As well there may be; junketings and dances
Are good occasions for lascivious glances.
Such things as these may soon too easily
Make a child bold and ripe, as one can see;
That's very dangerous and long has been,
For all too soon she learns to play the queen
And show how bold she is, when she's a wife.

A nd all you ladies that in middle life
Are put in charge of younger gentlefolk,
Pray do not think I speak as to provoke
Your anger; think that your appointment springs
From either one or other of two things,
Either that you were chaste and did not fail
To guard your honour, or that you were frail,
And therefore, knowing well the ancient dance,
You have forsaken your intemperance
For ever. Teach them then for Jesu's sake
And never slacken; virtue is at stake.
Just as a poacher who forsakes his crimes
And leaves his trade in villainy betimes,
Makes the best gamekeeper – he's just the man –
Keep you your charges; if you will you can.
Never belittle or connive at vice
Lest you should pay damnation as the price;
For those who do are traitors, never doubt it,
And so give heed to what I say about it.
Top of all treason, sovereign pestilence,
Is the betrayal done on innocence.

Y ou Fathers and you Mothers, let me add,
However many children you have had,
Yours is the duty of their supervision
As long as they are bound by your decision.
Beware lest the example you present
Or your neglect in giving chastisement
Cause them to perish; otherwise I fear,
If they should do so, you will pay it dear.
Shepherds too soft who let their duty sleep
Encourage wolves to tear the lambs and sheep.
One parable's enough, you understand;
Let me return to what I had in hand.

T his girl who is the theme of my address
Was such as not to need a governess.
The way she lived, if other girls would look,
Could teach them more of goodness than a book.
In all that should concern a virtuous maid,
She was so prudent, bountiful and staid;
And common fame was eager to confess

Her matchless beauty and her kindliness.
Lovers of virtue praised her and gave proof
Of her deserts, though envy stood aloof,
Envy that glowers at favour like a thief
And gloats to see another come to grief
(A phrase that St Augustine noted down).

T his girl one morning went into the town
Towards the temple, with her mother too,
As one may see a girl will often do.
Now at that time there was a judge in charge
Over the city and the land at large,
And so it happened that he cast his eye
Upon this girl as she was passing by
And narrowly appraised her. As he viewed
Her loveliness, a sudden change of mood
Entered his heart and, feeling himself caught
By her attraction, secretly he thought,
'I'll have that girl whether I sink or swim!'
At once the devil entered into him,
Whose machinations then began to stir
And teach him how to have his will of her.
He knew quite well that neither force nor fee
Could suit his purpose in the least degree,
For she had powerful friends and what was more
Her sovereignty of goodness closed the door
On his desires, he could not hope to win
Her soul or body to an act of sin.
So, after much reflection, he sent down
For a known blackguard living in the town,
As low in cunning tricks as he was bold.
He came; in secret then the tale was told
And having heard it he was made to swear
Never to tell a soul, and should he dare
So much as whisper, he should lose his head.
When he agreed to all that had been said
Of his accursed plan the judge was glad
And gave him precious gifts, the best he had.

W hen they had framed their whole conspiracy
From point to point to suit the lechery
That was to be enacted on the sly
(Though you shall hear about it by and by)
Home went the fellow, Claudius was his name;
This treacherous judge that was so lost to shame
Was surnamed Appius – for the thing's no fable
But quite historical, and many able
Historians will vouch the gist of it –
This treacherous judge, I tell you, set his wit
To work and went about without delay
To gratify his lust. There came a day
When the false judge (authorities report)
As was his custom, took his seat in court
And gave his judgement upon various cases.
All of a sudden in this fellow races
Crying, 'My Lord, I beg with your permission
For justice in my pitiful petition
Touching my suit against Virginius.
If he denies it, says it was not thus,
Then I shall prove it and produce good witness

To testify the truth of it, and fitness.'
'In absence,' said the judge, 'of the accused
Definitive award must be refused.
Summon him, state your case, and I will hear it
Gladly; you shall have justice, never fear it.'

Virginius came to learn the judge's will,
And instantly they read the cursed bill;
These were the terms of it, as you shall hear:
'To you, Lord Appius, it shall appear
On showing of your poor servant Claudius
How that a certain knight, Virginius,
Against the law, against all equity,
And an express injunction lodged by me
Retains a servant that is mine by right,
One that was stolen from my house by night
When she was very young. I can support
The charge on witness, may it please the court.
My lord the judge, whatever he may say
The girl is not his daughter and I pray
My slave may be restored, by your good will.'
This was the tenor of his cursed bill.

Virginius stared in horror at the churl,
But quickly, ere he could defend his girl
And prove it on his honour as a knight,
Or bring a host of witness, as he might,
That all was false his enemy had stated,
This cursed judge, who never so much as waited
To hear the answer of Virginius,
Spoke out at once and gave his judgement thus:
'I rule this fellow is to have his slave
Immediately. The case is very grave.

'This treacherous judge that was so lost to shame/Was surnamed Appius – for the thing's no fable/But quite historical...'. This graphic illustration of Appius comes from a Flemish illuminated manuscript of the 'Roman de la Rose' that gave another account of the story.

Your house shall not protect her. Fetch the girl.
I say the court awards her to the churl.'

And when Virginius, this excellent knight,
Had understood the judge's doom aright
And knew his daughter, on compulsion, must
Be handed over to the judge's lust,
Home he returned and seated in his hall
He sent a servant, bidding him to call
His daughter to him, and with ashen face
Deathly and cold, gazed on her lowly grace.
Fatherly pity pierced him to the heart
And yet he did not falter in his part.

'Daughter,' he said. 'Virginia, I must name
The ways that lie before you, death or shame.'
One you must take. Alas, that I was born!
O judgement undeserved! O my forlorn
And innocent girl to die upon the knife!

'Blessed be God that I shall die a maid!/I take my death rather than take my shame.' The climax of this moral tale comes when Virginius sees no alternative but to kill his beloved daughter, rather than hand her over to the lustful Appius. Another illustration from the Flemish illuminated manuscript of the 'Roman de la Rose'.

O my dear daughter, ender of my life,
You that I fostered up with such delight,
Whose thought has never left me day or night,
O daughter, you that are my last of woe
And last of any joy that I shall know,
Be patient, O my gem of chastity,
And take your death, for that is my decree.
And it is love, not hate, would have you dead;
My pitying hand must strike, and take your head.
Alas that ever Appius saw your face

To give false judgement in a treacherous case!'
He told her then all you have heard before
Of what had happened; I need say no more.
'O mercy, dearest father!' said the maid
And as she spoke she came to him and laid
Her arms about his neck, as oft she did,
And the tears flooded under either lid.
Thus as she wept, 'O father dear,' said she,
'Am I to die? Is there no remedy?'
'None, none, my dearest daughter. Hope is dead.'
'O give me time, dear father,' then she said,
'Let me lament my death a little space,
For Jephtha gave his daughter so much grace
As to allow her time to sorrow in,
Before he slew her. She had done no sin,
God knows, but ran, the first among them all,
To welcome him in solemn festival.'
And on the word she fell into a swoon;
But when her faintness passed she rose as soon
And thus addressed her father, unafraid,
'Blessed be God that I shall die a maid!
I take my death rather than take my shame,
So do your will upon me in God's name!'
And having spoken thus the child implored
That he would smite her softly with his sword
And then once more she fainted and lay still.
Her father sorrowful in heart and will
Smote off her head and took it by the hair,
Sought out the judge and gave it to him there
Sitting in judgement, in the open court.
When he beheld it, Livy makes report,
He rose and gave the order to his men
To take the knight and hang him. There and then
A thousand men came surging from the city
Thrusting their way into the court, in pity
And hope to save the knight; the news had flown,
The treacherous iniquity was known,
For there had been suspicion of the thing
Bred from the way the churl had sought to bring
His charge against the knight with the consent
Of Appius. They knew his lecherous bent,
And so it was the people had arisen.

In this fifteenth-century French woodcut of 'Doctor and Patient' the physician holds up a urinal while his assistant prepares medicines. In the background are a pestle and mortar and shelves full of 'bottles and boxes'. The Host claims to be touched with 'heart disease, or very near' by the Physician's pitiful tale, but he rejects any medical treatment in favour of a good drink!

They took that judge and cast him into prison
And there he slew himself; and Claudius,
Him that was instrument to Appius,
They took and would have hanged upon a tree
But that Virginius in clemency
Begged for his exile. They could scarce refuse,
Else he would certainly have got his dues.
The rest were hanged, the greater and the less,
That had been party to this cursedness.
Here one can see how sin is paid its wages;
Beware, for no one knows how God engages
Or when to smite the sinner, or how the worm
Of conscience will bring terror to the firm
In wickedness, however secretly,
Though none should know of it but God and he.
Be he illiterate or a man of learning,
How soon the blow will fall there's no discerning.
I offer you this counsel; let it make you
Forsake your sins before your sins forsake you.

Words of the Host to the Physician and to the Pardoner

OUR Host began a violent tirade.
'God's nails and blood,' he said, 'alas, poor maid!
What a low blackguard! What a treacherous judge!
Death to all lawyers that will bribe and fudge
To trap you, be they judge or advocate!
Well, the poor girl was killed at any rate.

Alas, her beauty cost her all too dear!
Just as I always say, it's pretty clear
The handsome gifts that fate and nature lend us
Are very often those that least befriend us.
Her beauty was her death as one might say;
How pitifully she was made away!
Those gifts that I was mentioning just now
Do us more harm than good, one must allow,

Well, my dear sir, if I may speak sincere,
Your tale was truly pitiful to hear.
Nevertheless, pass on. No sense in fretting.
God's blessing on you, Doctor, not forgetting
Your various urinals and chamber-pots,
Bottles, medicaments and cordial tots
And boxes brimming all with panaceas,
God's blessing on them all and St Maria's!
You look a proper fellow! Pills and pellets!
St Ronyan, you've a figure like a prelate's!
Don't I say well? – although I lack the art
To talk like you; your story touched my heart,
It gave me heart-disease, or very near.
By corpus bones! I'll need a dose, I fear,

Or else a good wet draught of malted ale
If someone doesn't tell a cheerful tale;
I'm lost in pity for that poor girl dead.
Come on, old chum and Pardoner,' he said,
'Tell us a funny story, break a joke!'
'Right, by St Ronyan! but I'll have a soak
First at this pub. I've got a thirst to slake,'
Said he, 'I'll drink and eat a bit of cake.'
Outcry arose among the gentlefolk.
'No, no, don't let him tell a dirty joke!
Tell something with a moral, something clear
And profitable, and we'll gladly hear.'
'Granted,' he said, 'but first I'll have to think;
I'll ponder something decent while I drink.'

Coment herodes feet a la table a vue feste ouvekes tiplefin degent. E la fili
herodie femeift deuaunt li: ceo eft afauoir de toumler + de aurie Abatement fount
herodes enout graunt ioie. E difoit: fili demaunde ceo q tu vors cuuerter E
deubartert a la te coundie. E ele allar a fa mere herodie p la cuurfcher quoi ele de
uoit demander. E ele la difoit la tefte fefn ian en vue efquele q eftoit en prifon. E ele al
lat demander la tefte fefn ian le Baptift q eftoit en fa prifon. E herodes la ottreat.

Coment fefn ian le Baptift eftoit decole de vn turmentour. E la tefte mife dedenz vue
efquele. E la fili herondie la aportat deuaunt herodes + herondie fa mere q enout
graunt ioie.

THE PARDONER'S TALE

The Pardoner's Prologue

M Y lords,' he said, 'in churches where I preach
I cultivate a haughty kind of speech
And ring it out as roundly as a bell;
I've got it all by heart, the tale I tell.
I have a text, it always is the same
And always has been, since I learnt the game,
Old as the hills and fresher than the grass,
Radix malorum est cupiditas.

B ut first I make pronouncement whence I come,
Show them my bulls in detail and in sum.
And flaunt the papal seal for their inspection
As warrant for my bodily protection,
That none may have the impudence to irk
Or hinder me in Christ's most holy work.
Then I tell stories, as occasion calls,
Showing forth bulls from popes and cardinals,
From patriarchs and bishops; as I do,
I speak some words in Latin – just a few –
To put a saffron tinge upon my preaching
And stir devotion with a spice of teaching.
Then I bring all my long glass bottles out
Cram-full of bones and ragged bits of clout,
Relics they are, at least for such are known.
Then, cased in metal, I've a shoulder-bone,
Belonging to a sheep, a holy Jew's.
"Good men," I say, "take heed, for here is news.
Take but this bone and dip it in a well;
If cow or calf, if sheep or ox should swell
From eating snakes or that a snake has stung,
Take water from that well and wash its tongue,
And it will then recover. Furthermore,
Where there is pox or scab or other sore,
All animals that water at that well
Are cured at once. Take note of what I tell.

A preacher and congregation, c.1400. The Pardoner reminisces about his own techniques as a preacher, explaining how he flaunts his papal seals before producing his array of relics.

Left: An illustration from the Holkham Bible of the drunken King Herod ordering the death of John the Baptist. The Pardoner cites King Herod's example when introducing his horrific tale about the three drunken revellers who set out to kill Death – and end by killing each other.

If the good man – the owner of the stock –
Goes once a week, before the crow of cock,
Fasting, and takes a draught of water too,
Why then, according to that holy Jew,
He'll find his cattle multiply and sell.

The punishment of the avaricious, from a manuscript on Heaven and Hell. Chaucer's Pardoner is motivated entirely by avarice.

And it's a cure for jealousy as well;
For though a man be given to jealous wrath,
Use but this water when you make his broth,
And never again will he mistrust his wife,
Though he knew all about her sinful life,
Though two or three clergy had enjoyed her love.
"Now look; I have a mitten here, a glove.
Whoever wears this mitten on his hand
Will multiply his grain. He sows his land
And up will come abundant wheat or oats,
Providing that he offers pence or groats.
"Good men and women, here's a word of warning;
If there is anyone in church this morning
Guilty of sin, so far beyond expression
Horrible, that he dare not make confession,
Or any woman, whether young or old,
That's cuckolded her husband, be she told
That such as she shall have no power or grace
To offer to my relics in this place.
But those who can acquit themselves of blame
Can all come up and offer in God's name,
And I will shrive them by the authority
Committed in this papal bull to me."

"That trick's been worth a hundred marks a year
Since I became a Pardoner, never fear.
Then, priestlike in my pulpit, with a frown,
I stand, and when the yokels have sat down,
I preach, as you have heard me say before,
And tell a hundred lying mockeries more.
I take great pains, and stretching out my neck
To east and west I crane about and peck
Just like a pigeon sitting on a barn.
My hands and tongue together spin the yarn
And all my antics are a joy to see.
The curse of avarice and cupidity
Is all my sermon, for it frees the pelf.
Out come the pence, and specially for myself,
For my exclusive purpose is to win
And not at all to castigate their sin.
Once dead what matter how their souls may fare?
They can go blackberrying, for all I care!
"Believe me, many a sermon or devotive
Exordium issues from an evil motive.
Some to give pleasure by their flattery
And gain promotion through hypocrisy,
Some out of vanity, some out of hate;

Or when I dare not otherwise debate
I'll put my discourse into such a shape,
My tongue will be a dagger; no escape
For him from slandering falsehood shall there be.
If he has hurt my brethren or me.
For though I never mention him by name
The congregation guesses all the same
From certain hints that everybody knows,
And so I take revenge upon our foes
And spit my venom forth, while I profess
Holy and true – or seeming holiness.
But let me briefly make my purpose plain;
I preach for nothing but for greed of gain
And use the same old text, as bold as brass,
Radix malorum est cupiditas.
And thus I preach against the very vice
I make my living out of – avarice.
And yet however guilty of that sin
Myself, with others I have power to win
Them from it, I can bring them to repent;
But that is not my principal intent.
Covetousness is both the root and stuff
Of all I preach. That ought to be enough.
Well, then I give examples thick and fast
From bygone times, old stories from the past.
A yokel mind loves stories from of old,

Being the kind it can repeat and hold.
What! Do you think, as long as I can preach
And get their silver for the things I teach,
That I will live in poverty, from choice?
That's not the counsel of my inner voice!
No! Let me preach and beg from kirk to kirk
And never do an honest job of work,
No, nor make baskets, like St Paul, to gain
A livelihood. I do not preach in vain.
There's no apostle I would counterfeit;
I mean to have money, wool and cheese and wheat
Though it were given me by the poorest lad
Or poorest village widow, though she had
A string of starving children, all agape.
No, let me drink the liquor of the grape
And keep a jolly wench in every town!
But listen, gentlemen; to bring things down
To a conclusion, would you like a tale?
Now as I've drunk a draught of corn-ripe
ale,
By God it stands to reason I can strike
On some good story that you all will like.
For though I am a wholly vicious man
Don't think I can't tell moral tales. I can!
Here's one I often preach when out for winning;
Now please be quiet. Here is the beginning.'

The Pardoner's Tale

IN Flanders once there was a company
Of youngsters haunting vice and ribaldry,
Riot and gambling, stews and public-houses
Where each with harp, guitar or lute carouses,
Dancing and dicing day and night, and bold

A den of iniquity. The Pardoner gives a vivid denunciation of gluttony, drunkenness, swearing and gambling, but paradoxically his skill as a preacher lends his description a horrific power.

To eat and drink far more than they can hold,
Doing thereby the devil sacrifice
Within that devil's temple of cursed vice,
Abominable in superfluity,
With oaths so damnable in blasphemy
That it's a grisly thing to hear them swear.
Our dear Lord's body they will rend and tear
As if the Jews had rent Him not enough;
And at the sin of others every tough
Will laugh, and presently the dancing-girls,
Small pretty ones, come in and shake their curls,
With youngsters selling fruit, and ancient bawds,
And girls with cakes and music, devil's gauds
To kindle and blow the fires of lechery
That are so close annexed to gluttony.
Witness the Bible, which is most express
That lust is bred of wine and drunkenness.
Look how the drunken and unnatural Lot
Lay with his daughters, though he knew it not;
He was too drunk to know what he was doing.
Take Herod, too, his tale is worth pursuing.
Replete with wine and feasting, he was able
To give the order at his very table
To kill the innocent Baptist, good St John.

The punishment of lechers, from a French mid-fifteenth-century manuscript. This would be one of the few vices the Pardoner knew little about for Chaucer gives several hints – his high bleating voice, his long yellow hair and his beardlessness – that he was a eunuch.

Seneca has a thought worth pondering on;
No difference, he says, that he can find
Between a madman who has lost his mind
And one who is habitually mellow
Except that madness when it takes a fellow
Lasts longer, on the whole, than drunkenness.
O cursed gluttony, our first distress!
Cause of our first confusion, first temptation,
The very origin of our damnation,
Till Christ redeemed us with his blood again!
O infamous indulgence! Cursed stain
So dearly bought! And what has it been worth?
Gluttony has corrupted all the earth.

Adam, our father, and his wife as well,
From Paradise to labour and to Hell
Were driven for that vice, they were indeed.
While she and Adam fasted, so I read,
They were in Paradise; when he and she

Gluttony, from a late medieval French manuscript. All the sins described by the Pardoner are seen as interdependent – to commit one leads to the others and all are forms of blasphemy, the greatest sin of all. Thus any sin draws the sinner irrevocably on to damnation.

Ate of the fruit of that forbidden tree
They were at once cast forth in pain and woe.
O gluttony, it is to thee we owe
Our griefs! O if we knew the maladies
That follow on excess and gluttonies,
Sure we would diet, we would temper pleasure
In sitting down at table, show some measure!
Alas the narrow throat, the tender mouth!
Men labour east and west and north and south
In earth, in air, in water – Why, d'you think?
To get a glutton dainty meat and drink!
How well of this St Paul's Epistle treats!
'Meats for the belly, belly for the meats,
But God shall yet destroy both it and them.'
Alas, the filth of it! If we contemn
The name, how far more filthy is the act!
A man who swills down vintages in fact
Makes a mere privy of his throat, a sink
For cursed superfluities of drink!

So the Apostle said, whom tears could soften:
'Many there are, as I have told you often,
And weep to tell, whose gluttony sufficed
To make them enemies of the cross of Christ,
Whose ending is destruction and whose God
Their belly!' O thou belly! stinking pod
Of dung and foul corruption, that canst send
Thy filthy music forth at either end,
What labour and expense it is to find
Thy sustenance! These cooks that strain and grind
And bray in mortars, transubstantiate
God's gifts into a flavour on a plate,
To please a lecherous palate. How they batter
Hard bones to put some marrow on your platter,
Spicery, root, bark, leaf – they search and cull it
In the sweet hope of flattering a gullet!
Nothing is thrown away that could delight
Or whet anew lascivious appetite.
Be sure a man whom such a fare entices
Is dead indeed, though living in his vices.

Wine is a lecherous thing and drunkenness
A squalor of contention and distress.
O drunkard, how disfigured is thy face,
How foul thy breath, how filthy thy embrace!
And through thy drunken nose a stertorous snort
Like *'samson-samson'* – something of the sort.
Yet Samson never was a man to swig.
You totter, lurch and fall like a stuck pig,
Your manhood's lost, your tongue is in a burr.
Drunkenness is the very sepulchre
Of human judgement and articulation.
He that is subject to the domination
Of drink can keep no secrets, be it said.
Keep clear of wine, I tell you, white or red,
Especially Spanish wines which they provide
And have on sale in Fish Street and Cheapside.
That wine mysteriously finds its way
To mix itself with others – shall we say
Spontaneously! – that grow in neighbouring regions.

'Gambling's the very mother of robbed purses,/Lies, double-dealing, perjury, and curses ...' The Pardoner's description with its powerful rhetoric is not really prohibitive at all.

Out of the mixture fumes arise in legions,
So when a man has had a drink or two
Though he may think he is at home with you
In Cheapside, I assure you he's in Spain
Where it was made, at Lepé I maintain,
Not even at Bordeaux. He's soon elate
And very near the *'samson-samson'* state.
But seriously, my lords, attention, pray!
All the most notable acts, I dare to say,
And victories in the Old Testament,
Won under God who is omnipotent,
Were won in abstinence, were won in prayer.
Look in the Bible, you will find it there.
Or else take Attila the Conqueror;
Died in his sleep, a manner to abhor,
In drunken shame and bleeding at the nose.
A general should live sober, I suppose.
Moreover to call to mind and ponder well
What was commanded unto Lemuel
– Not Samuel, but Lemuel I said –
Read in the Bible, that's the fountain-head,
And see what comes of giving judges drink.
No more of that. I've said enough, I think.
Having put gluttony in its proper setting
I wish to warn you against dice and betting.
Gambling's the very mother of robbed purses,
Lies, double-dealing, perjury, and curses,
Manslaughter, blasphemy of Christ, and waste
Of time and money. Worse, you are debased
In public reputation, put to shame.

'A common gambler' is a nasty name.
The more exalted such a man may be
So much the more contemptible is he.
A gambling prince would be incompetent
To frame a policy of government,
And he will sink in general opinion
As one unfit to exercise dominion.
Stilbon, that wise ambassador whose mission
Took him to Corinth, was of high position;
Sparta had sent him with intent to frame
A treaty of alliance. When he came,
Hoping for reinforcement and advice,
It happened that he found them all at dice,
Their very nobles; so he quickly planned
To steal away, home to his native land.
He said, 'I will not lose my reputation,
Or compromise the honour of my nation,
By asking dicers to negotiate.
Send other wise ambassadors of state,
For on my honour I would rather die
Than be a means for Sparta to ally
With gamblers; Sparta, glorious in honour,
Shall take no such alliances upon her
As dicers make, by any act of mine!'
He showed his sense in taking such a line.
Again, consider King Demetrius;
The King of Parthia – history has it thus –
Sent him a pair of golden dice in scorn,
To show he reckoned him a gambler born
Whose honour, if unable to surmount

The vice of gambling, was of no account.
Lords can amuse themselves in other ways
Honest enough, to occupy their days.
Now let me speak a word or two of swearing
And perjury; the Bible is unsparing.
It's an abominable thing to curse
And swear, it says; but perjury is worse.
Almighty God has said, 'Swear not at all',
Witness St Matthew, and you may recall
The words of Jeremiah, having care
To what he says of lying: 'Thou shalt swear
In truth, in judgement and in righteousness.'
But idle swearing is a sin, no less.
Behold and see the tables of the Law
Of God's Commandments, to be held in awe;
Look at the third where it is written plain,
'Thou shalt not take the name of God in vain.'
You see He has forbidden swearing first;
Not murder, no, nor other thing accurst
Comes before that, I say, in God's commands.
That is the order; he who understands
Knows that the third commandment is just that.
And in addition, let me tell you flat,
Vengeance on him and all his house shall fall
That swears outrageously, or swears at all.
'God's precious heart and passion, by God's nails
And by the blood of Christ that is at Hailes,
Seven's my luck, and yours is five and three;
God's blessed arms! If you play false with me
I'll stab you with my dagger!' Overthrown
By two small dice, two bitching bits of bone,
Their fruit is perjury, rage and homicide.
O for the love of Jesus Christ who died
For us, abandon curses, small or great!
But, sirs, I have a story to relate.
It's of three rioters I have to tell
Who, long before the morning service bell,
Were sitting in a tavern for a drink.
And as they sat, they heard the hand-bell clink
Before a coffin going to the grave;
One of them called the little tavern-knave
And said 'Go and find out at once – look spry! –
Whose corpse is in that coffin passing by;
And see you get the name correctly too.'
'Sir,' said the boy, 'no need, I promise you;
Two hours before you came here I was told.
He was a friend of yours in days of old,
And suddenly, last night, the man was slain,
Upon his bench, face up, dead drunk again.
There came a privy thief, they call him Death,
Who kills us all round here, and in a breath
He speared him through the heart, he never stirred.
And then Death went his way without a word.
He's killed a thousand in the present plague,
And, sir, it doesn't do to be too vague
If you should meet him; you had best be wary.
Be on your guard with such an adversary,
Be primed to meet him everywhere you go,

That's what my mother said. It's all I know.'
The publican joined in with, 'By St Mary,
What the child says is right; you'd best be wary,
This very year he killed, in a large village
A mile away, man, woman, serf at tillage,
Page in the household, children – all there were.
Yes, I imagine that he lives round there.
It's well to be prepared in these alarms,
He might do you dishonour.' 'Huh, God's arms!'
The rioter said, 'Is he so fierce to meet?
I'll search for him, by Jesus, street by street.
God's blessed bones! I'll register a vow!
Here, chaps! The three of us together now,
Hold up your hands, like me, and we'll be brothers
In this affair, and each defend the others,
And we will kill this traitor Death, I say!
Away with him as he has made away
With all our friends. God's dignity! Tonight!'
They made their bargain, swore with appetite,
These three, to live and die for one another
As brother-born might swear to his born brother.
And up they started in their drunken rage
And made towards this village which the page
And publican had spoken of before.
Many and grisly were the oaths they swore,
Tearing Christ's blessed body to a shred;

*The image of sinners encountering intimations of their own mortality
or skeletal personifications of Death was a recurrent one.*

'If we can only catch him, Death is dead!'
When they had gone not fully half a mile,
Just as they were about to cross a stile,
They came upon a very poor old man
Who humbly greeted them and thus began,
'God look to you, my lords, and give you quiet!'
To which the proudest of these men of riot
Gave back the answer, 'What, old fool? Give place!
Why are you all wrapped up except your face?
Why live so long? Isn't it time to die?'
The old, old fellow looked him in the eye
And said, 'Because I never yet have found,
Though I have walked to India, searching round
Village and city on my pilgrimage,
One who would change his youth to have my age.
And so my age is mine and must be still
Upon me, for such time as God may will.
Not even Death, alas, will take my life;
So, like a wretched prisoner at strife
Within himself, I walk alone and wait
About the earth, which is my mother's gate,
Knock-knocking with my staff from night to noon
And crying, "Mother, open to me soon!
Look at me, mother, won't you let me in?
See how I wither, flesh and blood and skin!
Alas! When will these bones be laid to rest?
Mother, I would exchange – for that were best –
The wardrobe in my chamber, standing there
So long, for yours! Aye, for a shirt of hair
To wrap me in!" She has refused her grace,
Whence comes the pallor of my withered face.
But it dishonoured you when you began
To speak so roughly, sir, to an old man,
Unless he had injured you in word or deed.
It says in holy writ, as you may read,
"Thou shalt rise up before the hoary head
And honour it." And therefore be it said
"Do no more harm to an old man than you,
Being now young, would have another do
When you are old" – if you should live till then.
And so may God be with you, gentlemen,
For I must go whither I have to go.'
'By God,' the gambler said, 'you shan't do so,
You don't get off so easy, by St John!
I heard you mention, just a moment gone,
A certain traitor Death who singles out
And kills the fine young fellows hereabout.
And you're his spy, by God! You wait a bit.
Say where he is or you shall pay for it,
By God and by the Holy Sacrament!
I say you've joined together by consent
To kill us younger folk, you thieving swine!'
'Well, sirs,' he said, 'if it be your design
To find out Death, turn up this crooked way
Towards that grove, I left him there today
Under a tree, and there you'll find him waiting.
He isn't one to hide for all your prating.
You see that oak? He won't be far to find.

And God protect you that redeemed mankind,
Aye, and amend you!' Thus that ancient man.
At once the three young rioters began
To run, and reached the tree, and there they
found
A pile of golden florins on the ground,
New-coined, eight bushels of them as they thought.
No longer was it Death those fellows sought,
For they were all so thrilled to see the sight,
The florins were so beautiful and bright,
That down they sat beside the precious pile.
The wickedest spoke first after a while.
'Brothers,' he said, 'you listen to what I say.
I'm pretty sharp although I joke away.
It's clear that Fortune has bestowed this treasure
To let us live in jollity and pleasure.
Light come, light go! We'll spend it as we ought.
God's precious dignity! Who would have thought
This morning was to be our lucky day?
If one could only get the gold away,
Back to my house, or else to yours, perhaps –
For as you know, the gold is ours, chaps –
We'd all be at the top of fortune, hey?
But certainly it can't be done by day.
People would call us robbers – a strong gang,
So our own property would make us hang.
No, we must bring this treasure back by night
Some prudent way, and keep it out of sight.
And so as a solution I propose
We draw for lots and see the way it goes;
The one who draws the longest, lucky man,
Shall run to town as quickly as he can
To fetch us bread and wine – but keep things dark –
While two remain in hiding here to mark
Our heap of treasure. If there's no delay,
When night comes down we'll carry it away,
All three of us, wherever we have planned.'
He gathered lots and hid them in his hand
Bidding them draw for where the luck should
fall.
It fell upon the youngest of them all,
And off he ran at once towards the town.
As soon as he had gone the first sat down
And thus began a parley with the other:
'You know that you can trust me as a brother;
Now let me tell you where your profit lies;
You know our friend has gone to get supplies
And here's a lot of gold that is to be
Divided equally amongst us three.
Nevertheless, if I could shape things thus
So that we shared it out – the two of us –
Wouldn't you take it as a friendly act?'
'But how?' the other said. 'He knows the fact
That all the gold was left with me and you;
What can we tell him? What are we to do?'
's it a bargain,' said the first, 'or no?
For I can tell you in a word or so
What's to be done to bring the thing about.'

This beautifully carved elmwood panel depicts scenes from 'The Pardoner's Tale'. It is dated from between 1400 and 1410 and was probably once part of a massive coffer.

'Trust me,' the other said, 'you needn't doubt
My word. I won't betray you, I'll be true.'
'Well,' said his friend, 'you see that we are two,
And two are twice as powerful as one.
Now look; when he comes back, get up in fun
To have a wrestle; then, as you attack,
I'll up and put my dagger through his back
While you and he are struggling, as in game;
Then draw your dagger too and do the same.
Then all this money will be ours to spend,
Divided equally of course, dear friend.
Then we can gratify our lusts and fill
The day with dicing at our own sweet will.'
Thus these two miscreants agreed to slay
The third and youngest, as you heard me say.
The youngest, as he ran towards the town,
Kept turning over, rolling up and down
Within his heart the beauty of those bright
New florins, saying, 'Lord, to think I might
Have all that treasure to myself alone!
Could there be anyone beneath the throne
Of God so happy as I then should be?'
And so the Fiend, our common enemy,
Was given power to put it in his thought
That there was always poison to be bought,
And that with poison he could kill his friends.
To men in such a state the Devil sends
Thoughts of this kind, and has a full permission
To lure them on to sorrow and perdition;
For this young man was utterly content
To kill them both and never to repent.

And on he ran, he had no thought to tarry,
Came to the town, found an apothecary
And said, 'Sell me some poison if you will,
I have a lot of rats I want to kill
And there's a polecat too about my yard
That takes my chickens and it hits me hard;
But I'll get even, as is only right,
With vermin that destroy a man by night.'
The chemist answered, 'I've a preparation
Which you shall have, and by my soul's salvation
If any living creature eat or drink
A mouthful, ere he has the time to think,
Though he took less than makes a grain of wheat,
You'll see him fall down dying at your feet;
Yes, die he must, and in so short a while
You'd hardly have the time to walk a mile,
The poison is so strong, you understand.'
This cursed fellow grabbed into his hand
The box of poison and away he ran
Into a neighbouring street, and found a man
Who lent him three large bottles. He withdrew
And deftly poured the poison into two.
He kept the third one clean, as well he might,
For his own drink, meaning to work all night
Stacking the gold and carrying it away.
And when this rioter, this devil's clay,
Had filled his bottles up with wine, all three,
Back to rejoin his comrades sauntered he.
Why make a sermon of it? Why waste breath?
Exactly in the way they'd planned his death
They fell on him and slew him, two to one.

Then said the first of them when this was done,
'Now for a drink. Sit down and let's be merry,
For later on there'll be the corpse to bury.'
And, as it happened, reaching for a sup,
He took a bottle full of poison up
And drank; and his companion, nothing loth,
Drank from it also, and they perished both.

There is, in Avicenna's long relation
Concerning poison and its operation,
Trust me, no ghastlier section to transcend
What these two wretches suffered at their end.
Thus these two murderers received their due,
So did the treacherous young poisoner too.

O cursed sin! O blackguardly excess!
O treacherous homicide! O wickedness!
O gluttony that lusted on and diced!
O blasphemy that took the name of Christ
With habit-hardened oaths that pride began!
Alas, how comes it that a mortal man,
That thou, to thy Creator, Him that wrought thee,
Art so unnatural and false within?

Dearly beloved, God forgive your sin
And keep you from the vice of avarice!
My holy pardon frees you all of this,
Provided that you make the right approaches,
That is with sterling, rings, or silver brooches.
Bow down your heads under this holy bull!
Come on, you women, offer up your wool!
I'll write your name into my ledger; so!
Into the bliss of Heaven you shall go.
For I'll absolve you by my holy power,
You that make offering, clean as at the hour
When you were born. . . . That, sirs, is how I preach.
And Jesu Christ, soul's healer, aye, the leech
Of every soul, grant pardon and relieve you
Of sin, for that is best, I won't deceive you.

One thing I should have mentioned in my tale,
Dear people. I've some relics in my bale
And pardons too, as full and fine, I hope,
As any in England, given me by the Pope.
If there be one among you that is willing
To have my absolution for a shilling

Devoutly given, come! and do not harden
Your hearts but kneel in humbleness for pardon;
Or else, receive my pardon as we go.
You can renew it every town or so
Always provided that you still renew
Each time, and in good money, what is due.
It is an honour to you to have found
A pardoner with his credentials sound
Who can absolve you as you ply the spur
In any accident that may occur.
For instance – we are all at Fortune's beck –
Your horse may throw you down and break your neck.
What a security it is to all
To have me here among you and at call
With pardon for the lowly and the great
When soul leaves body for the future state!
And I advise our Host here to begin,
The most enveloped of you all in sin.
Come forward, Host, you shall be the first to pay,
And kiss my holy relics right away.
Only a groat. Come on, unbuckle your purse!'

No, no,' said he, 'not I, and may the curse
Of Christ descend upon me if I do!
You'll have me kissing your old breeches too
And swear they were the relic of a saint
Although your fundament supplied the paint!
Now by St Helen and the Holy Land
I wish I had your ballocks in my hand
Instead of relics in a reliquarium;
Have them cut off and I will help to carry 'em.
We'll have them shrined for you in a hog's turd.'

The Pardoner said nothing, not a word;
He was so angry that he couldn't speak.
'Well,' said our Host, 'if you're for showing pique,
I'll joke no more, not with an angry man.'

The worthy Knight immediately began,
Seeing the fun was getting rather rough,
And said, 'No more, we've all had quite enough.
Now, Master Pardoner, perk up, look cheerly!
And you, Sir Host, whom I esteem so dearly,
I beg of you to kiss the Pardoner.
Come, Pardoner, draw nearer, my dear sir.
Let's laugh again and keep the ball in play.'
They kissed, and we continued on our way.

'The Wife of Bath's Tale' is the first in the manuscript often referred to as 'the marriage group'. The love of Dante for Beatrice represented the ideal of love, but although Chaucer credits her with a familiarity with Dante's works, the Wife of Bath's own matrimonial career represented a complete contrast....

THE WIFE OF BATH'S TALE

The Wife of Bath's Prologue

IF there were no authority on earth
Except experience, mine, for what it's worth,
And that's enough for me, all goes to show
That marriage is a misery and a woe;
For let me say, if I may make so bold,
My lords, since when I was but twelve years old,
Thanks be to God Eternal evermore,
Five husbands have I had at the church door;
Yes, it's a fact that I have had so many,
All worthy in their way, as good as any.
Someone said recently for my persuasion
That as Christ only went on one occasion
To grace a wedding – in Cana of Galilee –
He taught me by example there to see
That it is wrong to marry more than once.
Consider, too, how sharply, for the nonce,
He spoke, rebuking the Samaritan
Beside the well, Christ Jesus, God and man.
"Thou has had five men husband unto thee
And he that even now thou hast," said He,
"Is not thy husband." Such the words that fell;
But what He meant thereby I cannot tell.
Why was her fifth – explain it if you can –
No lawful spouse to the Samaritan?
How many might have had her, then, to wife?
I've never heard an answer all my life
To give the number final definition.
People may guess or frame a supposition,
But I can say for certain, it's no lie,
God bade us all to wax and multiply.
That kindly text I well can understand.
Is not my husband under God's command
To leave his father and mother and take me?
No word of what the number was to be,
Then why not marry two or even eight?
And why speak evil of the married state?
Take wise King Solomon of long ago;
We hear he had a thousand wives or so.
And would to God it were allowed to me
To be refreshed, aye, half so much as he!

The Wife of Bath holds the other pilgrims fascinated with her long and shamelessly frank account of her five marriages. She admits that she is looking forward to welcoming her sixth husband!

He must have had a gift of God for wives,
No one to match him in a world of lives!
This noble king, one may as well admit,
On the first night threw many a merry fit
With each of them, he was so much alive.
Blessed be God that I have wedded five!
Welcome the sixth, whenever he appears.
I can't keep continent for years and years.
No sooner than one husband's dead and gone
Some other Christian man shall take me on,
For then, so says the Apostle, I am free
To wed, o'God's name, where it pleases me.
Wedding's no sin, so far as I can learn.
Better it is to marry than to burn.
What do I care if people choose to see
Scandal in Lamech for his bigamy?
I know that Abraham was a holy man

And Jacob too – I speak as best I can –
Yet each of them, we know, had several brides,
Like many another holy man besides.
Show me a time or text where God disparages
Or sets a prohibition upon marriages
Expressly, let me have it! Show it me!
And where did He command virginity?
I know as well as you do, never doubt it,
All the Apostle Paul has said about it;
He said that as for precepts he had none.
One may advise a woman to be one;
Advice is no commandment in my view.
He left it in our judgement what to do.

Had God commanded maidenhood to all
Marriage would be condemned beyond recall,
And certainly if seed were never sown,
How ever could virginity be grown?
Paul did not dare pronounce, let matters rest,
His Master having given him no behest.
There's a prize offered for virginity;
Catch as catch can! Who's in for it? Let's see!

It is not everyone who hears the call;
On whom God wills He lets His power fall.
The Apostle was a virgin, well I know;
Nevertheless, though all his writings show
He wished that everyone were such as he,
It's all mere counsel to virginity.
And as for being married, he lets me do it
Out of indulgence, so there's nothing to it
In marrying me, suppose my husband dead;
There's nothing bigamous in such a bed.
Though it were good a man should never touch
A woman (meaning here in bed and such)
And dangerous to assemble fire and tow
– What this allusion means you all must know –
He only says virginity is fresh,
More perfect than the frailty of the flesh
In married life – except when he and she
Prefer to live in married chastity.

I grant it you. I'll never say a word
Decrying maidenhood although preferred
To frequent marriage; there are those who mean
To live in their virginity, as clean
In body as in soul, and never mate.
I'll make no boast about my own estate.
As in a noble household, we are told,
Not every dish and vessel's made of gold,
Some are of wood, yet earn their master's praise,
God calls His folk to Him in many ways.
To each of them God gave His proper gift,
Some this, some that, and left them to make shift.
Virginity is indeed a great perfection,
And married continence, for God's dilection,
But Christ, who of perfection is the well,
Bade not that everyone should go and sell
All that he had and give it to the poor
To follow in His footsteps, that is sure.
He spoke to those that would live perfectly,

Chastity is assailed by both Beauty and Ugliness. Chastity was a virtue extolled by the medieval Church but not by the Wife of Bath, who vigorously attacks the canon law which forbade a woman to remarry.

And by your leave, my lords, that's not for me.
I will bestow the flower of life, the honey,
Upon the acts and fruit of matrimony.

Tell me to what conclusion or in aid
Of what were generative organs made?
And for what profit were those creatures wrought?
Trust me, they cannot have been made for naught.
Gloze as you will and plead the explanation
That they were only made for the purgation
Of urine, little things of no avail
Except to know a female from a male,
And nothing else. Did somebody say no?
Experience knows well it isn't so.
The learned may rebuke me, or be loth
To think it so, but they were made for both,
That is to say both use and pleasure in
Engendering, except in case of sin.
Why else the proverb written down and set
In books: "A man must yield his wife her debt"?
What means of paying her can he invent
Unless he use his silly instrument?
It follows they were fashioned at creation
Both to purge urine and for propagation.

But I'm not saying everyone is bound
Who has such harness as you heard me expound
To go and use it breeding; that would be
To show too little care for chastity.
Christ was a virgin, fashioned as a man,
And many of his saints since time began
Were ever perfect in their chastity.
I'll have no quarrel with virginity.
Let them be pure wheat loaves of maidenhead
And let us wives be known for barley-bread;
Yet Mark can tell that barley-bread sufficed
To freshen many at the hand of Christ.
In that estate to which God summoned me

I'll persevere; I'm not pernickety
In wifehood I will use my instrument
As freely as my Maker me it sent.
If I turn difficult, God give me sorrow!
My husband, he shall have it eve and morrow
Whenever he likes to come and pay his debt,
I won't prevent him! I'll have a husband yet
Who shall be both my debtor and my slave
And bear his tribulation to the grave
Upon his flesh, as long as I'm his wife.
For mine shall be the power all his life
Over his proper body, and not he,
Thus the Apostle Paul has told it me,
And bade our husbands they should love us well;
There's a command on which I like to dwell . . .'

The Pardoner started up, and thereupon
'Madam,' he said, 'by God and by St John,
That's noble preaching no one could surpass!
I was about to take a wife; alas!
Am I to buy it on my flesh so dear?
There'll be no marrying for me this year!'

'You wait,' she said, 'my story's not begun.
You'll taste another brew before I've done;
You'll find it doesn't taste as good as ale;
And when I've finished telling you my tale
Of tribulation in the married life
In which I've been an expert as a wife,
That is to say, myself have been the whip.
So please yourself whether you want to sip

At that same cask of marriage I shall broach.
Be cautious before making the approach,
For I'll give instances, and more than ten.
And those who won't be warned by other men,
By other men shall suffer their correction,
So Ptolemy has said, in this connection.
You read his *Almagest*; you'll find it there.'

'Madam, I put it to you as a prayer,'
The Pardoner said, 'go on as you began!
Tell us your tale, spare not for any man.
Instruct us younger men in your technique.'
'Gladly,' she said, 'if you will let me speak,
But still I hope the company won't reprove me
Though I should speak as fantasy may move me,
And please don't be offended at my views;
They're really only offered to amuse.

Now, gentlemen, I'll on and tell my tale
And as I hope to drink good wine and ale
I'll tell the truth. Those husbands that I had,
Three of them were good and two were bad.
The three that I call 'good' were rich and old.
They could indeed with difficulty hold
The articles that bound them all to me;
(No doubt you understand my simile).
So help me God, I have to laugh outright
Remembering how I made them work at night!
And faith I set no store by it; no pleasure
It was to me. They'd given me their treasure,
And so I had no need of diligence
Winning their love, or showing reverence.
They loved me well enough, so, heavens above,
Why should I make a dainty of their love?

A knowing woman's work is never done
To get a lover if she hasn't one,
But as I had them eating from my hand
And as they'd yielded me their gold and land,
Why then take trouble to provide them pleasure
Unless to profit and amuse my leisure?
I set them so to work, I'm bound to say;
Many a night they sang, "Alack the day!"
Never for them the flitch of bacon though
That some have won in Essex at Dunmow!
I managed them so well by my technique
Each was delighted to go out and seek
And buy some pretty thing for me to wear,
Happy if I as much as spoke them fair.
God knows how spitefully I used to scold them.

Listen, I'll tell you how I used to hold them,
You knowing women, who can understand,
First put them in the wrong, and out of hand.
No one can be so bold – I mean no man –
At lies and swearing as a woman can.
This is no news, as you'll have realized,
To knowing ones, but to the misadvised.
A knowing wife if she is worth her salt
Can always prove her husband is at fault,
And even though the fellow may have heard
Some story told him by a little bird

A fourteenth-century view of King Arthur's wedding night from a French manuscript, the 'Roman de Artas', shows an unabashed enjoyment that the Wife of Bath clearly knew very well. She defends her marriages on the practical grounds that, if marriage was displeasing to God, He would not have given men and women their generative organs – 'Trust me, they cannot have been made for naught.'

She knows enough to prove the bird is crazy
And get her maid to witness she's a daisy,
With full agreement, scarce solicited.
But listen. Here's the sort of thing I said:

"Now, sir old dotard, what is that you say?
    Why is my neighbour's wife so smart and gay?
    She is respected everywhere she goes.
I sit at home and have no decent clothes.
Why haunt her house? What are you doing there?
Are you so amorous? Is she so fair?
What, whispering secrets to our maid? For shame,
Sir ancient lecher! Time you dropped that game.
And if I see my gossip or a friend
You scold me like a devil! There's no end
If I as much as stroll towards his house.
Then you come home as drunken as a mouse,
You mount your throne and preach, chapter and verse
– All nonsense – and you tell me it's a curse
To marry a poor woman – she's expensive;
Or if her family's wealthy and extensive
You say it's torture to endure her pride
And melancholy airs, and more beside.
And if she has a pretty face, old traitor,
You say she's game for any fornicator
And ask what likelihood will keep her straight
With all those men who lie about in wait.

"You say that some desire us for our wealth,
    Some for our shapeliness, our looks, our health,
    Some for our singing, others for our dancing,
    Some for our gentleness and dalliant glancing,
And some because our hands are soft and small;
By your account the devil gets us all.

"You say what castle wall can be so strong
    As to hold out against a siege for long?
    And if her looks are foul you say that she
    Is hot for every man that she can see,

'*...what castle wall can be so strong/As to hold out against a seige for long?*' *The god of love assaults the castle in this illumination from the late fifteenth-century copy of the 'Roman de la Rose'. This image of Chastity being protected by a castle wall while being assailed from without by Love was a recurrent one.*

Leaping upon them with a spaniel's airs
Until she finds a man to buy her wares.
Never was goose upon the lake so grey
But that she found a gander, so you say.
You say it's hard to keep a girl controlled
If she's the kind that no one wants to hold.
That's what you say as you stump off to bed,
You brute! You say no man of sense would wed,
That is, not if he wants to go to Heaven.
Wild thunderbolts and fire from the Seven
Planets descend and break your withered neck!

"You say that buildings falling into wreck,
    And smoke, and scolding women, are the three
    Things that will drive a man from home. Dear
        me!
What ails the poor old man to grumble so?

"We women hide our faults but let them show
    Once we are safely married, so you say.
    There's a fine proverb for a popinjay!

"You say that oxen, asses, hounds and horses
    Can be tried out on various ploys and courses;
    And basins too, and dishes when you buy them,
    Spoons, chairs and furnishings, a man can try them
As he can try a suit of clothes, no doubt,
But no one ever tries a woman out
Until he's married her; old dotard crow!
And then you say she lets her vices show.

"You also say we count it for a crime
    Unless you praise our beauty all the time,
    Unless you're always poring on our faces
    And call us pretty names in public places;
Of if you fail to treat me to a feast
Upon my birthday – presents at the least –
Or to respect my nurse and her grey hairs,
Or be polite to all my maids upstairs
And to my father's cronies and his spies.
That's what you say, old barrelful of lies!

"Then there's our young apprentice, handsome
        Johnny,
    Because he has crisp hair that shines as bonny
As finest gold, and squires me up and down
You show your low suspicions in a frown.
I wouldn't have him, not if you died to-morrow!

"And tell me this, God punish you with sorrow,
    Why do you hide the keys of coffer doors?
    It's just as much my property as yours.
Do you want to make an idiot of your wife?
Now, by the Lord that gave me soul and life,
You shan't have both, you can't be such a noddy
As think to keep my goods and have my body!
One you must do without, whatever you say.
And do you need to spy on me all day?
I think you'd like to lock me in your coffer!
'Go where you please, dear wife,' you ought to offer,
'Amuse yourself! I shan't give ear to malice,
I know you for a virtuous wife, Dame Alice.'
We cannot love a husband who takes charge
Of where we go. We like to be at large.

"Above all other men may God confer
His blessing on that wise astrologer
Sir Ptolemy who, in his *Almagest*,
Has set this proverb down: 'Of men, the best
And wisest care not who may have in hand
The conduct of the world.' I understand
That means, 'If you've enough, you shouldn't care
How prosperously other people fare.'
Be sure, old dotard, if you call the bluff,
You'll get your evening rations right enough.
He's a mean fellow that lets no man handle
His lantern when it's just to light a candle;
He has lost no light, he hasn't felt the strain;
And you have light enough, so why complain?

Fourteenth-century books were objects of great value. But when the Wife of Bath quarrels with her fifth husband she tears one of his books and finally, to assert her dominance, makes him burn it!

"And when a woman tries a mild display
In dress or costly ornament, you say
It is a danger to her chastity,
And then, bad luck to you, start making free
With Bible tags in the Apostle's name;
'And in like manner, chastely and with shame,
You women should adorn yourselves,' said he,
'And not with braided hair or jewelry,
With pearl or golden ornament.' What next!
I'll pay as much attention to your text
And rubric in such things as would a gnat.

"And once you said that I was like a cat,
For if you singe a cat it will not roam
And that's the way to keep a cat at home.
But when she feels her fur is sleek and gay
She can't be kept indoors for half a day
But off she takes herself as dusk is falling
To show her fur and go a-caterwauling.
Which means if I feel gay, as you suppose,
I shall run out to show my poor old clothes.

"Silly old fool! You and your private spies!
Go on, beg Argus with his hundred eyes
To be my bodyguard, that's better still!
But yet he shan't, I say, against my will.
I'll pull him by the beard, believe you me!

"And once you said that principally three
Misfortunes trouble earth, east, west and north,
And no man living could endure a fourth.
My dear sir shrew, Jesu cut short your life!
You preach away and say a hateful wife
Is reckoned to be one of these misfortunes.
Is there no other trouble that importunes
The world and that your parables could condemn?
Must an unhappy wife be one of them?

"Then you compared a woman's love to Hell,
To barren land where water will not dwell,
And you compared it to a quenchless fire,
The more it burns the more is its desire
To burn up everything that burnt can be.
You say that just as worms destroy a tree
A wife destroys her husband and contrives,
As husbands know, the ruin of their lives."

Such was the way, my lords, you understand
I kept my older husbands well in hand.
I told them they were drunk and their unfitness
To judge my conduct forced me to take witness
That they were lying. Johnny and my niece
Would back me up. O Lord, I wrecked their peace,
Innocent as they were, without remorse!
For I could bite and whinney like a horse
And launch complaints when things were all my fault;
I'd have been lost if I had called a halt.
First to the mill is first to grind your corn;
I attacked first and they were overborne,
Glad to apologize and even suing
Pardon for what they'd never thought of doing.

I'd tackle one for wenching, out of hand,
Although so ill the man could hardly stand,
Yet he felt flattered in his heart because
He thought it showed how fond of him I was.
I swore that all my walking out at night
Was just to keep his wenching well in sight.
That was a dodge that made me shake with mirth;
But all such wit is given us at birth.
Lies, tears and spinning are the things God gives
By nature to a woman, while she lives.
So there's one thing at least I can boast,
That in the end I always ruled the roast;
Cunning or force was sure to make them stumble,

The Wife of Bath battered her first three husbands into submissive exhaustion by her sexual voraciousness and masterful energy. But at the beginning of her fifth marriage she impulsively abandoned both authority and possessions to her young husband, the one she loved the best: 'in our bed he was so fresh and gay'.

And always keeping up a steady grumble.
But bed-time above all was their misfortune;
That was the place to scold them and importune
And baulk their fun. I never would abide
In bed with them if hands began to slide
Till they had promised ransom, paid a fee:
And then I let them do their nicety.
And so I tell this tale to every man,
"It's all for sale and let him win who can."
No empty-handed man can lure a bird.
His pleasures were my profit; I concurred,
Even assumed fictitious appetite,
Though bacon never gave me much delight.
And that's the very fact that made me chide them.
And had the Pope been sitting there beside them
I wouldn't have spared them at their very table,
But paid them out as far as I was able.
I say, so help me God Omnipotent,
Were I to make my will and testament
I owe them nothing, paid them word for word
Putting my wits to use, and they preferred
To give it up and take it for the best
For otherwise they would have got no rest.
Though they might glower like a maddened beast
They got no satisfaction, not the least.
I then would say, "My dear, just take a peep!
What a meek look on Willikin our sheep!
Come nearer, husband, let me kiss your cheek;
You should be just as patient, just as meek;
Sweeten your heart. Your conscience needs a probe.
You're fond of preaching patience out of Job,
and so be patient; practise what you preach,
And if you don't, my dear, we'll have to teach
You that it's nice to have a quiet life.
One of us must be master, man or wife,
And since a man's more reasonable, he
Should be the patient one, you must agree.

"What ails you, man, to grumble so and groan?
Just that you want my what-not all your own?
Why, take it all, man, take it, every bit!
St Peter, what a love you have for it!
For if I were to sell my *belle chose*,
I could go walking fresher than a rose;
But I will keep it for your private tooth.
By God, you are to blame, and that's the truth."
That's how my first three husbands were undone.
Now let me tell you of my last but one.

He was a reveller, was number four;
That is to say he kept a paramour.
Young, strong and stubborn, I was full of rage
And jolly as a magpie in a cage.
Play me the harp and I would dance and sing,
Believe me, like a nightingale in spring,
If I had had a draught of sweetened wine.
Metellius, that filthy lout – the swine
Who snatched a staff and took his woman's life
For drinking wine – if I had been his wife
He never would have daunted me from drink.
Whenever I take wine I have to think
Of Venus, for as cold engenders hail
A lecherous mouth begets a lecherous tail.
A woman in her cups has no defence,
As lechers know from long experience.
But Christ! Whenever it comes back to me,
When I recall my youth and jollity,
It fairly warms the cockles of my heart!
This very day I feel a pleasure start,
Yes, I can feel it tickling at the root.
Lord, how it does me good! I've had my fruit,
I've had my world and time, I've had my fling!
But age that comes to poison everything
Has taken all my beauty and my pith.
Well, let it go, the devil go therewith!
The flour is gone, there is no more to say,
And I must sell the bran as best I may;
But still I mean to find my way to fun . . .
Now let me tell you of my last but one.
I told you how it filled my heart with spite
To see another woman his delight,
By God and all His saints I made it good!
I carved him out a cross of the same wood,
Not with my body in a filthy way,
But certainly by seeming rather gay
To others, frying him in his own grease
Of jealousy and rage; he got no peace.
By God on earth I was his purgatory,
For which I hope his soul may be in glory.
God knows he sang a sorry tune, he flinched,
And bitterly enough, when the shoe pinched.

The Christian world with Jerusalem at its centre. We know from the Prologue that the Wife of Bath has made the long journey there three times – we suspect as much for the company a pilgrimage could provide as for any more spiritual reasons.

And God and he alone can say how grim,
How many were the ways I tortured him.

He died when I came back from Jordan Stream
And he lies buried under the rood-beam,
Albeit that his tomb can scarce supply us
With such a show as that of King Darius
– Apelles sculped it in a sumptuous taste –
Expensive funerals are just a waste.
Farewell to him, God give his spirit rest!
He's in his grave, he's nailed up in his chest.

Now of my fifth, last husband let me tell.
God never let his soul be sent to Hell!
And yet he was my worst, and many a blow
He struck me still can ache along my row
Of ribs, and will until my dying day.

But in our bed he was so fresh and gay,
So coaxing, so persuasive . . . Heaven knows
Whenever he wanted it – my *belle chose* –
Though he had beaten me in every bone
He still could wheedle me to love, I own.
I think I loved him best, I'll tell no lie.

*A wife tries to entice her husband into revealing a secret. Wives had
a reputation for indiscretion and the Wife of Bath admits that she
confided everything about her fifth husband to her godmother, her
niece and to another worthy wife. Not surprisingly her gossiping
'used to set him blushing like a rose/and he would blame his lack of
sense/In telling me secrets of such consequence.'*

He was disdainful in his love, that's why.
We women have a curious fantasy
In such affairs, or so it seems to me.
When something's difficult, or can't be had,
We crave and cry for it all day like mad.
Forbid a thing, we pine for it all night,
Press fast upon us and we take to flight;
We use disdain in offering our wares.
A throng of buyers sends prices up at fairs,
Cheap goods have little value, they suppose;
And that's a thing that every woman knows.

My fifth and last – God keep his soul in health!
The one I took for love and not for wealth,
Had been at Oxford not so long before

But had left school and gone to lodge next door,
Yes, it was to my godmother's he'd gone.
God bless her soul! *Her* name was Alison.
She knew my heart and more of what I thought
Than did the parish priest, and so she ought!
She was my confidante, I told her all.
For had my husband pissed against a wall
Or done some crime that would have cost his life,
To her and to another worthy wife
And to my niece, because I loved her well,
I'd have told everything there was to tell.
And so I often did, and Heaven knows
It used to set him blushing like a rose
For shame, and he would blame his lack of sense
In telling me secrets of such consequence.

And so one time it happened that in Lent,
As I so often did, I rose and went
To see her, ever wanting to be gay
And go a-strolling, March, April and May,
From house to house for chat and village malice.

Johnny (the boy from Oxford) and Dame Alice
And I myself, into the fields we went.
My husband was in London all that Lent;
All the more fun for me – I only mean
The fun of seeing people and being seen
By cocky lads; for how was I to know
Where or what graces Fortune might bestow?
And so I made a round of visitations,
Went to processions, festivals, orations,
Preachments and pilgrimages, watched the carriages
They use for plays and pageants, went to marriages,
And always wore my gayest scarlet dress.

These worms, these moths, these mites, I must
confess,
Got little chance to eat it, by the way.
Why not? Because I wore it every day.

Now let me tell you all that came to pass.
We sauntered in the meadows through the grass
Toying and dallying to such extent,
Johnny and I, that I grew provident
And I suggested, were I ever free
And made a widow, he should marry me.
And certainly – I do not mean to boast –
I ever was more provident than most
In marriage matters and in other such.
I never think a mouse is up to much
That only has one hole in all the house;
If that should fail, well, it's good-bye the mouse.

I let him think I was as one enchanted
(That was a trick my godmother implanted)
And told him I had dreamt the night away
Thinking of him, and dreamt that as I lay
He tried to kill me. Blood had drenched the bed.

But still it was a lucky dream," I said,
"For blood betokens gold as I recall."
It was a lie. I hadn't dreamt at all.
'Twas from my godmother I learnt my lore
In matters such as that, and many more.

ell, let me see . . . what had I to explain?
Aha! By God, I've got the thread again.

hen my fourth husband lay upon his bier
I wept all day and looked as drear as drear,
As widows must, for it is quite in place,
And with a handkerchief I hid my face.
Now that I felt provided with a mate
I wept but little, I need hardly state.

o church they bore my husband on the morrow
With all the neighbours round him venting
    sorrow,
And one of them of course was handsome Johnny.
So help me God, I thought he looked so bonny
Behind the coffin! Heavens, what a pair
Of legs he had! Such feet, so clean and fair!
I gave my whole heart up, for him to hold.
He was, I think, some twenty winters old,
And I was forty then, to tell the truth.
But still, I always had a coltish tooth.
Yes, I'm gap-toothed; it suits me well I feel,
It is the print of Venus and her seal.
So help me God I was a lusty one,
Fair, young and well-to-do, and full of fun!
And truly, as my husbands said to me
I had the finest *quoniam* that might be.
For Venus sent me feeling from the stars
And my heart's boldness came to me from Mars.
Venus gave me desire and lecherousness
And Mars my hardihood, or so I guess,
Born under Taurus and with Mars therein.
Alas, alas, that ever love was sin!
I ever followed natural inclination
Under the power of my constellation
And was unable to deny, in truth,
My chamber of Venus to a likely youth.
The mark of Mars is still upon my face
And also in another privy place.
For as I may be saved by God above,
I never used discretion when in love
But ever followed on my appetite,
Whether the lad was short, long, black or white.
Little I cared, if he was fond of me,
How poor he was, or what his rank might be.

hat shall I say? Before the month was gone
This gay young student, my delightful John,
Had married me in solemn festival.
I handed him the money, lands and all
That ever had been given me before;
This I repented later, more and more.
None of my pleasures would he let me seek.
By God, he smote me once upon the cheek
Because I tore a page out of his book,
And that's the reason why I'm deaf. But look,
Stubborn I was, just like a lioness;
As to my tongue, a very wrangleress.
I went off gadding as I had before
From house to house, however much he swore.

Johnny, the Wife of Bath's last husband, whom she married for love, was an Oxford scholar half her age. Alas, he uses his learning to humiliate her, and it is from his compilation of anti-feminist works that she learns of St Jerome, Valerius and Theophrastus.

Because of that he used to preach and scold,
Drag Roman history up from days of old,
How one Simplicius Gallus left his wife,
Deserting her completely all his life,
Only for poking out her head one day
Without a hat, upon the public way.

ome other Roman – I forget his name –
Because his wife went to a summer's game
Without his knowledge, left her in the lurch.

nd he would take the Bible up and search
For proverbs in Ecclesiasticus,
Particularly one that has it thus:
"Suffer no wicked woman to gad about."
And then would come the saying (need you doubt?)
    A man who seeks to build his house of sallows,
    A man who spurs a blind horse over fallows,
    Or lets his wife make pilgrimage to Hallows,
    Is worthy to be hanged upon the gallows.
But all for naught. I didn't give a hen
For all his proverbs and his wise old men.
Nor would I take rebuke at any price;
I hate a man who points me out my vice,
And so, God knows, do many more than I.
That drove him raging mad, you may rely.
Nor more would I forbear him, I can promise.

ow let me tell you truly by St Thomas
About that book and why I tore the page
And how he smote me deaf in very rage.

e had a book, he kept it on the shelf,
And night and day he read it to himself
And laughed aloud, although it was quite serious.
He called it *Theophrastus and Valerius*.
There was another Roman, much the same,
A cardinal; St Jerome was his name.
He wrote a book against Jovinian,
Bound up together with Tertullian,
Chrysippus, Trotula and Heloise,
An abbess, lived near Paris. And with these
Were bound the parables of Solomon,
With Ovid's *Art of Love* another one.
All these were bound together in one book
And day and night he used to take a look
At what it said, when he had time and leisure
Or had no occupation but his pleasure,
Which was to read this book of wicked wives;
He knew more legends of them and their lives
Than there are good ones mentioned in the Bible.
For take my word for it, there is no libel
On women that the clergy will not paint,
Except when writing of a woman-saint,
But never good of other women, though.
Who called the lion savage? Do you know?
By God, if women had but written stories
Like those the clergy keep in oratories,
More had been written of man's wickedness
Than all the sons of Adam could redress.
Children of Mercury and we of Venus
Keep up the contrariety between us;
Mercury stands for wisdom, thrift and science,
Venus for revel, squandering and defiance.
Their several natures govern their direction;
One rises when the other's in dejection.
So Mercury is desolate when halted

A Swiss woodcut on 'the influence of Venus'. Venus accounts for the sexual appetites of the pleasure-loving Wife of Bath: 'Venus gave me desire and lecherousness.' But she is also influenced by Mars and Taurus and admits that a combative disposition underlies her pleasure-seeking.

In *Pisces*, just where Venus is exalted,
And Venus falls where Mercury is raised,
And women therefore never can be praised
By learned men, old scribes who cannot do
The works of Venus more than my old shoe.
These in their dotage sit them down to frowse
And say that women break their marriage-vows!

ow to my purpose as I told you; look,
Here's how I got a beating for a book.
One evening Johnny, glowering with ire,
Sat with his book and read it by the fire.
And first he read of Eve whose wickedness
Brought all mankind to sorrow and distress,
Root-cause why Jesus Christ Himself was slain
And gave His blood to buy us back again.
Aye, there's the text where you expressly find
That woman brought the loss of all mankind.

e read me then how Samson as he slept
Was shorn of all his hair by her he kept,
And by that treachery Samson lost his eyes.
And then he read me, if I tell no lies,
All about Hercules and Deianire;
She tricked him into setting himself on fire.

e left out nothing of the miseries
Occasioned by his wives to Socrates.
Xantippe poured a piss-pot on his head.
The silly man sat still, as he were dead,
Wiping his head, but dared no more complain
Than say, "Ere thunder stops, down comes the rain."

ext of Pasiphaë the Queen of Crete;
For wickedness he thought that story sweet;
Fie, say no more! It has a grisly sting,
Her horrible lust. How could she do the thing!

nd then he told of Clytemnestra's lechery
And how she made her husband die by
treachery.
He read that story with a great devotion.

e read me what occasioned the commotion
By which Amphiaraüs lost his life;
My husband had a legend about his wife
Eriphyle, who for a gaud in gold
Went to the Greeks in secret, and she told
Them where to find him, in what hiding-place.
At Thebes it was; he met with sorry grace.

f Livia and Lucilia then he read,
And both of course had killed their husbands dead,
The one for love, the other out of hate.
Livia prepared some poison for him late
One evening and she killed him out of spite,
Lucilia out of lecherous delight.
For she, in order he might only think
Of her, prepared an aphrodisiac drink;
He drank it and was dead before the morning.
Such is the fate of husbands; it's a warning.

nd then he told how one Latumius
Lamented to his comrade Arrius
That in his orchard-plot there grew a tree
On which his wives had hanged themselves, all three,

Or so he said, out of some spite or other;
To which this Arrius replied, "Dear brother,
Give me a cutting from that blessed tree
And planted in my garden it shall be!"
'Of wives of later date he also read,
    How some had killed their husbands when in bed,
    Then night-long with their lechers played the
whore,
While the poor corpse lay fresh upon the floor.
'One drove a nail into her husband's brain
    While he was sleeping, and the man was slain;
    Others put poison in their husbands' drink.
He spoke more harm of us than heart can think
And knew more proverbs too, for what they're worth,
Than there are blades of grass upon the earth.
'"Better," says he, "to share your habitation
    With lion, dragon, or abomination
    Than with a woman given to reproof.
Better," says he, "take refuge on the roof
Than with an angry wife, down in the house;
They are so wicked and cantankerous
They hate the things their husbands like," he'd say.
"A woman always casts her shame away
When she casts off her smock, and that's in haste.
A pretty woman, if she isn't chaste,
Is like a golden ring in a sow's snout."
'Who could imagine, who could figure out
    The torture in my heart? It reached the top
    And when I saw that he would never stop
Reading this cursed book, all night no doubt,
I suddenly grabbed and tore three pages out
Where he was reading, at the very place,
And fisted such a buffet in his face
That backwards down into our fire he fell.
'Then like a maddened lion, with a yell
    He started up and smote me on the head,
    And down I fell upon the floor for dead.
'And when he saw how motionless I lay
    He was aghast and would have fled away,
    But in the end I started to come to.
"O have you murdered me, you robber, you,
To get my land?" I said. "Was that the game?
Before I'm dead I'll kiss you all the same."
'he came up close and kneeling gently down
    He said, "My love, my dearest Alison,
    So help me God, I never again will hit
You, love; and if I did, you asked for it.

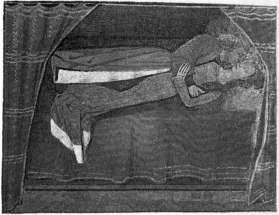

The lover embraces the rose in this illustration to a fifteenth-century copy of the 'Roman de la Rose'. The Wife of Bath's outspokenness presents a complete contrast to the elusive ideals of courtly love. Robust, outrageous – 'gloriously awful', as one expert has called her – she stands out as one of Chaucer's most vital creations. Unlike some of the other pilgrims, she is no mere caricature and, for all her faults, we end up feeling more sympathy than dislike. She represents an endearing sexual gusto, spontaneity and zest for life.

Forgive me!" But for all he was so meek,
I up at once and smote him on the cheek
And said, "Take that to level up the score!
Now let me die, I can't speak any more."
'We had a mort of trouble and heavy weather
    But in the end we made it up together.
    He gave the bridle over to my hand,
Gave me the government of house and land,
Of tongue and fist, indeed of all he'd got.
I made him burn that book upon the spot.
And when I'd mastered him, and out of deadlock
Secured myself the sovereignty in wedlock,
And when he said, "My own and truest wife,
Do as you please for all the rest of life,
But guard your honour and my good estate,"
From that day forward there was no debate.
So help me God I was as kind to him
As any wife from Denmark to the rim
Of India, and as true. And he to me.
And I pray God that sits in majesty
To bless his soul and fill it with his glory.
Now, if you'll listen, I will tell my story.'

Words between the Summoner and the Friar

'THE Friar laughed when he had heard all this.
    'Well, Ma'am,' he said, 'as God may send me bliss,
    This is a long preamble to a tale!'
    But when the Summoner heard the Friar rail,
'Just look!' he cried, 'by the two arms of God!

These meddling friars are always on the prod!
Don't we all know a friar and a fly
Go prod and buzz in every dish and pie!
What do you mean with your "preambulation"?
Amble yourself, trot, do a meditation!

You're spoiling all our fun with your commotion.'
The Friar smiled and said, 'Is that your motion?
I promise on my word before I go
To find occasion for a tale or so
About a summoner that will make us laugh.'
'Well, damn your eyes, and on my own behalf,'
The Summoner answered, 'mine be damned as well
If I can't think of several tales to tell
About the friars that will make you mourn

Before we get as far as Sittingbourne.
Have you no patience? Look, he's in a huff!'
Our Host called out, 'Be quiet, that's enough!
Shut up, and let the woman tell her tale.
You must be drunk, you've taken too much ale.
Now, Ma'am, you go ahead and no demur.'
'All right,' she said, 'it's just as you prefer,
If I have licence from this worthy friar.'
'Nothing,' said he, 'that I should more desire.'

The Wife Of Bath's Tale

WHEN good King Arthur ruled in ancient days
(A king that every Briton loves to praise)
This was a land brim-full of fairy folk.
The Elf-Queen and her courtiers joined and
  broke
Their elfin dance and many a green mead,
Or so was the opinion once, I read,
Hundreds of years ago, in days of yore.
But no one now sees fairies any more.
For now the saintly charity and prayer
Of holy friars seem to have purged the air;
They search the countryside through field and stream
As thick as motes that speckle a sun-beam,
Blessing the halls, the chambers, kitchens, bowers,
Cities and boroughs, castles, courts and towers,
Thorpes, barns and stables, outhouses and dairies,
And that's the reason why there are no fairies.
Wherever there was wont to walk an elf
To-day there walks the holy friar himself
As evening falls or when the daylight springs,
Saying his mattins and his holy things,
Walking his limit round from town to town.
Women can now go safely up and down
By every bush or under every tree;
There is no other incubus but he,
So there is really no one else to hurt you
And he will do no more than take your virtue.
Now it so happened, I began to say,
Long, long ago in good King Arthur's day,
There was a knight who was a lusty liver.
One day as he came riding from the river
He saw a maiden walking all forlorn
Ahead of him, alone as she was born.
And of that maiden, spite of all she said,
By very force he took her maidenhead.
This act of violence made such a stir,
So much petitioning to the king for her,
That he condemned the knight to lose his head
By course of law. He was as good as dead
(It seems that then the statutes took that view)

But that the queen, and other ladies too,
Implored the king to exercise his grace
So ceaselessly, he gave the queen the case
And granted her his life, and she could choose
Whether to show him mercy or refuse.
The queen returned him thanks with all her might,
And then she sent a summons to the knight
At her convenience, and expressed her will:
'You stand, for such is the position still,
In no way certain of your life,' said she,
'Yet you shall live if you can answer me:
What is the thing that women most desire?
Beware the axe and say as I require.
If you can't answer on the moment, though,
I will concede you this: you are to go
A twelvemonth and a day to seek and learn
Sufficient answer, then you shall return.
I shall take gages from you to extort
Surrender of your body to the court.'
Sad was the knight and sorrowfully sighed,
But there! All other choices were denied,
And in the end he chose to go away
And to return after a year and day
Armed with such answer as there might be sent
To him by God. He took his leave and went.
He knocked at every house, searched every place,
Yes, anywhere that offered hope of grace.
What could it be that women wanted most?
But all the same he never touched a coast,
Country or town in which there seemed to be
Any two people willing to agree.
Some said that women wanted wealth and treasure,
'Honour,' said some, some 'Jollity and pleasure,'
Some 'Gorgeous clothes' and others 'Fun in bed,'
'To be oft widowed and remarried,' said
Others again, and some that what most mattered
Was that we should be cosseted and flattered.
That's very near the truth, it seems to me;
A man can win us best with flattery.
To dance attendance on us, make a fuss,

172

The tale told by the Wife of Bath is based on a well-known story known as 'the Loathly Lady'. Some scholars believe that Chaucer originally intended it for the Shipman.

Ensnares us all, the best and worst of us.
Some say the things we most desire are these:
 Freedom to do exactly as we please,
 With no one to reprove our faults and lies,
Rather to have one call us good and wise.
Truly there's not a woman in ten score
Who has a fault, and someone rubs the sore,
But she will kick if what he says is true;
You try it out and you will find so too.
However vicious we may be within
We like to be thought wise and void of sin.
Others assert we women find it sweet
When we are thought dependable, discreet
And secret, firm of purpose and controlled,
Never betraying things that we are told.
But that's not worth the handle of a rake;
Women conceal a thing? For Heaven's sake!
Remember Midas? Will you hear the tale?

Among some other little things, now stale,
 Ovid relates that under his long hair
 The unhappy Midas grew a splendid pair
Of ass's ears; as subtly as he might,
He kept his foul deformity from sight;
Save for his wife, there was not one that knew.
He loved her best, and trusted in her too.
He begged her not to tell a living creature
That he possessed so horrible a feature.
And she – she swore, were all the world to win,
She would not do such villainy and sin

As saddle her husband with so foul a name;
Besides to speak would be to share the shame.
Nevertheless she thought she would have died
Keeping this secret bottled up inside;
It seemed to swell her heart and she, no doubt,
Thought it was on the point of bursting out.

Fearing to speak of it to woman or man,
 Down to a reedy marsh she quickly ran
 And reached the sedge. Her heart was all on fire
And, as a bittern bumbles in the mire,
She whispered to the water, near the ground,
'Betray me not, O water, with thy sound!
To thee alone I tell it: it appears
My husband has a pair of ass's ears!
Ah! My heart's well again, the secret's out!
I could no longer keep it, not a doubt.'
And so you see, although we may hold fast
A little while, it must come out at last,
We can't keep secrets; as for Midas, well,
Read Ovid for his story; he will tell.

This knight that I am telling you about
 Perceived at last he never would find out
 What it could be that women loved the best.
Faint was the soul within his sorrowful breast,
As home he went, he dared no longer stay;
His year was up and now it was the day.

As he rode home in a dejected mood
 Suddenly, at the margin of a wood,
 He saw a dance upon the leafy floor

173

Of four and twenty ladies, nay, and more.
Eagerly he approached, in hope to learn
Some words of wisdom ere he should return;
But lo! Before he came to where they were,
Dancers and dance all vanished into air!
There wasn't a living creature to be seen
Save one old woman crouched upon the green.
A fouler-looking creature I suppose
Could scarcely be imagined. She arose
And said, 'Sir knight, there's no way on from here.
Tell me what you are looking for, my dear,
For peradventure that were best for you;
We old, old women know a thing or two.'

'Dear Mother,' said the knight, 'alack the day!
I am as good as dead if I can't say
What thing it is that women most desire;
If you could tell me I would pay your hire.'
'Give me your hand,' she said, 'and swear to do

An old lady tells the lover how to get into the castle in the 'Roman de la Rose'. In Chaucer's version of the Loathly Lady, the hag saves the knight's life by telling him that what women most desire is 'the self-same sovereignty' over their husbands as their lovers, an answer that the Wife of Bath herself would have agreed with.

Whatever I shall next require of you
– If so to do should lie within your might –
And you shall know the answer before night.'
'Upon my honour,' he answered. 'I agree.'
'Then,' said the crone, 'I dare to guarantee
Your life is safe; I shall make good my claim.
Upon my life the queen will say the same.
Show me the very proudest of them all
In costly coverchief or jewelled caul
That dare say no to what I have to teach.
Let us go forward without further speech.'
And then she crooned her gospel in his ear
And told him to be glad and not to fear.

They came to court. This knight, in full array,
Stood forth and said, 'O Queen, I've kept my day
And kept my word and have my answer ready.'

There sat the noble matrons and the heady
Young girls, and widows too, that have the grace
Of wisdom, all assembled in that place,
And there the queen herself was throned to hear
And judge his answer. Then the knight drew near
And silence was commanded through the hall.

The queen gave order he should tell them all
What thing it was that women wanted most.
He stood not silent like a beast or post,
But gave his answer with the ringing word
Of a man's voice and the assembly heard:

'My liege and lady, in general,' said he,
'A woman wants the self-same sovereignty
Over her husband as over her lover,
And master him; he must not be above her.
That is your greatest wish, whether you kill
Or spare me; please yourself. I wait your will.'

In all the court not one that shook her head
Or contradicted what the knight had said;
Maid, wife and widow cried, 'He's saved his life!'

And on the word up started the old wife,
The one the knight saw sitting on the green,
And cried, 'Your mercy, sovereign lady queen!
Before the court disperses, do me right!
'Twas I who taught this answer to the knight,
For which he swore, and pledged his honour to it,
That the first thing I asked of him he'd do it,
So far as it should lie within his might.
Before this court I ask you then, sir knight,
To keep your word and take me for your wife;
For well you know that I have saved your life.
If this be false, deny it on your sword!'

'Alas!' he said, 'Old lady, by the Lord
I know indeed that such was my behest,
But for God's love think of a new request,
Take all my goods, but leave my body free.'
'A curse on us,' she said, 'if I agree!
I may be foul, I may be poor and old,
Yet will not choose to be, for all the gold
That's bedded in the earth or lies above,
Less than your wife, nay, than your very love!'

'My love?' said he. 'By heaven, my damnation!
Alas that any of my race and station
Should ever make so foul a misalliance!'
Yet in the end his pleading and defiance
All went for nothing, he was forced to wed.
He takes his ancient wife and goes to bed.

Now peradventure some may well suspect
A lack of care in me since I neglect
To tell of the rejoicings and display
Made at the feast upon their wedding-day.
I have but a short answer to let fall;
I say there was no joy or feast at all,
Nothing but heaviness of heart and sorrow.
He married her in private on the morrow
And all day long stayed hidden like an owl,
It was such torture that his wife looked foul.

Great was the anguish churning in his head
When he and she were piloted to bed;
He wallowed back and forth in desperate style.
His ancient wife lay smiling all the while;
At last she said 'Bless us! Is this, my dear,
How knights and wives get on together here?
Are these the laws of good King Arthur's house?
Are knights of his all so contemptuous?
I am your own beloved and your wife,
And I am she, indeed, that saved your life;
And certainly I never did you wrong.
Then why, this first of nights, so sad a song?
You're carrying on as if you were half-witted
Say, for God's love, what sin have I committed?
I'll put things right if you will tell me how.'

Put right?' he cried. 'That never can be now!
Nothing can ever be put right again!
You're old, and so abominably plain,
So poor to start with, so low-bred to follow;
It's little wonder if I twist and wallow!
God, that my heart would burst within my breast!'

Is that,' said she, 'the cause of your unrest?'
'Yes, certainly,' he said, 'and can you wonder?'

I could set right what you suppose a blunder,
That's if I cared to, in a day or two,
If I were shown more courtesy by you.
'Just now,' she said, 'you spoke of gentle birth,
Such as descends from ancient wealth and worth.
If that's the claim you make for gentlemen

King Arthur and his Knights of the Round Table. Another well-known version of the story of the Loathly Lady is the story of Sir Gawain and Dame Ragnell. One of the key themes in Chaucer's version is his discussion of 'gentilesse', which he relates firmly to behaviour, not to rank.

Such arrogance is hardly worth a hen.
Whoever loves to work for virtuous ends,
Public and private, and who most intends
To do what deeds of gentleness he can,
Take him to be the greatest gentleman.
Christ wills we take our gentleness from Him,
Not from a wealth of ancestry long dim,
Though they bequeath their whole establishment
By which we claim to be of high descent.
Our fathers cannot make us a bequest
Of all those virtues that became them best
And earned for them the name of gentlemen,
But bade us follow them as best we can.

Thus the wise poet of the Florentines,
Dante by name, has written in these lines,
For such is the opinion Dante launches:
"Seldom arises by these slender branches
Prowess of men, for it is God, no less,
Wills us to claim of Him our gentleness."
For of our parents nothing can we claim
Save temporal things, and these may hurt and maim.

But everyone knows this as well as I;
For if gentility were implanted by
The natural course of lineage down the line,
Public or private, could it cease to shine
In doing the fair work of gentle deed?
No vice or villany could then bear seed.

Take fire and carry it to the darkest house
Between this kingdom and the Caucasus,
And shut the doors on it and leave it there,
It will burn on, and it will burn as fair
As if ten thousand men were there to see,
For fire will keep its nature and degree,
I can assure you, sir, until it dies.

But gentleness, as you will recognize,
Is not annexed in nature to possessions.
Men fail in living up to their professions;
But fire never ceases to be fire.
God knows you'll often find, if you enquire,
Some lording full of villainy and shame.
If you would be esteemed for the mere name
Of having been by birth a gentleman
And stemming from some virtuous, noble clan,
And do not live yourself by gentle deed
Or take your father's noble code and creed,
You are no gentleman, though duke or earl.
Vice and bad manners are what make a churl.

Gentility is only the renown
For bounty that your fathers handed down,
Quite foreign to your person, not your own;
Gentility must come from God alone.
That we are gentle comes to us by grace
And by no means is it bequeathed with place.

Reflect how noble (says Valerius)
Was Tullius surnamed Hostilius,
Who rose from poverty to nobleness.
And read Boethius, Seneca no less,
Thus they express themselves and are agreed:

An illumination depicting Venus and her children, from a fifteenth-century 'Boke of Astronomy'. Chaucer's constant use of astronomical terminology reflected a genuine scientific interest in the subject. Rather unexpectedly, the list of his own works includes a 'Treatise on the Astrolabe' (an instrument used in making astrological calculations), which he wrote for his own young son Lewis.

"Gentle is he that does a gentle deed."
And therefore, my dear husband, I conclude
That even if my ancestors were rude,
Yet God on high – and so I hope He will –
Can grant me grace to live in virtue still,
A gentlewoman only when beginning
To live in virtue and to shrink from sinning.
As for my poverty which you reprove,
Almighty God Himsef in whom we move,
Believe and have our being, chose a life
Of poverty, and every man or wife
Nay, every child can see our Heavenly King
Would never stoop to choose a shameful thing.
No shame in poverty if the heart is gay,
As Seneca and all the learned say.
He who accepts his poverty unhurt

I'd say is rich although he lacked a shirt.
But truly poor are they who whine and fret
And covet what they cannot hope to get.
And he that, having nothing, covets not,
Is rich, though you may think he is a sot.
True poverty can find a song to sing.
Juvenal says a pleasant little thing:
"The poor can dance and sing in the relief
Of having nothing that will tempt a thief."
Though it be hateful, poverty is good,
A great incentive to a livelihood,
And a great help to our capacity
For wisdom, if accepted patiently.
Poverty is, though wanting in estate,
A kind of wealth that none caluminate.
Poverty often, when the heart is lowly,
Brings one to God and teaches what is holy,
Gives knowledge of oneself and even lends
A glass by which to see one's truest friends.
And since it's no offence, let me be plain;
Do not rebuke my poverty again.
Lastly you taxed me, sir, with being old.
Yet even if you never had been told
By ancient books, you gentlemen engage
Yourselves in honour to respect old age.
To call an old man "father" shows good breeding,
And this could be supported from my reading.
You say I'm old and fouler than a fen.
You need not fear to be a cuckold, then.
Filth and old age, I'm sure you will agree,
Are powerful wardens over chastity.
Nevertheless, well knowing your delights,
I shall fulfil your worldly appetites.
You have two choices; which one will you try?
To have me old and ugly till I die,
But still a loyal, true, and humble wife
That never will displease you all her life,
Or would you rather I were young and pretty

A drawing, based on an earlier woodcut, of a wedding. When the knight grants his old and ugly bride sovereignty in their marriage, he receives the reward of a young and lovely wife – an example off submission which the Wife of Bath wishes all husbands should follow.

And chance your arm what happens in a city
Where friends will visit you because of me,
Yes, and in other places too, maybe.
Which would you have? The choice is all your own.'
The knight thought long, and with a piteous
  groan
  At last he said, with all the care in life,
'My lady and my love, my dearest wife,
I leave the matter to your wise decision.
You make the choice yourself, for the provision
Of what may be agreeable and rich
In honour to us both, I don't care which;
Whatever pleases you suffices me.'
And have I won the mastery?' said she,
  'Since I'm to choose and rule as I think fit?'
  'Certainly, wife,' he answered her, 'that's it.'
'Kiss me,' she cried. 'No quarrels! On my oath
And word of honour, you shall find me both,
That is, both fair and faithful as a wife;
May I go howling mad and take my life
Unless I prove to be as good and true

As ever wife was since the world was new!
And if to-morrow when the sun's above
I seem less fair than any lady-love,
Than any queen or empress east or west,
Do with my life and death as you think best.
Cast up the curtain, husband. Look at me!'
And when indeed the knight had looked to see,
  Lo, she was young and lovely, rich in charms.
  In ecstasy he caught her in his arms,
His heart went bathing in a bath of blisses
And melted in a hundred thousand kisses,
And she responded in the fullest measure
With all that could delight or give him pleasure.
So they lived ever after to the end
  In perfect bliss; and may Christ Jesus send
  Us husbands meek and young and fresh in bed,
And grace to overbid them when we wed.
And – Jesu hear my prayer! – cut short the lives
Of those who won't be governed by their wives;
And all old, angry niggards of their pence,
God send them soon a very pestilence!

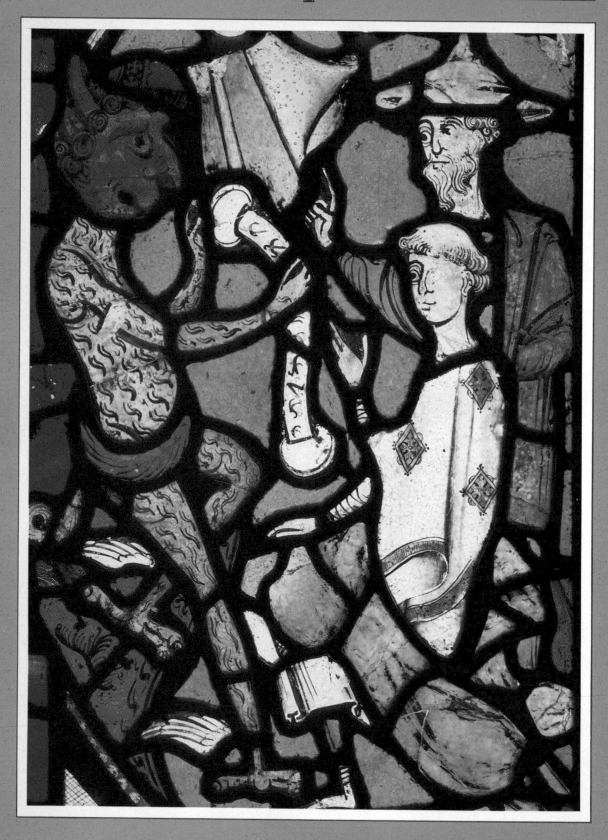

THE FRIAR'S TALE

The Friar's Prologue

OUR worthy limiter, the noble Friar,
Kept glancing with a lowering sort of ire
Towards the Summoner, but, to keep polite,
As yet had said no ugly word outright.
At last he turned towards the Wife of Bath,
'Madam,' he said, 'God be about your path!
You here have touched on many difficult rules
Debated, I assure you, in the Schools.
Much you advanced was excellent, I say!
But, Madam, as we ride along the way
We're only called upon to speak in game.
Let's leave the authorities, in Heaven's name,
To preachers and to schools for ordinands.
But if it meets the company's demands,
I'll talk about a summoner, for a game,
Lord knows, one can be certain from the name
A summoner isn't much to be commended.

I hope that none of you will be offended.
A summoner's one who runs about the nation
Dealing out summonses for fornication,
Is beaten up every villager
At the town's end . . .' 'Now, mind the manners, sir,'
Our Host called out, 'befitting your estate.
In company we do not want debate.
You tell your tale and let the Summoner be.'
'Nay,' said the Summoner, 'makes no odds to me.
Say what he likes, and when my turn's to come
I'll pay him back, by God! I'll strike him dumb!
I'll tell him what an honour it is, none higher,
To be a limiter, a flattering friar!
I'll tell him all about that job of his.'
Our Host replied, 'Let's have no more of this.'
Then turning to the Friar, 'We prefer,'
He said, 'to hear your story, my dear sir.'

The Friar's Tale

IN my own district once there used to be
A fine archdeacon, one of high degree,
Who boldly did the execution due
On fornication and on witchcraft too,
Bawdry, adultery and defamation,
Breaches of wills and contract, spoliation
Of church endowment, failure in the rents
And tithes and disregard of sacraments,
All these and many other kinds of crime
That need have no rehearsal at this time,

Left: Satan in one of the windows at Lincoln cathedral. The Devil played an active role in medieval Christianity and 'The Friar's Tale' which centres on a roadside meeting with him would have had a sinister plausibility.

Usury, simony too. But he could boast
That lechery was what he punished most.
They had to sing for it if they were caught,
Like those who failed to pay the tithes they ought.
As for all such, if there was an informant,
Nothing could save them from pecunial torment.
For those whose tithes and offerings were small
Were made to sing the saddest song of all,
And ere the bishop caught them with his crook
They were all down in the archdeacon's book,
And he had jurisdiction, on inspection,
And powers to administer correction.
He had a summoner ready to his hand.
There was no slyer boy in all the land,
For he had subtly formed a gang of spies

This fifteenth-century manuscript portrays the ecclesiastical hierarchy. The clergy could not be tried in ordinary courts of law, but only in ecclesiastical ones which also tried laymen for moral offences. Wrongdoers would be ordered to attend by 'summoners'.

Who taught him where his profit might arise,
And he would spare one lecher from his store
To teach the way to four-and-twenty more.
Though it may drive him mad as a March hare,
Our Summoner here, I mean, I will not spare
His harlotries. He has no jurisdiction
On friars and he cannot make infliction
Upon us, now or ever, or take dues
From friars ... 'Nor from women of the stews!'
The Summoner shouted, 'We have no control
On either lot.' 'The devil take your soul!'
Called out the Host, 'I say I won't have squalls.
On with your story, sir, and if it galls
The Summoner, spare him not, my worthy master! ... '
This treacherous thief (the Friar said) was pastor
To certain bawds that ate out of his hand,
Lures for a hawk, none such in all the land.
They told him all the secret things they drew
From sinners; their acquaintance was not new.
Each was his agent, say, his private spy;
He drew large profits to himself thereby.
Even the archdeacon didn't always know
How much he got. He didn't have to show
A warrant when he chose to make things hot
For some obscure, uneducated sot;
For he could summon under threat of curse

And they were glad enough to fill his purse
Or give him banquets at the *Lamb and Flag.*
And just as Judas kept a little bag
And was a thief, just such a thief was he.
His master got no more than half the fee.
To give the man his due and not to skimp,
He was a thief, a summoner, and a pimp.
And he had wenches in his retinue,
So when the Reverend Robert or Sir Hugh
Or Jack or Ralph, whoever it was, drew near
And lay with them, they told it in his ear.
He and these wenches made a gang at it.
Then he would fetch forth a fictitious writ,
Summon them both before the Chapter-bench
And skin the man while letting off the wench,
Saying, 'Dear friend, I know you would prefer
Her name were struck from our black register;
Trouble yourself no further, my good man,
On her account. I'll help you all I can.'
He knew so much of bribery and blackmail
I should be two years telling you the tale.
There is no sporting dog that's more expert
At knowing a wounded deer from one unhurt
Than was this summoner who could spot for sure
Lecher, adulterer or paramour.
Indeed on that his whole attention went

Because it was the source of all his rent.

So it befell that on a certain day
This summoner rode forth to catch his prey,
A poor old fiddle of the widow-tribe
From whom, on a feigned charge, he hoped a bribe.
Now as he rode it happened that he saw
A gay young yeoman under a leafy shaw;
He bore a bow with arrows bright and keen
And wore a little jacket of bright green
And had a black-fringed hat upon his head
'Hail, welcome and well met!' the Summoner said.
'Welcome to you and all good lads,' said he.
'Whither away under the greenwood tree?'
Pursued the yeoman, 'Have you far to go?'

The summoner paused a moment and said, 'No,
Just here, close by. In fact I'm only bent
On going for a ride, to raise a rent
That's owing to my lord, a little fee.'
'Why then you are a bailiff?' 'Yes,' said he.
He did not dare, for very filth and shame,
Say that he was a summoner, for the name.

Well, I'll be damned!' the yeoman said. 'Dear
  brother,
You say you are a bailiff? I'm another.
But I'm a stranger round about this part.
I'll beg acquaintance with you for a start,
And brotherhood, if that is fair to offer.
I have some gold and silver in my coffer
And should you chance to cross into our shire
All shall be yours, as much as you desire.'
'My word!' the summoner answered, 'Thanks a lot!'
The pair of them shook hands upon the spot,
Swore to be brothers to their dying day
And, chatting pleasantly, rode on their way.

This summoner, always ready with a word,
As full of venom as a butcher-bird,
And sticking his nose into one thing or other
Went on, 'And where do you live at home, dear brother?
I might come calling there some other day.'

The yeoman said in his soft-spoken way,
'O, far away up north; I'll tell you where.
I hope that some time I shall see you there.
Before we part I shall be so explicit
About my home I'm sure you'll never miss it.'

Brother,' the summoner said, 'I'd like to know
If you can teach me something as we go.
Since you're a bailiff just the same as me,
Tell me your subtler tricks. Now, seriously,
How can I win most money at the game?
Keep nothing back for conscience, or from shame.
Talk like a brother. How do you make out?'

Well, I break level, brother, just about.
I'll tell a truthful story; all in all
My wages are extremely tight and small.
My master's hard on me and difficult,
My job laborious and with poor result,
And so it's by extortion that I live.
I take whatever anyone will give.

At any rate by tricks and violences
From year to year I cover my expenses.
I can't say better, speaking truthfully.'

The summoner said, 'It's just the same with me.
I'm ready to take anything, God wot,
Unless it is too heavy or too hot.
What I can get out of a little chat
In private – why should conscience boggle at that?
Without extortion, how could I make a living?
My little jokes are hardly worth forgiving.
Bowels of pity, conscience, I have none.
Plague on these penance-fathers every one!
We make a pair, by God and by St James!
But, brother, what do you say to swopping names?'

The summoner paused; the yeoman all the while
The summoner spoke had worn a little smile.
'Brother,' he answered, 'would you have me tell?
I am a fiend, my dwelling is in Hell.
I ride on business and have so far thriven
By taking anything that I am given.
That is the sum of all my revenue.
You seem to have the same objective too,
You're out for wealth, acquired no matter how,
And so with me. I'll go a-riding now
As far as the world's end in search of prey.'

'Usurers in Hell', from a fifteenth-century manuscript. Usury was one of the many offences that would have been dealt with in the church courts. Chaucer's Summoner is one of the most loathsome of all his characters – a vivid example of both personal and institutional corruption.

Yet since you ask why we're a busy band,
It's thus: at times we are God's instruments,
A means of forwarding divine events,
When He so pleases, that concern His creatures,
By various arts, disguised by various features.
We have no power without Him, that's a fact,
If it should please Him to oppose some act.
Sometimes, at our request, He gives us leave
To hurt the body, though we may not grieve
The soul. Take Job; his is a case in point.
At other times the two are not disjoint,
That is to say, the body and the soul.
Sometimes we are allowed to take control
Over a man and put his soul to test,
But not his body; all is for the best;
For every time a man withstands temptation
It is a partial cause of his salvation,
Though our intention is, when we beset him,
Not that he should be saved, but we should get him.
At times we slave for men without complaint
As on Archbishop Dunstan, now a saint;
Why, I was servant to the apostle once.'

'Tell me,' the summoner said, '– I'm just a dunce –
But do you make new bodies as you go
Out of the elements?' The fiend said, 'No;

The fiends of hell were always quick to snatch their prey. In this woodcut they dance eagerly around a corpse in its coffin and carry it away from the open church door towards the mouth of Hell.

'Lord!' said the summoner. 'What did I hear you
         say?
         I thought you were a yeoman, certainly
You have the body of a man like me.
And have you, then, another shape as well
Appointed for your high estate in Hell?'
'No,' he replied, 'for Hell admits of none.
   But when we like we can appropriate one,
   Or rather make you think we have a shape;
Sometimes it's like a man, sometimes an ape,
Even an angel riding into bliss.
There's nothing very wonderful in this;
A lousy conjuror can trick your eye,
And he, God knows, has far less power than I.'
'But why,' pursued the summoner, 'track your game
   In various shapes? Why don't you stay the same?'
   'Just to appear,' he said, 'in such a way
As will enable us to snatch our prey.'
'But why do you have to go to all this bother?'
'For very many reasons, my dear brother;
You shall know all about it in good time.
The day is short and it is long past prime,
And yet I've taken nothing the whole day,
And I must think of business, if I may,
Rather than air my intellectual gift;
Besides, you lack the brains to catch my drift.
If I explained you wouldn't understand;

According to one story of how Archbishop Dunstan outwitted the Devil, he thrust burning tongs into the Devil's nose. There were reputedly several other incidents too in which he managed to subject a fiend to his will.

We just create illusions, or we raise
A corpse and use it; there are many ways.
And we can talk as trippingly and well
As, to the Witch of Endor, Samuel.
And yet some people say it wasn't he;
I have no use for your theology.

'One thing I warn you of, it is no jape;
You will be learning all about our shape
In any case, hereafter, my dear brother,
Where you'll not need me, no, nor yet another,
To teach you; for your own experience
Will furnish you sufficient evidence
To give a lecture on it, and declare
As well as from a professorial chair,
Better than Virgil when he was alive,
Or Dante either. Now, if we're to thrive
Let's hurry on; I'll keep you company
Unless it chance that you abandon me.'

'What?' said the summoner, 'Leave you on your own?
I am a yeoman, pretty widely known;
I'll hold to my engagement, on the level,
Though you were Satan's self, the very Devil!
I keep my word of honour to a brother,
As I have sworn, and so shall each to other;
True brothers we shall be; the bargain's made
And both of us can go about our trade.
You take your share – whatever people give –
And I'll take mine, and that's our way to live.
If either should do better than the other,
Let him be true and share it with his brother.'

'Agreed,' the devil answered. 'As you say.'
And on the word they trotted on their way.
Just at the entry of the very village
The summoner had it in his mind to pillage
They saw a farm-cart loaded up with hay.
There was a carter driving, but the way
Was deep and muddy and the cart stood still.
The carter lashed and shouted with a will,
'Hey, Brock! Hup, Scottie! Never mind for stones!
The foul fiend come and fetch you, flesh and bones,
As sure as you were foaled! Mud, ruts and rubble!
Lord, what a team! I've never known such trouble!
The devil take all, cart, horse and hay in one!'

The summoner said, 'Now we shall have some fun!'
And, as if nothing were happening, he drew near
And whispered softly in the devil's ear;
'Listen to that, dear brother, use your head!
Didn't you hear what the old carter said?
Take it at once, he gave them all to you,
His hay, his cart and his three horses too.'

*The road was 'deep and muddy and the cart stood still'. Most roads
would have been no better than muddy tracks, particularly in
winter – and heavily-laden carts would have often needed a good
push. This painting is from the Luttrell Psalter.*

This woodcut of a summoner comes from the edition of 'The Canterbury Tales' printed by Richard Pynson in the early sixteenth-century. Early printers often reused the same cut and this one was used for the Franklin as well as the Summoner.

on't you believe it!' said the fiend. 'I heard,
But he meant nothing by it, take my word.
Go up and ask him if you don't trust me,
Or else keep quiet for a bit and see.'

he carter thwacked his horses, jerked the rein,
And got them moving; as they took the strain,
'Hup, there!' he shouted, 'Jesus bless you, love,
And all His handiwork! Hey! Saints above!
Well tugged, old fellow, that's the stuff, Grey Boy!
God save you all, my darlings, send you joy!
That's lifted the old cart out of the slough!'

hat did I tell you,' said the fiend, 'just now?
That ought to make it clear to you, dear brother,
The chap said one thing but he meant another.
So let's go on a bit. You mustn't scoff,
But here there's nothing I can carry off.'

hen they were out of town a little way
The summoner whispered to the fiend to say,
'There's an old fiddle here, an ancient wreck,
Dear brother, who would rather break her neck
Than lose a penny of her goods. Too bad,
She'll have to pay me twelve-pence. She'll be mad,
But if she doesn't pay she'll face the court.
And yet, God knows there's nothing to report,
She has no vices. But as you failed just now
To earn your keep, I'd like to show you how.'

he summoner battered at the widow's gate.
'Come out,' he said, 'you old inebriate!
I'll bet you've got a friar or priest inside!'

ho's knocking? Bless us, Lord!' the widow cried,
'God save you, sir, and what is your sweet will?'

ere!' said the summoner. 'I've a summons-bill.
On pain of excommunication, see
That you're at court at the archdeacon's knee
To-morrow morning. There are certain things

To answer for.' 'Christ Jesus, King of Kings,'
She said, 'have mercy! What am I to say?
I can't! I'm ill, and have been many a day.
I couldn't walk so far, nor even ride,
'Twould kill me. There's a pricking in my side.
Couldn't you write it down and save a journey,
And let me answer it through my attorney,
The charge I mean, whatever it may be?'

es, if you pay at once,' he said. 'Let's see.
Twelve pence to me and I'll secure acquittal.
I get no profit from it – very little.
My master gets the profit and not me.
Come off it, I'm in haste. It's got to be.
Give me twelve pence. No time to wait, old fairy.'

welve pence!' said she. 'O blessed Virgin Mary,
Help me and keep me clear of sin and dearth!
Why, if you were to offer me the earth
I couldn't! There's not twelve pence in my bag!
You know I'm nothing but a poor old hag,
Show kindness to a miserable wretch!'

f I excuse you may the devil fetch
Me off! Though it should break you! Come along,
Pay up!' he said. 'But I've done nothing wrong!'
'You pay at once, or by the sweet St Anne,'
He said, 'I'll carry off your frying-pan
For debt, the new one, owed me since the day
You cuckolded your husband. Did I pay
For the correction then or did I not?'

The Devil's trick on the Summoner turns on the popular belief that a curse is effective when it comes from the heart. After the widow's heartfelt damnation, the Devil can promise, 'You yet shall be in Hell with me tonight.' This representation of the flames of hell is from a French manuscript of St Augustine's 'City of God', dated c.1400.

ou lie!' she said. 'On my salvation! What?
Correction? Whether as widow or as wife
I've never had a summons in my life;
I never cuckolded my poor old man!
And as for you and for your frying-pan
The hairiest, blackest devil out of Hell
Carry you off and take the pan as well!'

eeing her kneel and curse, the devil spoke:
'Now, Mother Mabel, is this all a joke,
Or do you really mean the things you say?'

he devil,' she said, 'can carry him away
With pan and all unless he will repent!'
'No, you old cow, I have no such intent,'
The summoner said, 'there's no repentance due
For anything I ever had of you.
I'd strip you naked, smock and rag and clout!'

he devil said, 'What are you cross about,
Dear brother? You and this pan are mine by right.
You yet shall be in Hell with me tonight,
Where you'll know more about our mystery
Than any Doctor of Divinity.'

nd on the word this foul fiend made a swoop
And dragged him, body and soul, to join the
troupe

In Hell, where summoners have their special shelf.
And God, who in the image of Himself
Created man, guide us to Abraham's lap,
And make this Summoner here a decent chap!

y lords, I could have told you, never fear,
Had I the time to save this Summoner here,
Following texts from Christ and Paul and John
And many teachers who are dead and gone,
Of torments that are fit to terrorize
Your hearts, though tongue of man can scarce devise
Such things, or in a thousand winters tell
The pain of that accursed house of Hell.
Watch therefore, and pray Jesus of his grace
To keep us out of that accursed place
And ward off Satan, tempting us from glory;
Ponder my words, reflect upon my story.
The lion's always on the watch for prey
To kill the innocent, if so he may;
And so dispose your heart that it withstand
The fiend who would enslave you in his band.
He may not tempt you, though, above your might,
For Christ will be your champion and your knight.
And, Summoners, flee the sins that so beset you,
And learn repentance ere the devil get you.

The Summoner immediately gets his revenge on the Friar in his topical tale about an ailing man on his sickbed who is preyed on by a hypocritical and greedy friar. The outbreaks of bubonic plague gave many opportunities for such abuse. This picture of a household visited by plague is from a window in Canterbury Cathedral.

THE SUMMONER'S TALE

The Summoner's Prologue

THE Summoner rose in wrath against the Friar
High in his stirrups, and he quaked with ire.
He stood there trembling like an aspen leaf.
'I've only one desire,' he said, 'it's brief,
And one your courtesy will not deny;
Since you have heard this filthy friar lie,
Let me refute him. I've a tale to tell!
This friar boasts his knowledge about Hell,
And if he does, God knows it's little wonder;
Friars and fiends are seldom far asunder.
Lord knows you must have often heard them tell
Of how a friar was ravished down to Hell
Once in a vision, taken there in spirit.
An angel led him up and down to ferret
Among the torments – various kinds of fire –
And yet he never saw a single friar,
Though he saw plenty of other kinds of folk
In pain enough. At last this friar spoke:
"Sir, are the friars in such a state of grace,"
He said, "none ever come into this place?"
"Why, yes," the angel answered, "many a million!"
And led him down to Lucifer's pavilion.

"Satan," the angel said, "has got a tail
As broad or broader than a barge's sail.
Hold up thy tail, thou Satan!" then said he,
"Show forth thine arse and let the friar see
The nest ordained for friars in this place!"
Ere the tail rose a furlong into space
From underneath it there began to drive,
Much as if bees were swarming from a hive,
Some twenty thousand friars in a rout
And swarmed all over Hell and round about,
And then came back as fast as they could run
And crept into his arse again, each one.
He clapped his tail on them and then lay still.
And after when the friar had looked his fill
On all the torments in that sorry place
His spirit was restored by Heaven's grace
Back to his body again and he awoke.
But all the same the terror made him choke,
So much the devil's arse was in his mind,
The natural heritage of all his kind.
God save you all except this cursed Friar,
For that is all the prologue I require.'

The Summoner's Tale

MY lords, there lies – in Yorkshire, as I guess –
A marshy district known as Holderness,
In which a friar, a limiter, went about
To preach his sermons and to beg, no doubt.
And on a certain day it so befell,
When he had preached in church, and cast his spell
With one main object, far above the rest,
To fire his congregation with a zest
For buying trentals, and for Jesu's sake
To give the wherewithal for friars to make

Their holy houses, where the Lord is dowered
With truest honour, not to be devoured
By those to whom there is no need to give
Like those endowed already, who can live,
Thanks be to God, in affluence and glory.
'Trentals,' he said, 'can fetch from Purgatory
The souls of all your friends, both old and young,
Yes, even when they're very quickly sung
– Not that a priest is frivolous or gay
Because he only sings one mass a day –

187

In his savage parody of the predatory friar, Chaucer was voicing a widespread criticism that in the fourteenth century the power of ecclesiastics to absolve people from their sins was frequently abused. This drawing of a priest selling pardons and papal indulgences is from that other fourteenth-century literary masterpiece, Langland's 'Piers Plowman'.

Release the souls,' he thundered, 'from the pit,
Deliver them from the flesh-hook and the spit!
What agony to be clawed, to burn, to bake!
Be quick, exert yourselves, for Jesu's sake!'
 hen he had finished all he had to say,
 With *qui cum Patre* off he went his way.
 When folk had put their pennies in the plate
He used to go away, he wouldn't wait.
With scrip and pointed staff uplifted high
He went from house to house to poke and pry
And beg a little meal and cheese, or corn.
His comrade had a staff was tipped with horn,

And bore two ivory tablets, wax-anointed,
Also a stylus elegantly pointed.
He always wrote the names down as he stood
Of those who gave him offerings or food
(Pretence of praying for them by and by).
' ive us a bushel of barley, malt or rye,
 A wee God's cookie, then, a slice of cheese,
 It's not for us to choose, but as you please;
A penny to say mass, or half a penny,
Some of your brawn perhaps – you haven't any? –
Well then, a bit of blanket, worthy dame,
Our well-beloved sister! There's your name,
It's down. Beef? Bacon? Anything you can find!'
A sturdy varlet followed them behind –
The servant for their guests, and bore a sack,
What they were given he carried on his back.
Once out of doors again and business done,
He used to plane the names out, every one
That he had written on his waxen tables.
He'd served them all with fairy-tales and fables.
'No, there you lie, you Summoner!' cried the Friar;
'Peace!' said our Host. 'Who cares if he's a liar?
Tell on your story! Let the Friar keep still
Never you spare him, Summoner!' 'Nor I will.'
 n went this friar from house to house till he
 Came upon one where he was wont to be
 Better refreshed than anywhere in town.
The householder was sick and lying down.
Bedridden on a couch the fellow lay.
'*Deus hic!* Friend Thomas, how are we today?'
The Friar said, taking pains to soften
His voice politely; 'God protect you! Often –
How often! – I've sat upon this very bench to steal
Your kindness and enjoyed a merry meal!'
And, from the bench, he drove away the cat,
And, laying down his pointed staff, his hat,
And then his scrip, he settled softly down.
 is comrade was off walking in the town;
 He and his varlet had gone off to see
 The hostel where they aimed, that night, to be.
 my dear master,' said this ailing man,
 'How have things been with you since March
 began?
Ain't seen you this last fortnight now, or more.'
'God knows,' he answered, 'I have laboured sore
And, more especially, have said in care
Of your salvation many a precious prayer,
And for our other friends, but let that pass.
I went this morning to your church for Mass,
And preached according to my simple wit;
It wasn't all on texts from Holy Writ,
For that's too hard for you as I suppose,
And I prefer to paraphrase or gloze.
Glozing's a glorious thing, and anyway
"The letter killeth" as we clerics say.
And so I taught them to be charitable
And spend their goods where it is reasonable;
And there I saw your wife – Ah, where is she?'

'Out in the yard, I think, or ought to be,'
The fellow said; 'she'll come, she can't be far.'

'Why, sir, you're welcome, by St John you are!'
The woman said, 'I hope you're keeping
    sprightly?'
Up from his bench the friar rose politely
Embracing her – the clasp was somewhat narrow –
And kissed her sweetly, chirping like a sparrow
As his lips parted. 'Ma'am,' he said, 'I'm fine.
Your servant, Ma'am,' he said, 'in all that's mine.
Thanks be to God that gave you soul and life
I haven't seen a prettier little wife
In all the church today, upon my word!'
'Well, God amend defects!' the woman purred.
'At any rate you're welcome, I'll be bound.'
'My warmest thanks! That's what I've always found.
If I may trespass – you're so very kind –
On your good nature; if you wouldn't mind,
I want to talk to Thomas here; you know
These curates are so negligent and slow
At groping consciences with tenderness.
I study how to preach and to confess,
Earnestly read St Peter and St Paul
And walk about to fish and make a haul
Of Christian souls, pay Christ his proper rent,
And if I spread His word I am content.'

'Now, my dear master, by your leave,' said she,
'Scold the man well, for by the Trinity,
He is as irritable as an ant,
Though he has everything a man can want.
I try to keep him warm at night, I squeeze him,
Put my leg over him, or arm, to please him,
And all he does is grunt, like boar in sty!
I get no other sport of him, not I.
No way of pleasing him at all, I promise.'

'O Thomas, *je vous dis*, O Thomas, Thomas!
That is the devil's work and must be chidden.
Anger's a thing by Heavenly God forbidden;
I mean to speak of that, a word or so.'

'Now, master,' said the wife, 'before I go,
What would you like for dinner? What would suit?'
'Well, Ma'am,' he answered, '*je vous dis sans doute*,
If I could have a little chicken-liver
And some of your soft bread – the merest shiver –
And then a pig's head roasted – but, do you see?
I won't have any creature killed for me –
It would be homely and sufficient fare.
The sustenance I take is very spare;
You see, my spirit draws its nourishment
Out of the Bible, and my body's spent
In pains and prayers; my stomach is destroyed.
However, Ma'am, you mustn't be annoyed
To hear me speak as frankly as I do,
For these are things I tell to very few.'

'Before I leave you, sir, you ought to know,'
She said, 'my baby died two weeks ago,
Just after you left town on visitation.'

'I know. I saw his death by revelation,'
Replied the friar, 'in our dormitory.
I saw the little fellow borne to glory,
I dare say it was less than half an hour
After his death indeed. To God the power!
Our sexton and our infirmarian,
They saw it too, both friars, boy and man,
These fifty years, thank God. They now are free
To walk alone, they've reached their jubilee.
I rose at once, in fact the entire place
Rose, and the tears were trickling down my face;
There was no noise, no clattering bells were rung,
But a *Te Deum* – nothing else – was sung,
Save that I made an act of adoration
To Christ, to thank Him for His revelation.
For I assure you both, believe me well,
Our orisons are more effectual
And we see more of Christ's most secret things
Than common people do, or even kings.
We live in poverty and abstinence
But common folk in riches and expense
On food and drink, and other foul delight;
But we contemn all worldly appetite.

'Dives and Lazarus lived differently,
And different their guerdon had to be.
Whoever prays must fast, he must keep clean,
Fatten his soul and make his body lean.
We follow the Apostle; clothes and food

An illustration from Savanarola's 'Art of Dying Well'. Life in the middle ages was always dominated by death, and fear of damnation gave ecclesiastics great power over ordinary people. In this picture a man lies on his deathbed surrounded by his wife and attendants while the forces of heaven and hell prepare to do battle for his immortal soul. Also around the bed can be seen the skeletal figure of Death and the fiends of hell. Such images and the fears they expressed would make any sick man an easy customer for the Friar's offer of absolution – or so he hoped!

Suffice us though they may be rough and rude,
Our purity and fasting have sufficed
To make our prayers acceptable to Christ.

Moses had fasted forty days and nights
Before Almighty God, upon the heights
Of Sinai, came down to speak with him,
And with an empty stomach, frail of limb,
Moses received the law Jehovah drew
With his own finger; and Elijah too
When in Mount Horeb, ere he could have speech
With that Almighty Lord, who is the leech
Of life, had fasted long on contemplation.

Aaron no less, under whose domination
The temple was, and other Levites too,
When they approached the temple to renew
Their services and supplications, they
Refrained from drinking – drinking, that's to say,
That might have made them drunk – attending there
In abstinence, in watching and in prayer
Lest they should die. Take heed of what I say;
Unless the priest is sober who would pray
For you – but there! I've said enough of it.

Jesus our Lord, it says in Holy Writ,
Fasted and prayed, and patterned our desires,
And so we mendicants, we simple friars
Have wedded poverty and continence,
Charity, humbleness and penitence,
And persecution too for righteousness;
Pure, merciful, austere, but quick to bless
Though weeping often. Therefore our desires
– I'm speaking of ourselves, mendicant friars –
Are more acceptable to God, more able
Than yours, with all your feasts upon the table.

I speak the truth; gluttony was the vice
That first flung Adam out of Paradise;
And man was chaste in Eden, I may mention.

But listen to me, Thomas, pay attention.
Though there's no text exactly, I suppose,
Yet in a manner of speaking, if I gloze
A little, you will see our Lord referred
Especially to friars in the word
"Blessed are the poor in spirit." Think and look,
Study the gospels, search the Holy Book,
And see if it be liker our profession
Than theirs who swim in riches and possession.
Fie on their pomp! Fie on their gluttony!
Their ignorance is a disgrace to see.

Jovinian makes a good comparison,
"Fat as a whale and waddling like a swan,"
They stink of wine like bottles in a bar;
How reverent their supplications are!
When they say prayers for souls their psalm of David
Is just a "Burp! *Cor meum eructavit!*"
Who follows on the gospel, tracks the spoor
Of Christ, but we the humble, chaste and poor,
The doers of the word, not hearers only?
And as a hawk springs up into the lonely
Regions of heaven, so the prayer aspires
Of charitable, chaste and busy friars,
Takes flight and enters in at God's two ears.
O Thomas, Thomas! Let me say with tears
And by that patron who is called St Ives,
Where were your hope to be as one that thrives
If you were not our brother? Day and night
Our Chapter prays the Lord to send you might,
Strengthen your body, girdle it and belt it!'
'God knows,' the fellow said, 'I haven't felt it.
So help me Christ, I've spent a lot in hire,
These last few years, on various kinds of friar,
Aye, many a pound; and yet I'm none the better.
I've poured it out. I'm very near a debtor.
Farewell my gold, it's gone; no more to go!'

O Thomas!' said the friar. 'Did you so?
What need to seek out "various kinds of friar"?
Who, with a perfect doctor, could require
To seek out other doctors in the town?
Your own inconstancy has let you down.

This picture from York Minster shows a donor presenting the window to the Minister. Friars had a reputation for granting absolution simply in return for generous donations to their churches, many of which became notable for their magnificent stained glass windows.

Do you suppose our convent, and I too,
Are insufficient, then, to pray for you?
Thomas, that joke's not good. Your faith is brittle.
You're ill because you've given us too little.
"Ah! give that convent half a quarter of oats!"
"Ah! give that convent four and twenty groats!"
"Ah! give that friar a penny and let him go?"
No, Thomas, Thomas, it should not be so!
What is a farthing worth if split in twelve?
An undivided thing is (if you delve
Into your wits) stronger than when it's scattered.
Thomas, by me you never shall be flattered.
You're trying to get our work for nothing, eh?
What does Almighty God who made us say?
"The labourer is worthy of his hire."
Thomas, you know it's not that I desire
Your treasure for myself; it should be spent,
Seeing our convent is so diligent
In prayer for you, to build the church of Christ.
Thomas! If you would learn or be enticed
To learn what good there is in building churches,
Your namesake's life will further your researches,
St Thomas of India. There you lie in ire,
The devil having set your heart on fire,
And chide this foolish, innocent woman here,
Your wife, so meek, so patient, so sincere.
So, Thomas, please let this be understood:
No wrangling with your wife! It's for your good.
And take this thought away to fill your head
Touching this matter; wisely was it said:
"Then be not as a lion in thy house,
A terror to thy household, tyrannous,
Nor such that thine acquaintance flees away."
I charge you, Thomas, once again and say,
Beware of her that in your bosom sleeps;
Beware the serpent that so slyly creeps
Amidst the grass and stings with subtlety.
Beware, my son, and listen patiently,
For twenty thousand men have lost their lives
For wrangling with their lovers and their wives.
And since you have so holy and meek a wife,
What, Thomas, is the need for all this strife?
No serpent is so cruel, truth to tell,
If one should tread upon his tail, so fell
As women who have given way to ire.
Vengeance is then the sum of their desire.
Ire is a sin, one of the deadly seven,
Abominable unto God in Heaven,
And a destruction to yourself, none quicker.
Every illiterate parson, every vicar
Can tell that ire engenders homicide.
For ire is the executor of pride.
Were I to say what ire can bring in sorrow
To man, my tale would last until tomorrow.
So day and night I pray as best I can
God send no power to an angry man!
Great harm can come of it, great misery,
When angry men are set in high degree.

'Once on a time an angry potentate,
Seneca says, bore rule over a state.
A certain day two knights went riding out
And fortune willed that it should come about
That one of them returned, the other not.
The knight was brought to judgement on the spot;
This judge gave sentence: "You have killed your friend.
You are condemned to death and that's the end."
And to another knight was standing by
He turned and said, "Go, lead him out to die."
And so it happened as they went along
To the appointed place, towards the throng
There came the knight that was reported dead.
So it seemed best that both of them be led
Together back before the judge again.
"My lord," they said, "the knight has not been slain;
His friend is guiltless. As you see, they thrive."
"You all shall die," said he, "as I'm alive!
You first, the second, you, and you the third!"
And turning to the first he said this word:
"I have condemned you. You must therefore die."
Then to the next, "You too, and this is why:
Your comrade clearly owes his death to you."
Then to the third he turned and said, "You too;
You had my orders; they were not fulfilled."
And so it was the three of them were killed.

'An angry man and drunken was Cambyses,
Who took great joy in showing off his vices.
A knight, it happened, in his company,
Given to virtue and morality,
In private conference with him began:
"A lord is lost if he's a vicious man,
And drunkenness if filthy to record
Of any man, especially a lord.
Many the eye and ear that takes good care
To spy on lords, they can't be certain where.
For God's love be more temperate in your drink,
For wine will rob you of your power to think
And incapacitate your members too."
"You'll see," said he, "the opposite is true,
And prove it by your own experience
That wine has no such power of offence.
There is no wine so strong as to deny
Strength to my hand or foot or sight of eye."
And out of spite he drank as much, nay, more
A hundred times than he had drunk before
And right away this angry, cursed wretch
Gave an immediate command to fetch
This noble's son, and there he made him stand;
Then snatching up a bow into his hand
Drew string to ear, and aiming it with care
He shot him with an arrow then and there.
"Now have I got a steady hand or not?
Now have my mental powers gone to rot?"
The tyrant said, "Has wine destroyed my sight?"
Why should I tell the answer of the knight?
His son was slain, there is no more to say.
Dealing with lords be careful in your play;

You sing *Placebo*! I shall if I can,
Except when talking to some poor old man.
To tell their vices to the poor is well,
But not to lords, though they should go to Hell.
'Cyrus the Persian was an evil-liver
And given to anger; he destroyed the river
Gyson in which his horse was drowned, upon
His expedition to take Babylon.
That river in his rage was so diminished
Women could wade it by the time he'd finished.
'Solomon teaches us as no one can:
"Make thou no friendship with an angry man;
And with a furious man take not thy way,
Lest thou repent it"; there's no more to say.
'Leave anger, Thomas; brother, have a care!
You'll find me just. I'm like a joiner's square.
That devil's knife, O draw it from your heart!
It is your anger causes you to smart.
Make your confession to me if you can.'
'No, by St Simon,' said the ailing man,
'The curate came and shrived me here today.
I told him everything I had to say.
There's no more need to speak of it,' said he,
'Unless I care to, from humility.'
'Then give me of your gold to make our cloister,'
Said he, 'for many a mussel, many an oyster,
When other men eat well and fill their cup,
Has been our food, to build our cloister up.
And yet we've hardly finished the foundation.
There's not a tile as yet or tessellation
Upon the pavement that we hope to own,
And forty pound is owing still for stone.
'Now, Thomas, help, for Him that harrowed Hell,
For otherwise we shall be forced to sell
Our books, and if you lacked our predication
The world would quickly fall to desolation.
To cheat it of our sermons and bereave
The world of us, dear Thomas, by your leave,
Were worse than to bereave it of the sun.
Who teaches and who works as we have done?
And for a long, long time,' he said, 'because
There have been friars since Elijah was;
Elisha too was one (the books record) –
In charity with us, I thank our Lord.
Now Thomas, help, for holy charity!'
And down at once he went upon his knee.
'The ailing man was nearly mad with ire;
He would have very gladly burnt the friar,
Him and his lying speech and false profession.
'I'll give you what I have in my possession,
Such as it is,' he said, 'I have none other.
You said a moment back I was your brother?'
'Believe it,' said the friar, 'and none better;
I brought your wife our sealed Fraternal Letter!'
'Well now,' he said, 'there's something I can give
Your holy convent, if I am to live.
And you shall have it in your hand to own
On one condition and on one alone,

That you divide it equally, dear brother,
And every friar to have as much as other.
But swear by your profession to the thing,
And without fraudulence or cavilling.'
'I swear it by my faith!' the friar said,
Clasping the hand of the poor man in bed.
'My hand on it! In me shall be no lack.'
'Well, then, reach down your hand along my back,'
The sick man said, 'and if you grope behind,
Beneath my buttocks you are sure to find
Something I've hidden there for secrecy.'
'Ah!' thought the friar, 'that's the thing for me!'
And down he launched his hand and searched the
        cleft
In hope of profiting by gift or theft.
When the sick man could feel him here and there
Groping about his fundament with care,
Into that friar's hand he blew a fart.
There never was a farmhorse drawing cart
That farted with a more prodigious sound.
'Mad as a lion then the friar spun round,
'You treacherous lout!' he cried, 'God's bones
        and blight!
You did it on purpose! It was done for spite!
You shall pay dearly for that fart, I say!'
'The sick man's servants, hearing the affray,
Came leaping in and chased away the friar,
And off he went still spluttering with ire
To find his comrade where he kept his goods.
He looked like a wild boar out of the woods,
Gnashing his teeth, he was so furious.
'He strode along towards the manor-house
Where lived a man of honour and possession
Who used to seek the friar in confession.
This worthy man was the manorial lord;
As he was sitting eating at his board
In came the friar in a towering rage
Almost past speech for anger by that stage,
But in the end 'God blesss you, sir,' said he.
The lord stared back. 'Hey, *benedicite*!
It's Friar John! What sort of world is this?
It's easy seen that something is amiss!
You look as if the thieves were in the wood;
Sit down and say if I can do you good;
I'll settle matters for you, if I can!'
'I have received an insult,' said the man.
'God give you joy – below here, in your village,
In all the world there is no serf at tillage
So poor but would have held in execration
And counted it as an abomination
The affront that I've been offered in your town.
And yet, what grieves me most, this hoary clown
Blasphemed against our holy convent too!'
'Now, master,' said the lord, 'I beg of you –'
'No master, sir,' he said, 'your servitor!
Although the Schools did me that honour, sir,
But still God wishes not that men should call
Us "Rabbi" either here in your large hall

St Francis, the founder of the Franciscan order of Friars, painted by Giotto. Chaucer's scorn indicates how far the friars had departed from the ideals of their founder.

In 'The Summoner's Tale', Chaucer's sense of outrage at the cynical exploitation of religion by ecclesiastical officials rises to a new pitch. The story was probably based on a current anecdote.

Or in the market.' 'Never mind,' said he,
'Tell me your trouble.' 'Sir, there was done to me,
And to my Order too, an odious wrong;
Per consequens to all that may belong
To Holy Church itself. May God amend it.'
'Sir,' said the lord, 'you know the way to end it.
Keep calm, you're my confessor; I know your
    worth.
You are the salt and savour of the earth.
For love of God be patient and unfold
The matter of your grief.' So then he told
The story (you have heard it) with a will.
The lady of the house sat very still
Till she had heard the friar's whole tirade.
'Mother of God,' she said, 'O blessed Maid!
And is there nothing else? Now tell me true.'
'Madam,' he answered, 'May I hear your view?'
'My view?' she said. 'God help us! What's the
    need?
I say a churl has done a churlish deed.
What should I say? May God deny him ease!

His poor sick head is full of vanities.
I think he must have had some kind of fit.'
'Madam,' said he, 'I'll pay him out for it,
By God I will! There are within my reach
Several ways; for instance I can preach,
I can defame him! I won't be derided
Or bidden divide what cannot be divided
In equal parts – God damn his ignorance!'
The lord had sat like someone in a trance,
Rolling in heart the problem up and down,
How the imagination of a clown
Had hit on this conundrum for the friar.
'I never before heard such a thing transpire;
I think the devil put it in his mind.
In all arithmetic you couldn't find
Until today so tricky an equation.
How could one set about a demonstration
Where every man alike should have his part
Both of the sound and savour of a fart?
Proud churl! O nice distinction! Damn his nerve!'
He then went on more gravely to observe,

194

'Who ever heard of such a thing till now!
"To every man alike?" Good Lord, but how?
It is impossible, it cannot be!
Aha, nice churl! God send him misery!
The rumbling of a fart or any sound
Is only air reverberating round,
What's more, diminishingly, bit by bit.
Upon my word! No one could have the wit
To see it was divided equally.
To think a churl, a churl of mine, could be
So shrewd, and to my own confessor too!
He's certainly demoniac in my view!
Now eat your food and leave the churl alone
And let the devil hang him for his own!'

Now the lord's squire was standing by and heard
The tale as he was carving, word for word,
And saw the problem you have heard defined.
'My lord,' he said, 'I hope you will not mind,
But, for a piece of cloth to make a gown,
I'd tell the friar – but he mustn't frown –
How such a fart could equally be shared
Between him and his convent, if I cared.'

His lord replied, 'Well, tell us then, go on,
And you shall have your gown-cloth, by St
John.'

Well, when the weather, sir,' he said, 'is fair,
When there's no wind or movement in the air,
Then have a cart-wheel brought into this hall,
But see the spokes are fitted – twelve in all,
A cartwheel has twelve spokes – then, by and by,
Bring me twelve friars. You will ask me why?
Well, thirteen make a convent, as I guess.
And this confessor here, for worthiness,
Shall bring the number to thirteen, my lord.
Then they shall all kneel down with one accord;
To each spoke's end a friar, I propose,
Shall very seriously lay his nose.
Your excellent confessor, whom God save,
Shall put his nose right up under the nave.
And then the churl, with belly stiff and taut
As drum or tabor, hither shall be brought,
Set on the wheel thus taken from the cart
Above the nave, and made to let a fart.
Then you will see, as surely as I live,

'As wise as Euclid or as Ptolemy'. The ancient Greek authorities
were regarded as the embodiment of wisdom. This painting,
showing Euclid with his sphere and dioptra and Hermannus
holding an astrolabe, is from a collection of fortune-telling tracts.

And by a proof that is demonstrative,
That equally the sound of it will wend,
Together with the stink, to the spokes' end,
Save that this worthy friar, your confessor,
Being of great honour, they of lesser,
Shall have the first-fruits, as is only right.
A noble custom, in which friars unite,
Is that a worthy man should first be served
And certainly it will be well-deserved.
Today his preaching did us so much good,
Being beneath the pulpit where he stood,
That I'd allow him, if it fell to me,
First smell of every fart, say up to three,
And so would all his convent I am sure,
His bearing is so holy, fair and pure.'

The lord and lady – all except the friar –
Thought Jacky's answer all they could desire,
As wise as Euclid or as Ptolemy.
As for the churl, it was his subtlety,
His wit, they said, to think of such a crack.
'He is no fool, he's no demoniac!'
And Jacky has acquired a new gown.
My tale is done; we've almost come to town.

Le premier chappie contient
vng dictie de francois petrac poete flo
rentin et de Iehan boccace acteur de
cestuy psalteur. Et commence
ou latin. Quid my. Et le recit
ne say que ie die
apres laccomplisse
ment de mon vn me
leure fort que ie me
repose mais ie crems

le repos. Car cette chose est que le soup
irans repos est cause de encommssent
Et si est repos contraire a soubtilete
de... Et combien que par ma folie
ie aie esprouue quelle chose est re
pos. toutesuoies ie suis maintenant cheus
en dommaigeuse peresse. Car pour
ce que ie desiroie repos ie habandon
nay mes membres et les lay fait choir
en arguant oysiuete. Ie oubliay tou

THE CLERK'S TALE

The Clerk's Prologue

'YOU, sir, from Oxford!' said the Host. 'God's
          life!
     As coy and quiet as a virgin-wife
     Newly espoused and sitting mum at table!
     You haven't said a word since we left stable.
Studying, I suppose? On wisdom's wing?
Says Solomon, "There's a time for everything."
'For goodness' sake cheer up, show animation!
     This is no time for abstruse meditation.
     Tell us a lively tale in Heaven's name;
For when a man has entered on a game
He's bound to keep the rules, it's by consent.
But don't you preach as friars do in Lent,
Dragging up all our sins to make us weep,
Nor tell a tale to send us all to sleep.
'Let it be brisk adventure, stuff that nourishes
     And not too much of your rhetorical flourishes.
     Keep the "high style" until occasion brings
A use for it, like when they write to kings,
And for the present put things plainly, pray,
So we can follow all you have to say.'
'This worthy cleric left the land of nod
     And said benignly, 'Sir, I kiss the rod!
     Our company is under your control
And I am all obedience heart and soul,
That is, as far as reason will allow.
'I heard the story I shall tell you now
     In Padua, from a learned man now dead,
     Of proven worth in all he did and said.
Yes, he is dead and nailed up in his chest,
And I pray God his spirit may have rest.
'Francis Petrarch, the poet laureate,
     They called him, whose sweet rhetoric of late
     Illumined Italy with poesy,
As Lynian did with his philosophy
And law, and other special kinds of learning.

*Left: Petrarch appearing to Boccaccio. 'The Clerk's Tale' can be
traced back to an old folk-tale. Petrarch translated it into Latin from
Boccaccio's 'Decameron' and Chaucer relied heavily on this version.*

*The Clerk, like Chaucer himself when it was his turn to tell a Tale,
has to be aroused from scholarly absorption by the Host, who begs
him to speak in plain, colloquial language.*

Death that allows no lingering or returning
In, as it were, the twinkling of an eye
Has slain them both; and we must also die.
'But, to return to this distinguished man
     From whom I learnt the tale, as I began,
     Let me say first he starts it by enditing
A preface in the highest style of writing,
Ere coming to the body of his tale,
Describing Piedmont, the Saluzzo vale,
And the high Apennines that one may see
Bounding the lands of western Lombardy;
And he is most particular to tell
Of Monte Viso, where, from a little well,
The river Po springs from its tiny source.
Eastwards it runs, increasing on its course,
Towards the Aemilian Way; Ferrara past,
It reaches Venice and the sea at last,
Which is not only far too long to tell
But, as I think, irrelevant as well,
Except to set the tale and engineer it
A frame-work. This is it, if you will hear it.'

The Clerk's Tale

PART I

UPON the western shores of Italy
Where Monte Viso lifts into the cold,
There lies a plain of rich fertility
With many a town and tower to behold,
Built by their forefathers in days of old,
And other lovely things to see in legion.
Saluzzo it is called, this splendid region.

There was a marquis once who ruled that land,
As had his ancestors in days gone by.
His vassals were obedient at his hand
Ready to serve, the lowly and the high.
Honoured and dreaded, under fortune's eye
He long had lived and found the living pleasant,
Beloved alike by nobleman and peasant.

He was, moreover, speaking of descent,
The noblest-born of all in Lombardy,
Handsome and young and strong; in him were
blent
High honour and a gentle courtesy.
He was discreet in his authority,
Though in some things he was indeed to blame,
As you shall hear, and Walter was his name.

I blame his failure in consideration
Of what the distant future might provide.
He always fed his present inclination,
Hawking and hunting round the countryside.
As to more serious cares, he let them slide,

The desire that his subjects express for the marquis to marry in order to perpetuate a dynasty touched on a topical subject, for Chaucer wrote 'The Canterbury Tales' in the reign of the childless king Richard II.

And worst of all, whatever might miscarry,
He could not be prevailed upon to marry.

This was the only point that really stung them,
And so one day a deputation went
To wait on him. The wisest man among them,
Or else the least unwilling to consent
To give the marquis their admonishment,
The ablest there to touch on such a head,
Boldly addressed the marquis thus and said:

My noble lord, your great humanity
Gives us assurance; we are therefore bold
To speak on any point of urgency
Or heavy care of which you should be told.
Then, sir, let not your clemency withhold
A hearing to our pitiful petition;
Do not disdain my voice or our position.

Though what I ask concerns me no more nearly
Than any of your subjects in this place,
Yet forasmuch as you have loved me dearly
And ever shown the favours of your grace,
I dare the better beg in such a case
For gentle audience; here is our request,
And you, my lord, must do as you think best.

We love you well, sir, are indeed rejoiced
In all you do or ever did, and we
Scarce can imagine thoughts that could be voiced

Hawking was a traditional sport for noblemen. In the earlier folk-tale, the hero was a supernatural being and this accounted for his reluctance to marry. In both Petrarch's and Chaucer's versions the fairy lover has become a mortal and the disparity between him and Griselda has dwindled to one of social class.

To lap us round in more felicity
Save one thing only, would that it might be!
Did you but choose, my lord, to take a wife,
What sovereign comfort to your country's life!

'Obow your neck under that blessed yoke!
It is a kingdom, not a slavery;
Espousal, wedlock, it is called. Invoke
Your wisdom, ponder carefully and see
How variously days pass; the seasons flee
Away in sleeping, waking, roaming, riding.
Time passes on and there is no abiding.

'Still in the flower of your youth's delights
Age creeps upon you, silent as a stone.
Death menaces all ages and he smites
The high and low, the known and the unknown;
We see for certain, are obliged to own
That we must die, but we are ignorant all
Of when the hour's to come, the blow to fall.

'Death menaces all ages and he smites/The high and low, the
known and the unknown;/We see for certain, are obliged to
own/That we must die, but we are ignorant all/Of when the hour's
to come, the blow to fall.' Death cuts the thread of life in this
illustration to the 'Roman de la Rose'.

'Incline to our petition for protection,
Hear us that never crossed your least behest,
And we, with your consent, will make election
Immediately and choose a wife possessed
Of gentlest quality and birth, the best
In all the land, beseeming to her place,
An honour both to God and to your Grace.

'Deliver us from anxious fears and rid
Our hearts of care, for blessed Jesu's sake;
For if it so befell – which God forbid! –
Your line should end, then might not fortune rake
Some strange successor in to come and take
Your heritage? Should we not all miscarry?
Therefore we beg you speedily to marry.'

'Their humble prayer and their imploring features
Made much impression on his clemency
And he replied, 'My people, fellow-creatures,
Married's a thing I never thought to be.
I go rejoicing in my liberty,
And that and marriage seldom go together;
Where I was free, am I to take the tether?

'Yet, since your offer is sincerely meant,
And since I trust you now as in the past,
I freely will admit myself content
To humour you and take a wife at last.
But as for the suggestion you should cast
About to find me a bride, I must remit
That duty; kindly say no more of it.

'God knows it's true that children in the main
Are much unlike their elders gone before,
Natural goodness comes of God, no strain
Of blood can give it, no, nor ancestor;
I trust in God's good bounty; say no more.
My marriage, my condition, rank and ease
I lay on Him. Do He as He may please.

'Leave me alone to choose myself a wife,
That is my burden, my prerogative.
But I command you, charge you, on your life,
That whomsoever I choose, you are to give
All honour to her, long as she may live,
In word and deed, here and elsewhere, no less
Than to an emperor's daughter or princess.

'And over this you furthermore shall swear
Never to grumble, never to check or strive
Against my choice, if I am to impair
My personal liberty that you may thrive.
Where I have set my heart I mean to wive;
If you withhold consent as to this latter
I beg you'll speak no more upon the matter.'

A woodcut illustration of a royal marriage – 'that blessed yoke'.

This painting of Italian courtiers is taken from a fifteenth-century illustration of Boccaccio's 'Il Filoco'. Chaucer's own career as a courtier led to his being entrusted with several important diplomatic missions. He first went to northern Italy at the end of 1372, an experience which had a decisive influence on his imaginative development and aroused his interest in the Italian writers who were to become so influential on his own work.

ith heart's goodwill they gave him their assent
To this demand, not one that made objection,
But begged the princely favour ere they went
That he would name a day for the election
Of his espoused and quickly, for a section
Among his folk were yet uneasy, dreading
The marquis had no real thought of wedding.

e granted them a day of their own choosing
When he would wed in sober certainty;
He said he did so not to seem refusing
Their reasonable request, and reverently
In grave obedience then they bent the knee
Thanking him one and all, and were content,
Having achieved their aim, and home they went.

nd thereupon he bade his ministers
To make such preparations as were fit
Against a feast, giving his officers
And squires such orders as he pleased for it,
And they obeyed him, setting all their wit
With diligence, the greatest and the least,
To make provision for a solemn feast.

PART II

OT far from where the noble palace stood
In which this marquis set about his wedding
There was a pretty village near a wood
Where the poor folk, each in his little steading,
Tended their animals with food and bedding
And took what sustenance they could from toil,
According to the bounty of the soil.

mong these poorer folk there dwelt a man
Who was esteemed the poorest of them all;
Yet there are times when God in Heaven can
Send grace into a little ox's stall.
Janicula the village used to call
This poor old man; his daughter was a pearl.
Griselda was the name of this young girl.

ut in the virtuous beauty of her heart
She was among the loveliest man could ask,
For being poorly bred, no sensual part
Had learnt to use her beauty as a mask.
More often from the well than from the cask
She drank, and loving virtue, sought to please
By honest labour, not by idle ease.

nd though as yet a girl of tender age,
Yet in the breast of her virginity
There was a ripeness, serious and sage.

With fostering love and reverent constancy
Her poor old father in his poverty
She tended, spun her wheel and watched his sheep
At pasture, never idle save asleep.

'The vigilance of the good Shepherd' from the 'Roman de la Rose'. Griselda's humble background is in no way sordid or mean. Her father's poverty is dignified by being associated with the Nativity, and the hardships of her life are described through images which evoke a biblical rather than a medieval background. The whole story is related in a gentle and leisurely manner that reflects the nature of its heroine.

hen she came homeward she would often bring
Roots, herbs and other grasses to the croft;
These she would shred and seethe for flavouring,
Then make her bed that was in nothing soft.
And thus she kept her father's heart aloft
With all the obedience, all the diligence
By which a child can show her reverence.

riselda, though among his poorest creatures,
Walter had often seen, for, riding by,
Hunting perhaps, a something in her features
Caught his regard, not that he sought to try
The frivolous glance of wantonness; his eye
Fell on her with a serious awareness
And he would often ponder on her fairness.

er womanliness was what his heart commended,
Her goodness too, far passing the condition
Of one so young, was beautifully blended
In looks and deeds. A vulgar intuition
Lacks insight into virtue; his position
Taught him to recognize it and decide,
Were he to marry, she should be his bride.

he day appointed for his wedding came
But no one knew what woman it should be,
In wonder at which his people would exclaim,
Talking among themselves in privacy,
'When will the marquis quit his vanity
And take a wife? Alas to see him thus!
Why does he try to fool himself and us?'

evertheless the marquis bade prepare
Brooches and rings, all for Griselda, lit
With jewels, gold and lapis; he took care
Her wedding-garment should be made to fit,
But by another girl they measured it,
Who was of equal stature; gems were sewn
On it to grace a wedding like his own.

nd as the morning opened on the day
Appointed when the wedding was to be,
They decked the palace out in full array,
The hall, the chambers, each in its degree:
The store-rooms, bulging with a quantity
Of delicate viands, held in plenteous strength
Italy's best from all its breadth and length.

he royal marquis in his richest dress
With lords and ladies in a company
Invited to the banquet, and no less
His household officers and soldiery,
Rode off with many a sound of minstrelsy
Towards the little thorpe I spoke about
And by the shortest road, in sumptuous rout.

ow could the innocent Griselda tell
That all this pomp was levelled at her head?
She had gone off for water to the well
And having drawn it, home she quickly sped,
For she had heard the marquis was to wed;
She knew it was the day and hoped she might
Be present as he passed, and see the sight.

he thought, 'I'll stand among the other girls,
My own companions, by our door and see
The marchioness, the marquis and his earls.
I'll hurry home as quickly as can be
And finish off the work that's there for me,
So that I can have leisure then to wait
And watch her riding to the castle gate.'

he reached the threshold with her water-pot
And as she did the marquis called her name.
She, putting down her vessel on the spot
Beside the cattle-stall, returned and came
Before him, falling on her knees, the same
Serious-looking girl; she knelt quite still
And waited quietly to hear his will.

*A medieval Italian 'cassone' or wedding chest. A bride would use
such a 'cassone' to take her belongings to her husband's house and
often the paintings on it were so fine that it would be dismantled so
that they could be hung on the walls. Griselda, of course, had no
dowry but Chaucer makes the marquis exact a promise of
uncomplaining constancy as the price of marriage.*

he thoughtful marquis, speaking with an air
  Of sober gravity, said thus to her:
  'Tell me, Griselda, is your father there?'
In all humility, without demur,
She answered, 'He is here and ready, sir.'
She rose at once and of her own accord
Fetched out her father to his overlord.

e took the poor old fellow by the hand,
  Leading him off to speak with him apart.
  'Janicula, I can no more withstand,
No, nor conceal, the pleasures of my heart.
If you consent, accepting from the start
Whatever follows, I will take to wife
Your daughter and will love her all my life.

ou love me as I know and would obey,
  Being my liege-man born and faithful too;
  Whatever pleases me I dare to say
  May well succeed in also pleasing you.
Yet in this point I specially pursue:
Tell me, I beg you, can my purpose draw
Consent to take me for your son-in-law?'

holly astounded at the news he heard
  The old man turned deep red and stood there
      quaking,
So troubled he could hardly say a word,
Except 'My lord, my will is in your making;
What you desire in any undertaking
Let me not hinder; I am bound to do,
My dear, dear master, what best pleases you.'

he marquis answered softly, 'None the less
  In your own cottage you and I and she
  Must have a conference. Why? You cannot
    guess?
I have to ask her if her will may be
To marry and submit herself to me.
This must be done while you are by to hear,
I will not speak unless I have you near.'

hile they were in the chamber and about
  The treaty, which you presently shall hear,
  The throng pressed round their dwelling-place
    without
And wondered at its decency and cheer,
How well she tended on her father dear.
But she, Griseld, might wonder even more,
For such a sight she'd never seen before.

or is it strange Griselda was astounded
  To see so great a guest in such a place,
  She was not used to being so surrounded
By noble visitors. How pale her face …
But let me keep my story up to pace;
These are the words in which her lord conveyed
His will to this benign, true-hearted maid:

riselda, I would have you understand
  As pleasing to your father and to me
  That I should marry you, and here's my hand
If, as I may conjecture, you agree.
But I would rather ask you first,' said he,
'Since all is done in such a hasty way,
Will you consent, or pause before you say?

warn you to be ready to obey
  My lightest whim and pleasure; you must show
  A willing heart, ungrudging night or day,
Whether I please to offer joy or woe.
When I say "Yes" you never shall say "No"
Either by word or frowning a defiance.
Swear this and I will swear to our alliance.'

n wonder at these words, quaking for dread,
  She answered, 'Lord, unworthy though I be
  Of so much honour, so unmerited,
If it seems good to you it is to me.
And here I promise never willingly
To disobey in deed or thought or breath
Though I should die, and yet I fear my death.'

hat is enough, Griselda mine!' said he.
  He left the chamber then with sober tread
  And reached the door; and after him came she.
And to the throng of people there he said:

*A fifteenth-century woodcut from an Italian version of the story
called the 'Novella de Gualtieri e Griselda'.*

'She stood transfigured in her gorgeous dress/Scarce recognizable for loveliness.' The dress of a court lady could literally cost a fortune and Griselda has to discard all her own humble clothing before she can be presented as a suitable bride. The court lady in this illumination is from the late fifteenth-century edition of the 'Roman de la Rose'.

'Here stands the wife it is my choice to wed.
Give her your reverence and love, I pray,
Whoever loves me. There's no more to say.'

And that she might not take the smallest bit
Of her old gear into his house, he bade
His women strip her there and I admit
Those ladies of the court were scarcely glad
To touch the rags in which the girl was clad.
Yet the bright beauty of her natural glow
Was clothed anew at last from top to toe.

They combed her hair that fell but rudely tressed
With slender hands as if preparatory
To coronation, and a crown was pressed
Upon her head with gems of changeful glory.
Why should I let her raiment stay my story?
She stood transfigured in her gorgeous dress
Scarce recognizable for loveliness.

The marquis then espoused her with a ring
Brought for the pupose; on a horse he set her,
It was a nobly-pacing snow-white thing.
And to the palace next with those that met her,
Leading the way with joyful heart he let her
Be brought in triumph, and the day had end
In revel till they saw the sun descend.

Shortly, to let my story quicken pace,
I say this young, new marchioness so stood
In favour with the Lord and Heaven's grace
It could not seem by any likelihood
That she was born and bred in servitude,

As in a cottage or an oxen-stall,
But rather nourished in an emperor's hall.

To all that looked on her she grew so dear,
So much to be revered, where she was born
Those who had watched her childhood year by year
Could hardly credit it, and dared have sworn
That she had never laboured in the corn
Nor was Janicula's child, for by her feature
Fancy would think she was some other creature.

Virtuous ever, as had long been known,
She had increased to such an excellence
Of grace she was as bounty on a throne,
Wise, and so lovely in her eloquence,
So grave and so benign, she charmed the sense
And gathered every heart in her embrace,
They loved her all that looked upon her face.

Nor only was Griselda thus renowned
Within Saluzzo, for her bounteous name
Was published forth in all the region round.
If one said well another said the same;
Indeed her goodness had so wide a fame,
Men, women too, the younger and the older,
Went to Saluzzo only to behold her.

And thus in humble, nay, in royal kind,
Walter espoused a love as fortunate
As it was fair. God's peace was in his mind
And he enjoyed the outward gifts of fate;
And in that he had seen in low estate
The hidden grace, men held him to have been
A prudent man, and that is seldom seen.

Nor was it only that by natural wit
She could accomplish all a woman should
In homely ways, for, were there call for it,
She also could advance the public good;
There was no rancour, no discordant mood
In all that country that she did not ease
Or use her grace and wisdom to appease.

She, in her husband's absence, did not cease
Her labours; if the nobles of the land
Fell into enmity she made their peace.
So wise and ripe the words at her command,
Her heart so equitable and her hand
So just, they thought that Heaven had sent her down
To right all wrongs and to protect the town.

And it was not long after, to her joy,
Griselda bore a daughter fine and fair,
And though she would have rather borne a boy,
Walter was glad and so his people were,
For though it was a girl, perchance an heir
Might yet be born to them and likely so,
Seeing she was not barren. Time would show.

PART III

IT happened, as it often does in life,
While yet the child was sucking at her breast
The marquis, in obsession for his wife,
Longed to expose her constancy to test.
He could not throw the thought away or rest,
Having a marvellous passion to assay her;
Needless, God knows, to frighten and dismay her,

He had assayed her faith enough before
And ever found her good; what was the need
Of heaping trial on her, more and more?
Though some may praise the subtlety, indeed
For my part I should say it could succeed
Only in evil; what could be the gain
In putting her to needless fear and pain?

But this was how he fed his prepossession;
He came alone one night to where she lay
With troubled features and a stern expression
And said, 'Griseld, do you recall the day
I came and took you from your poor array
And raised you to the height of nobleness?
You've not forgotten that, or so I guess.

I say, Griseld, this present dignity
To which I raised you cannot have, I know,
Made you forgetful of your debt to me
Who took you up from what was poor and low,
For all the little wealth that you could show.
Take heed of every word I say to you;
No one is here to hear it but us two.

You may remember your arrival here
Into this house, it's not so long ago;
And though I love you much and hold you dear,
My noblemen are far from doing so.
They say it is a scandal and a show
That they should serve you, lifted from the tillage
As you have been, born in a little village.

And now you've borne your daughter, all the
        more
No doubt they murmur phrases such as these.
But I desire, as I did before,
To live my life among them and in ease.
I cannot then ignore contingencies
And must dispose your daughter as is best,
Not as I wish to, but as they suggest.

But still God knows it's painful to me too;
Yet without your full knowledge and consent
I will do nothing, but it is for you
To acquiesce and show no discontent.
Summon your patience, show that they were meant,

Those promises you gave me to obey,
Down in your village on our wedding-day.'

Apparently unmoved as she received
What he had said, no change in her expression
Or tone of voice, Griselda unaggrieved
Replied, 'My child and I are your possession
And at your pleasure; on my heart's profession
We are all yours and you may spare or kill
What is your own. Do therefore as you will.

Nor is there anything, as God may save
My soul, that pleasing you displeases me,
Nor is there anything that I could crave
To have, or dread to lose, but you,' said she.
'This is my heart's will and shall ever be;
This may no length of time, no death deface;
My heart will never turn or change its place.'

If he were gladdened at her mild reply
There was no sign upon his face to show,
But gravely and with unrelenting eye
He gazed at her. At last he turned to go.
Soon after this, within a day or so,
He told a man in secret what he held
Was needful, and he sent him to Griseld.

He was a sort of secret agent, one
That had been ever faithful in pursuing
Important tasks. When wickedness is done
Such men are very useful in the doing.
He loved and feared his master, and reviewing
What was commanded of him, made his way
With silent stalk to where Griselda lay.

'Madam,' the fellow said, 'I must be pardoned
For doing that to which I am constrained;
You are too wise to let your heart be hardened,
You know a lord's command must be sustained
And not refused, although it be complained
Against and wept for. Servants must obey,
And so will I. There is no more to say.

It is commanded that I take this child.'
He said no more but grabbed the innocent
Despitefully, his countenance as wild
As if he would have slain it ere he went.
Griselda had to suffer and consent,
And like a lamb she lay there, meek and still,
And let the cruel fellow do his will.

He was a man of ominous ill-fame,
In voice and feature ominous, as are such,
And ominous the hour at which he came.

This painting of a scene from the 'Novella de Griselda' by Paisolino
was originally a panel of an Italian 'cassone'.

Alas, her daughter that she loved so much
Would, as she thought, be murdered at his touch.
Nevertheless she wept not nor lamented;
It was her husband's will and she consented.

She found her voice at last and she began
   Humbly imploring not to be denied
   This mercy, as he was a gentleman,
To let her kiss the child before it died;
She took it to her breast, with terrified
And stricken face, and lulled it in her loss;
She kissed it then and signed it with the cross,

Saying with love, 'Farewell, O sacrificed
   And blessed child that I shall never see;
   Look, I have marked thee with the cross of Christ.
He is thy Father, may He comfort thee,
Who died, for sake of us, upon a tree;
Thy little soul I offer in His sight
Since thou shalt die, for sake of me, tonight.'

And had there been a nurse with her, God knows
   She would have thought it pitiful to see;
   Well might a mother then have wept her woes.
Yet she was grave, and gazing steadfastly
As one who suffers all adversity
In meek submission, turned with sorrow-laden
Spirit and said, 'Take back your little maiden.

'Go now,' she said, 'and do as you are bidden.
   But one thing let me beg of you your grace;
   Bury the little body, be it hidden,
Unless my lord forbade it, in some place
That beasts and birds of prey can never trace.'
Yet not a word in answer would he say;
He took the little child and went his way,

Reporting to the marquis once again
   What she had said, how looked, if reconciled,
   As briefly point by point he made all plain
And having done he gave him up the child.
And though some touch of tenderness beguiled
His master, yet he held his purpose still
As lords will do that mean to have their will.

He bade the fellow secretly to take
   The child and wrap the softest winding round
   Her little form and carefully to make
A chest to bear it in; and then he bound
The man on pain of death that not a sound
Of his intention should be uttered, dumb
On whither he was going or whence come.

But to Bologna, to the marquis' sister,
   The Countess of Panaro, he must go,
   Taking the child, and he must there enlist her
To help him in this matter and bestow
All fostering care, so that the child might grow
In nobleness – and yet that none might trace
Or tell whose child she was, in any case.

The man went off and did as he was bidden.
   Now let us watch the marquis as he ranged
   In quick imagination for some hidden
Sign in his wife whether she were estranged;
Was there a chance word showing she had changed
Towards him? But he still could never find
Her anything but serious and kind,

As glad, as humble and as quick to serve,
   And in her love as she was wont to be;
   In everything the same, she did not swerve,
And of her daughter not a word said she.
There was no sign of that adversity
To see upon her; and her daughter's name
She never used, in earnest or in game.

PART IV

The birth of a prince and heir was an event of great political significance, as the marquis and his nobles all appreciate. 'The marquis being told, set greatest store/On it; not only he but the whole county,/and all gave thanks and honour to God's bounty.' This Flemish manuscript is a late-medieval representation of the birth of Alexander the Great, that perfect knightly prince.

FOUR years went by in this unaltered state
Before Griselda was with child once more,
And then she bore a boy as delicate
In grace and beauty as the child before.
The marquis, being told, set greatest store
On it; nor only he but he whole county,
And all gave thanks and honour to God's bounty.

When it was two years old, weaned from the breast
And taken from its nurse, there came a day
When Walter yet again was moved to test
The patience of his wife in the same way.
O needless, needless was the test, I say!
But married men too often use no measure
That have some patient creature at their pleasure.

Wife,' said the marquis, 'as I said at first,
My people take it ill that we were married.
Now that my son is born they think the worst;
Never were things so bad, for I am harried
By murmurings and rumours that are carried
About my ears; I feel a deadly smart
That has indeed almost destroyed my heart.

For now they say, "When Walter's reign is done
Old Janicle's descendants will succeed
And be our masters, either that or none."
Such is the common talk, it is indeed.
Murmurs like that a ruler has to heed,
And certainly I dread all such opinions,
Though secretly advanced, in my dominions.

I mean to live in quiet if I may,
And so am utterly disposed in mind
To serve the brother in the self-same way
As I have served his sister. I designed
To give this warning lest you were inclined
To do some outrage in your violent grief;
I beg you to be patient then, in brief.'

I long have said,' she answered, 'Oh, believe
me,
Nothing I will, nor yet would have unwilled,
But as it pleases you. It does not grieve me
At all, though son and daughter both be killed
At your commandment; let it be fulfilled.
In my two children I have had no part
But sickness first, then pain and grief of heart.

You are our sovereign, do with what is yours
Just as you please and do not bid me frame
Advice for you; for at my father's doors
I left my clothing. Was it not the same
To leave my will and freedom when I came?

The legends associated with King Arthur and his knights provided a rich source of inspiration for late medieval writers. This woodcut shows the birth of Tristram, who was to become ruler of the legendary kingdom of Lyonesse. The taking of Griselda's children in 'The Clerk's Tale' is one of the most sadistic tests her husband can devise, yet still she accepts it with complete submissiveness.

I took your clothing and I therefore pray
Your pleasure may be done. I will obey.

And surely had I had the prescience
To know your will before you told it me
I had performed it without negligence.
But knowing what your pleasure is to be,
I hold to it with firmest constancy.
For if I knew my death itself would ease you,
Then I would die, and gladly die, to please you.

For death can never make comparison
Beside your love.' And when the marquis saw
Her faithfulness he could not look upon
Her face and dropped his eyes in wondering awe,
Thinking, 'What patience to endure the law
Of my caprices!' and he left the room
Happy at heart, but set his face in gloom.

The ugly officer as brutally
As he had snatched her daughter, or with more
Brutality if more in man could be,
Seized on her son, so beautiful, and tore
Him from her arms; she, patient as before,
Gave him no sign of suffering in her loss
But kissed her son and signed him with the cross.

But yet she begged the fellow, if he might,
To close the little body in a grave.
His tender limbs so delicate to sight
She sought in her extremity to save
From birds and beasts, but not a sign he gave
And snatched the child with careless cruelty,
But bore it to Bologna tenderly.

The marquis wondered ever more and more
At so much patience in her misery;
Had he not known for certain long before
How perfectly she loved her children, he
Would have supposed some cunning devilry
Of malice, some heart's cruelty or base
Indifference beneath her constant face.

But well the marquis knew it was no mask,
For she had ever loved her children best,
Next to himself. Now, I would like to ask
Of women, had he made sufficient test?
Could stubborn husband fancy or suggest
More that would prove a steadfast wifeliness
To one continuing stubborn to excess?

But there are folk in such a state of mind
That, if they finally resolve to take
Some certain course to which they feel inclined,
Cannot hold back, but fettered to their stake,
Hold to their purposes and cannot slake
Their fevered wills. So too this marquis nursed
His purposes, to test her as at first.

And so he waited for a word or glance
To show her change of heart, but there was none,
No variation in her countenance
Could he discover; face and heart were one.
And as she aged the love in her begun
Continued even truer, made addition,
If that could be, in love and true submission.

Therefore there seemed to be between these two
One undivided will; if Walter pressed
For something, it became her joy to do;
And God be thanked all happened for the best.
And she gave proof that in whatever test
A wife, as of herself, in nothing should
Direct her will but as her husband would.

Walter's ill-fame began to mount and spread;
His cruel soul had led him to embark
For having wed a pauper, people said,
On murdering both his children in the dark.
Such was the common murmur and remark.
No wonder; common rumours all concurred:
He'd murdered them. There came no other word.

And so the love his people felt of yore
Turned into hatred; scandal and ill-fame
Are things a man may well be hated for;
To be called a murderer is a hateful name.
Yet he, in game or earnest, with the same
Cruel device drove on to what he sought;
To test her further was his only thought.

Now when his daughter was some twelve years old
He sent to Rome, long cunningly apprised
Of his intentinos, and the court was told
That such a papal bull should be devised,
That his fell purpose might be realized,
And that the Pope, to set all minds at rest,
Should bid him wed again, as he thought best.

I say he ordered them to counterfeit
A papal bull declaring approbation
Of a divorce, for Walter then could meet
Objection with a papal dispensation
And calm the rancour and the indignation
Between his people and him. They framed the bull
And published the whole forgery in full.

The common people, and no wonder, held,
Or else supposed, that things were even so.
But when these tidings came to poor Griseld
I deem her heart was weighted down with woe.
But she, and now no less than long ago,
Was ready, humble creature, faithfully
To meet misfortune and adversity.

And still she waited on his will and pleasure
To whom she had been given, heart and soul,
As to her one unfailing worldly treasure.
Yet to be brief about it and control
My tale, the marquis now to reach his goal
Devised a letter that declared his aim,
And to Bologna secretly it came.

It was for Lord Panaro, for the earl
Who had espoused his sister, and requested
That he would send him home his boy and girl
In public state and openly invested
With every honour, but it still protested
That upon no account should he declare,
Even if questioned, whose the children were,

But say the maid was shortly to espouse
The Marquis of Saluzzo; and thereto
The earl agreed. As day began to rouse
He started on the journey and he drew
Towards Saluzzo with a retinue
Of many lords in rich array, to guide
This maiden and the brother at her side.

All in her wedding-dress and fresh as heaven,
She rode in pearl and gold without alloy.
Her brother too, a little lad of seven,
Looked freshly, in the tunic of a boy;
So with great splendour, every face in joy,
They shaped their journey, riding all the way;
And thus they neared Saluzzo day by day.

PART V

MEANWHILE, according to his cruel bent,
The Marquis sought to test his wife yet more.
And by the uttermost experiment
To prove her spirit to the very core,
Whether she still were steadfast as before;
And so in open audience one day
And in a blustering voice he chose to say:

It was agreeable enough, forsooth,
To marry you, Griselda, in the flower
Of your obedient love and simple truth,
And not for lineage or for worldly dower;
But now I know in very truth that power,
If one reflects, is nothing much to praise;
It is a servitude in many ways.

I may not do as any ploughman may;
My subjects are constraining me to take
Another wife, they clamour day by day.
Even the Pope has thought it fit to slake
Their rancour by consenting, you need make
No doubt of that; indeed I have to say
My second wife is now upon her way.

Strengthen your heart to give her up your place.
As for the dowry that you brought of old,
Take it again, I grant it as a grace;
Go home, rejoin your father in his fold.
No one can count upon his luck to hold,
And I enjoin you to endure the smart
Of fortune's buffets with an even heart.'

She answered patiently without pretence:
'My lord, I know as I have always done
That, set against your high magnificence,

My poverty makes no comparison.
It cannot be denied, and I for one
Was never worthy, never in my life,
To be your chambermaid, much less your wife.

And in this house whose lady you have made me,
As God's my witness whom I love and fear,
And as His power may gladden me and aid me,
I never thought myself the mistress here,
Rather a servant, humble and sincere,
To your high honour; so I shall think for ever
Of you, above all creatures whatsoever.

That you so long of your benignity
Have held me high in honour and display,
Whereas I was not worthy so to be,
I thank my God and you; and now I pray
Revoke it, for there is no more to say.
Gladly I seek my father and will live
My life with him, whatever life may give.

For I was fostered there when I was small,
Only a child, and there I'll live and die
A widow clean in body, heart and all;
I gave my maidenhead to you, and I
Am still your faithful wife, I do not lie.
And God forbid a wife to one so great
Should take another man to be her mate.

Touching your second wife, may God in grace
Grant you both joy and long prosperity,
For I will gladly yield her up my place
That once was such a happiness to me.
But since it pleases you, my lord,' said she,

'In whom was formerly my whole heart's rest,
Then I will go when you shall think it best.

But as you proffer me what first I brought,
Such dowry as I had, it's in my mind
It was my wretched clothing and worth nought,
And would indeed be hard for me to find.
O blessed God, how noble and how kind
You seemed in speech, in countenance, in carriage,
That day, the day on which we made our marriage!

It's truly said, at least I find it true
For the effect of it is proved in me,
"A love grown old is not the love once new."
And yet whatever the adversity,
Though it were death, my lord, it cannot be
That ever I should repent, though I depart,
For having wholly given you my heart.

My lord, you know that in my father's place
You stripped me of my rags and in their stead
Gave me rich garments, as an act of grace.
I brought you nothing else it may be said
But faith and nakedness and maidenhead.
Here I return your garments and restore
My wedding-ring as well, for evermore.

And the remainder of the gems you lent
Are in your chamber I can safely say.
Naked out of my father's house I went
And naked I return again today;
Gladly I'll do your pleasure, if I may.
But yet I hope you will not make a mock
Of me or send me forth without a smock.

So infamous a thing you could not do
As let the womb in which your children lay
Be seen in nakedness, bare to the view

Hunger is represented by a meek, thin woman in a shabby brown dress in this early fifteenth-century French illumination. In medieval iconography personifications of abstracts relating to suffering were invariably female. Griselda can be seen as an emblem of the soul patiently undergoing the purifying ordeals of worldly tribulation.

Of all your people, let me not I pray
Go naked as a worm upon the way.
Bethink yourself, my own dear lord, because
I was your wife, unworthy though I was.

Therefore in guerdon of my maidenhead
Which, hither brought, returns with me no more.
Vouchsafe a payment, give to me instead
Just such a simple smock as once I wore
To hide the womb of one that heretofore
Has been your wife; and here at last I leave you
And bid farewell, dear lord, lest I should grieve you.'

Poverty is similarly always represented as a woman with bare feet. Bare feet, or at most rough sandals, were a symbol of humility for religious orders like the Franciscans. In Griselda's case, her humble background and lack of wealth do not prevent her from speaking with unaffected courtesy and behaving with womanly grace. Her virtuous behaviour springs from her own nature, not her social rank.

The smock,' he said, 'you have upon your back
You may retain; remove it to your stall.'
Yet as he spoke his voice began to crack
For pity, and he turned and left the hall.
She stripped her garments in the sight of all
And in her smock, head bare and feet unshod,
Home to her father and his house she trod.

Folk followed weeping when she passed them by,
They railed on fate for all that had occurred.
Her eyes withheld their weeping and were dry
And at this time she did not speak a word.
The news soon reached her father; when he heard
He cursed the day and hour of his birth
That fashioned him a man to live on earth.

He, never doubt it, though so old and poor,
Had ever been suspicious of the match,
Had always thought it never could endure,

In that the marquis, having had the snatch
Of his desires, would feel disgrace attach
To his estate in such a low alliance
And when he could would set it at defiance.

At her approach he hastened forth to meet her
Led by the sound of many a beholder
That wept to see her pass, and he to greet her
Brought her old cloak and cast it on her shoulder
And wept. It fitted not, for it was older
By many a day than was her wedding-dress;
The cloth was coarsely woven, comfortless.

Thus with her father for a certain space
This flower of love and wifely patience stayed.
Never a word or look upon her face
In front of others, or alone, conveyed
A hint that she had suffered, or betrayed
Any remembrance of her former glory;
Her countenance told nothing of her story.

And that's no wonder; in her high estate
Her spirit had a full humility,
No tender mouth for food, no delicate
Heart's hungering after royal brilliancy
Or show of pomp; benignly, patiently,
She had lived wise in honour, void of pride,
Meek and unchanging at her husband's side.

They speak of Job and his humility,
For clerics when they wish to can endite
Its praises nobly, and especially,

The biblical character of Job is synonymous with patience and restraint in the face of appalling suffering. Here he is being told of the destruction of his flocks, in a French manuscript 'Bible Historiale' dating from the early fourteenth century. Like Job, Griselda endures any test her husband can devise with unruffled patience and complete submission.

In men – they praise few women when they write;
Yet none can reach a humbleness as white
As women can, nor can be half so true
As women are, or else it's something new.

PART VI

NOW from Bologna he of whom I spoke,
The earl, arrived. The greater and the less
Got wind of it and all the common folk
Buzzed with the news a second marchioness
Was being brought in all the loftiness
Of pomp and splendour. Such a sight to see
Had never been known in all west Lombardy.

The marquis, who had planned and knew it all,
Before the earl had fully reached his place,
Sent down for poor Griselda in her stall;
And she with humble heart and happy face
Came at his bidding, all without a trace
Of swelling thought, and went upon her knees
And greeted him with reverence and at ease.

'Griseld,' said he, 'my will is firmly set.
This maiden hither brought to be my bride
Tomorrow shall as royally be met
As possible, with all I can provide
That's in my house. My servants, side by side
According to their rank, shall wait upon her
As may be best arranged in joy and honour.

'I have no woman of sufficient skill
To decorate the chambers as I hold
They should be decorated. If you will,
I should be glad to see it all controlled
By you who know me and my tastes of old.
And though your dress is not a thing of beauty,
I hope at least that you will do your duty.'

'Not only, lord, would I be glad,' said she,
'To do your will; I long and shall endeavour
To serve and please you in my own degree
And not to faint in service, now or ever.
For neither grief or happiness can sever
My love from me. My heart can never rest
Save in the ceaseless will to love you best.'

And she began upon the decorations;
There were the boards to set, the beds to make.
All she could do in many occupations
She did, and begged the maids for goodness' sake
To hurry and to sweep and dusk and shake,
While she, most serviceable of them all,
Went garnishing the chambers and the hall.

The earl arrived, beginning to alight
With the two children early in the day,
And all the people ran to see the sight
Of so much opulence and rich array.
And soon among them there were those to say
That Walter was no fool, and though obsessed
To change his wife, it might be for the best.

*The final test of Griselda's loyalty is being made to greet her
successor when she arrives in 'pomp and splendour'. Her courtesy
and lack of malice at last convince her husband of her steadfastness.*

'For she is lovelier,' they all agreed,
'And younger than Griselda. Put the case
That fruit will fall to them; a fairer breed
Will issue from such lineage and grace.'
Her brother had so beautiful a face
It caught them with delight, opinion changed.
They now applauded what had been arranged.

'O stormy people, frivolous and fickle,
Void of true judgement, turning like a vane,
Whom every novelty and rumour tickle,
How like the moon you are to wax and wane,
Clapping your praises, shouting your disdain,

False judges, dear at a penny as a rule,
Who trusts to your opinion is a fool.'

So said the serious people of the city
Who watched the throng go gazing up and down
Glad merely for the novelty, the pretty
New lady that had come to grace the town.
But let me leave the pleasure-seeking clown
And turn to my Griselda, in the press
Of all her labours, in her steadfastness.

Busy in all, she worked, disposed and settled,
Laboured and strove to cater and adorn,
Nor did she seem at all abashed or nettled
Although her clothes were coarse and somewhat torn,
But with a face as cheerful as the morn
Went to the gate with all her retinue
To greet the marchioness, and then withdrew.

She met the guests so cheerfully and greeted them
With so much skill according to their rank
That none could find a fault in how she treated them
And all were wondering whom they had to thank,
For how could such a pauper, to be frank,
Know all the rules of honour and degree?
They praised her prudence as a rarity.

And in the meanwhile ceaselessly she still
Praised the young bride and praised her brother too
With so much heart, with such benign goodwill
That no one could have given them better due.
And in the end when all the retinue
Sat down to meat, Walter began to call
Griselda who was busy in his hall.

'Griseld,' he said to her as if in jest,
'How do you like the beauty of my wife?'
'Indeed, my lord,' she said, 'I must protest
I never saw a lovelier in my life.
God give her joy and may there be no strife
Between you, and I pray that He may send
Your fill of happiness to your lives' end!

'One thing I beg of you, and warn you too,
Never to goad her, never put on trial
This tender girl as I have known you do;
For she was fostered preciously, a vial
More delicate. I think the self-denial
Adversity might force on her would be
Harder for her to suffer than for me.'

When Walter saw this patience in Griseld,
Her happy face, no malice there at all,
And thought of his offences long upheld
To test her, ever constant as a wall,
Grave, innocent and ever at his call,
The stubborn marquis could no more repress
His pity for such a wifely steadfastness.

In secret; take them back and never say
Your children have been lost or snatched away.

'Let those that otherwise have talked of me
Know that I did this, be it bad or good,
Neither in malice nor in cruelty
But for the trial of your womanhood.
What! Slay my children? God forbid I should!
Rather I kept them privately apart
Till I had proved the purpose of your heart.'

On hearing this Griselda fell aswoon
In piteous joy, but made recovery
And called her children to her and they soon
Were folded in her arms. How tenderly
She kissed them as the salt tears falling free
Bathed them and glistened on their face and hair;
How like a mother stood Griselda there!

And Oh how pitiful it was to see
Her fainting and to hear her humble tone!
'All thanks to you, my dearest lord,' said she,
'For you have saved my children, you alone!
Were I to die this moment I have known
Your love and have found favour in your sight,
And death were nothing, though I died tonight.

'O dear, O tender ones, so long away,
Your sorrowing mother steadfastly had thought
That some foul vermin, hound or beast of prey
Had eaten you. But God in mercy brought
You back to me and your kind father sought
In tender love to keep you safe and sound.'
She suddenly swooned again and fell to ground.

Though she had fainted, sadly, clingingly
She held her children in that first embrace,
And it was difficult for skill to free
Them from her arms, and touching to unlace.
O many a tear on many a pitying face
Ran down among those standing at her side,
Scarce able in her presence to abide.

Walter caressed her, loosed her from her grief,
And up she rose bewildered from her trance,
While all the rest in joy at her relief
Made much of her and cleared her countenance;
And Walter showed such loving vigilance
It was a dainty thing to see the air
Of new-found happiness between the pair.

The ladies round her, when the moment came,
Led her towards her chamber; there the old
Poor rags she wore, though never worn in shame,
They stripped and set on her a gown of gold;
A coronet of jewels manifold
They crowned her with and led her into hall
There to receive the homage of them all.

*Both 'The Clerk's Tale' and 'The Merchant's Tale' which follows
are set in northern Italy. The background to 'The Clerk's Tale' is
appropriately bleak and austere, conveying the atmosphere of a time
earlier than Chaucer's own.*

'It is enough,' he said, 'Griselda mine!
Have no more fears, let not your heart be sore.
Your faith and gentleness as far outshine
All other faith as you were tested more,
In wealth and want, than any wife before.
Dear wife, I know your steadfastness by this.'
He took her up into his arms to kiss.

She, lost in wonder, did not seem to grasp
Or even hear the words he uttered thus,
But as a sleeper breaking from the clasp
Of an amazement, woke incredulous.
'Griseld,' said he, 'by Him that died for us
You are my wife and I have none but you,
Nor ever had as God may judge me true!

'This is your daughter whom you so commended
As wife for me; the other on my oath
Shall be my heir as I have long intended,
They are the children of your body, both.
Bologna nourished them and fed their growth

Thus to a piteous day a blissful close,
And every man and woman, as they might,
Gave themselves up to revelry; there rose
The stars and all the welkin shone with light.
Greater the glad solemnities that night,
Greater the joy in feasting and defray
In treasure than upon their wedding-day.

For many a year in high prosperity
These two lived on in concord to the close;
Their daughter too they married worthily
And richly to a lord, best among those
In Italy. They also found repose
For old Janicula whom Walter kept
Safe at his court till soul from body crept.

Their son succeeded to the inheritance
After his father's day in peace and rest;
He married happily but did not chance
To put his wife to such a searching test.
This world of ours, it has to be confessed,
Is not so sturdy as it was of old.
Hear how my author ends the tale he told:

This story does not mean it would be good
For wives to ape Griseld's humility,
It would be unendurable they should.
But everybody in his own degree
Should be as perfect in his constancy
As was Griselda.' That is why Petrarch chose
To tell her story in his noble prose.

For since a woman showed such patience to
A mortal man, how much the more we ought
To take in patience all that God may do!
Reason He has to test what He has wrought,
Yet never tempts the souls that He has bought
Above what they are able, and St James
Tells us He tests us daily, and reclaims.

He will permit, to exercise our virtue,
The sharper scourges of adversity
To lash us often, not that they may hurt you,
Nor yet to test the will, for certainly
No one can know our frailty more than He
Who knew it ere our birth, and all is best;
Then let our virtues learn to suffer test.

But one word more, my lords, before I go.
It isn't very easy nowadays
To find Griseldas round the town, you know.
And if you try imposing these assays,
What gold they have is mixed with such allays
Of brass, that though the coin looks right perhaps,
When you begin to bend the thing, it snaps.

So, from affection for the Wife of Bath,
Whose life and all her sect may God maintain
In high authority upon their path
– And pity else – I sing you this refrain
With lusty heart, to gladden you again,
Dropping the note of earnest emphasis,
So listen to my song, it goes like this:

Chaucer's envoy to the Clerk's Tale

GRISELDA and her patience both are dead
And buried in some far Italian vale.
So let it then in open court be said,
Husbands, be not so hardy as to assail
The patience of your wives in hope to find
Griseldas, for you certainly will fail.

O noble wives, in highest prudence bred,
Allow no such humility to nail
Your tongues, nor give a scholar cause to shed
Such light on you as this astounding tale
Sheds of Griselda, patient still, and kind,
Lest Chichevache engulf you like a whale.

Imitate Echo, she that never fled
In silence, but returns you hail for hail,
Never let innocence besot your head,
But take the helm yourselves and trim the sail.
And print this lesson firmly in your mind
For common profit; it can never stale.

Arch-wives, stand up, defend your board and bed!
Stronger than camels as you are, prevail!
Don't swallow insults, offer them instead.
And all you slender little wives and frail,
Be fierce as Indian tigers, since designed
To rattle like a windmill in a gale.

Never revere them, never be in dread,
For though your husband wears a coat of mail
Your shafts of crabbed eloquence will thread
His armour through and drub him like a flail.
Voice your suspicions of him! Guilt will bind
Him down, he'll couch as quiet as a quail.

If you are beautiful, advance your tread,
Show yourself off to people, blaze the trail!
If you are ugly, spend and make a spread,
Get friends, they'll do the business of a male;
Dance like a linden-leaf if so inclined,
Leave him to weep and wring his hands and wail!

Mayus habet dies xxxi.
Luna xxx.

xi	b		Philippi et iacobi aploȝum
	c	Ñ	Athanasÿ epi et conf.
xix	d	Ñ	Inuentio sancte crucis.
viii	e	Ñ	festum corone dͦ.
	f	Ñ	Gotardi epi et conf.
xvi	a	Ñ	Johis ante portam latinã.
v		Ñ	Cleti pape et martiris.
	b	Id	
xiii	c	Id	Translatio sci nicholay.
ii	d	Id	Gordiani et epimachi mȝ.

THE MERCHANT'S TALE

The Merchant's Prologue

'WEEPING and wailing, care and other sorrow,
I know them well enough by eve and morrow,'
The Merchant said; 'like others I suppose
That have been married, that's the way it
goes;
I know too well that's how it goes with me.
I have a wife, the worst that there could be;
For if a fiend were coupled to my wife,
She'd overmatch him, you can bet your life.
Why choose a special instance to recall
Her soaring malice? She's a shrew in all.
There's a wide difference I'm bound to say
Between Griselda's patience and the way
My wife behaves; her studied cruelty
Surpasses everything. If I were free,
Never again, never again the snare!
We married men, our life is grief and care.

Try it who will, and he will find, I promise
That I have spoken truly, by St Thomas,
For most of us – I do not say for all,
And God forbid that such a thing befall.
Ah, my good Host, I have been wedded now
These two months past, no more than that,
I vow,
Yet I believe no bachelor alive,
Not if you were to take a knife and rive
Him to the heart, could tell of so much grief
As I could tell you of; beyond belief,
The curst malignity I get from her!'
Our Host replied, 'God bless you, my dear sir!
But since you know so much about the art
Of marriage, let me beg you to impart.'
With pleasure,' he said, 'but on the personal score
I'm so heart-scalded I shall say no more.'

The Merchant's Tale

THERE was a knight one time of good renown
In Lombardy, Pavia was the town.
He'd lived there very prosperously for more
Than sixty years and was a bachelor,
Though always taking bodily delight
On women, such as pleased his appetite,
As do these foolish worldlings, never fear.
Now when this knight had passed his sixtieth year
– Whether for holiness, or from a surge
Of dotage, who can say? – he felt an urge

So violent to be a wedded man
That day and night his eager fancies ran
On where and how to spy himself a bride,
Praying the Lord he might not be denied
Once to have knowledge of that blissful life
There is between a husband and his wife,
And live within the holy bond and tether
In which God first bound woman and man together.
'No other life,' he said, 'is worth a bean;
For wedlock is so easy and so clean
It is a very paradise on earth.'
Thus said this ageing knight, so full of worth.
And certainly, as sure as God is King,
To take a wife is a most glorious thing,
Especially if a man is old and hoary;

Left: The month of May, from the Playfair Hours. The in-appropriate union of an elderly merchant called January and a young girl, May, is the theme of 'The Merchant's Tale' which treats the subject of marriage with cynical realism.

Then she's the fruit of all his wealth and glory.
It's then he ought to take her, young and fair,
One upon whom he might beget an heir,
And lead a life of rapture and content,
Whereas these bachelors can but lament
And suffer, when in some adversity
From love, which is but childish vanity.
And it's no more than right it should be so
If bachelors are beset by grief and woe:
On brittle ground they build, so all is ready
For brittle love, though they expect a steady.
Their liberty is that of bird or beast,
They've no restraint, no discipline at least,
Whereas a married man achieves a state
Of bliss that's orderly and fortunate.
Under the yoke of matrimony bowed,
The heart, in bliss abounding, sings aloud.
For who is so obedient as a wife?
Who is so true, so careful for his life
Whether in health or sickness, as his mate?
For weal or woe she tends upon his state,
In service, and in love, she never tires,
Though he lie bedridden till he expires.

And yet some writers say this isn't so;
One such was Theophrastus long ago.
Who cares if Theophrastus was a liar?
'Don't take a wife,' he said, 'from a desire
To make economies and spare expense.
A faithful servant shows more diligence
In guarding your possessions than a wife
For she claims half you have throughout her life;
And if you're sick, as God may give me joy,
Your very friends, an honest serving-boy,
Do more than she, who's watching for a way
To corner your possessions night and day.
And if you take a wife into your bed
You're very likely to be cuckolded.'

Opinions such as these and hundreds worse
This fellow wrote, God lay him under curse!
But take no heed of all such vanity,
Defy foul Theophrastus and hear me.

A wife is verily the gift of God.
All other kinds of gift, the fruitful sod
Of land, fair pastures, movables in store,
Rents – they're the gifts of Fortune, nothing more,
That pass as does a shadow on a wall.

Still, if I must speak plainly, after all
A wife does last some time, and time may lapse
A good deal slower than one likes, perhaps.

Marriage is a momentous sacrament,
Bachelordom contemptible, and spent
In helpless desolation and remorse
– I'm speaking of the laity, of course.
I don't say this for nothing; listen why.
Woman was made to be a man's ally.
When God created Adam, flesh and bone,
And saw him belly-naked and alone,
He of His endless goodness thus began:

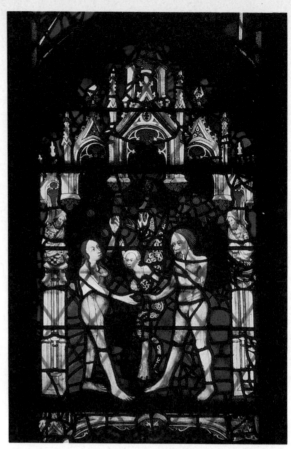

Eve tempts Adam in the Garden of Eden, in this stained glass window at York Minster. When January first thinks about marriage, he recalled Eve as Adam's companion in 'earthly paradise'. He forgets her subsequent betrayal. . . .

'Let us now make a help-meet for this man
Like to himself.' And He created Eve.
Here lies the proof of what we all believe,
That woman is man's helper, his resort,
His earthly paradise and his disport.
So pliant and so virtuous is she
They cannot but abide in unity.
One flesh they are; one flesh as I suppose
Has but a single heart in joys and woes.

A wife! Saint Mary, what a benediction!
How can a man be subject to affliction
Who has a wife? Indeed I cannot say.
There is a bliss between them such as may
No tongue tell forth, such as no heart can judge.
If he be poor she helps her man to drudge,
Sets guard upon his goods and checks the waste;
All that her husband likes is to her taste,
She never once says 'no' when he says 'yes.'
'Do this,' says he; 'already done,' she says.
O blissful state of wedlock, no way vicious
But virtuous and merry, nay, delicious,

And so commended and approved withal
That any man who's worth a leek should fall
On his bare knees, to thank God, all his life,
For having ordained and given him a wife,
Or else to pray that he vouchsafe to send
A wife to last him to the very end.
Then he can count upon security
And not be tricked, as far as I can see,
Provided that he works by her advice:
Jacob, the learned tell us, was precise
In following the good counsel of his mother,
And won his father's blessing from his brother,
By binding round his neck a pelt of kid.
Or Judith, one can read of what she did:
Her wisdom held God's people in its keeping
By slaying Holofernes, who was sleeping.
Take Abigail, what good advice she gave!
It saved her husband Nabal from the grave.
Take Esther too, whose wisdom brought relief
To all God's people, saved them from their grief
And made Ahasuerus grant promotion
To Mordecai for his true devotion.
There's no superlative that ranks in life,
Says Seneca, above a humble wife.
'The tongue of wife,' so Cato was to say,
'Commands the husband: suffer and obey.'
And yet she will obey by courtesy.
A wife is guardian of your husbandry;

This illumination of Judith celebrating the death of Holofernes comes from the Bible of Richard II. Chaucer skilfully uses Old Testament references to create a picture of the wiles and destructiveness of women – even when they appear virtuous. Judith saved the Israelites, but only through her murderous cunning.

Well may a man in sickness wail and weep
Who has no wife to nurse him and to keep
His house for him; do wisely then and search
For one and love her as Christ loves His Church.
For if you love yourself you love your wife,
For no one hates his flesh, nay all his life
He fosters it, and so I bid you wive
And cherish her, or you will never thrive.
Husband and wife, whatever the worldly say
In ribald jest, are on the straight, sure way.
They are so knit no accident or strife
Harms them, particularly not the wife.
So January thought, of whom I told,
Deeply considering as he grew old
The life of lusty joy and virtuous quiet
That marriage offers in its honey-diet.
And so one day he sent for all his friends
To ask their views on what he now intends.
With serious face he spoke, and solemn tongue.
'My friends,' he said, 'I am no longer young;
God knows, I'm near the pit, I'm on the brink:
I have a soul, of which I ought to think.
My body I have foolishly expended;
Blessed be God, that still can be amended.
I have resolved to be a wedded man,
And that at once, in all the haste I can,
To some fair virgin; one of tender years.
Prepare yourselves to help as overseers
Against my wedding, for I will not wait.
I for my own part will investigate
And find a hasty match, if there be any:
But in as much as you, my friends, are many,
You may discern more readily than I
Where it would most befit me to ally.
But, my dear friends, you may as well be told
The woman must on no account be old,
Certainly under twenty, and demure.
Flesh should be young though fish should be mature;
As pike, not pickerel, makes the tastier meal,
Old beef is not so good as tender veal.
I'll have no woman thirty years of age;
That's only fodder, bean-straw for a cage.
Old women are as tricky in their trade
Of making trouble as the Boat of Wade
And when they choose, they can be such a pest –
It's clear I'd never have a moment's rest.
Subtle is the scholar taught in several schools;
And women taught in many are no fools,
Half-scholars one might say; but when they're young
A man can still control them with his tongue
And guide them, should their duty seem too lax
Just as a man may model in warm wax.
So let me sum the matter in a clause;
I will have no old woman, for this cause.
For were I so unlucky as to marry
Where I could take no pleasure, I'd miscarry,
I should commit adultery and slide
Straight downwards to the devil when I died.

I could beget no child on her to greet me,
Yet I had rather that the dogs should eat me
Than that my fine inheritance should fall
Into strange hands, that let me tell you all.
I'm not a fool, I know the reason why
One ought to wed, though I could specify
Many who prate of it, but I engage
They know about as little as my page
Touching the reasons why to take a wife.
A man unable to be chaste in life
Should take a wife in holy dedication
And for the sake of lawful procreation
Of children, to the honour of God above,
Not as a paramour, or lady-love,
But to curb lechery, which he should eschew,
Paying his debt whenever it falls due,
Or each a willing helper to the other
In trouble, like a sister to a brother
And live a life of holy chastity;
But, by your leave, sirs, that would not suit me,
For, God be thanked, I dare to make the claim,
I feel my limbs sufficient, strong and game
For all that is belonging to a man,
And am my own best judge in what I can.
I may seem hoary, but I'm like a tree
That blossoms white before the fruit can be;
Blossoming trees are neither dry nor dead
And I am only hoary on my head.
My heart and all my members are as green
As laurel is; all the year round, I mean.
And now you are informed of my intention
I beg you to agree without dissension.'
Various men gave various examples
Of classic marriages, convincing samples;
Some praised it certainly, some reprehended,
But at the last (to get the matter ended),
As altercation happens every day
Among good friends who mean to say their say,
An argument was presently begun
Between two friends of his, Placebo one,
Justinus, as I recollect, the other.
Placebo said, 'O January, dear brother,
You have no need, sweet lord, it must appear,
To take advice from anybody here,
Save that your sapience, after meditation,
Would prudently resist the inclination
To set aside the word of Solomon,
For this is what he said for everyone:
"Do all things by advice," his saying went,
"And then you'll have no reason to repent."
Though that may be what Solomon commends,
Dear lord, my brother, nay, my best of friends,
As surely as the Lord may give me rest
I think your own opinion is the best.
Take it from me – if I can find the phrase –
You know I've been a courtier all my days,
God knows unworthily, I make admission,
Yet I have stood in quite a high position

An Italian woodcut from 'The Wedding of the Merchant's Daughter'. January is a Lombard merchant and 'The Merchant's Tale' is set in the northern Italian setting that Chaucer knew from his diplomatic missions.

And among lords of very great estate;
But I have never joined in a debate
With them, or offered contradiction. Why?
Well, obviously, my lord knows more than I,
And what he says I hold as firm and stable;
I echo it as far as I am able.
No counsellor is such a fool as he
That, serving on a lord of high degree,
Dares to presume or even thinks it fit
To be superior to him in wit.
Lords are no fools, believe me … May I say
That you have also shown yourself today
A man of lofty views, an eloquent,
A holy-minded man, and I consent
To all you said. It should be written down.
A speech like that – there isn't one in town,
No, nor all Italy, able to supply it!
Christ holds himself more than rewarded by it.
In anyone at all advanced in age
It shows a lively spirit to engage
In taking a young wife. Ah, Lord of grace!
You've pinned your heart up in a jolly place;
Follow your inclination; I protest
Whatever you decide on will be best.'
Justinus who sat silent, having heard
Placebo speaking, then took up the word.
'Brother,' he said, 'be patient with me, pray;
You spoke your mind, now hear what I would say;
Seneca gave a lot of sound advice;
He says it's always better to think twice
Before you give away estate or pelf.
And therefore if you should advise yourself
In giving property away or land,
If it's important you should understand
Who is to get your goods, how much the more
You ought to think things over well before
You give away your body. If I may

I'd like to warn you; it is no child's play
Choosing a wife. It needs consideration,
In fact it asks a long investigation.
Is she discreet and sober? Or a drinker?
Or arrogant? Or, in other ways, a stinker?
A scolder? Or extravagant? Too clannish?
Too poor? Too rich? Unnaturally mannish?
Although we know there isn't to be found
In all the world one that will trot quite sound,
Whether it's man or beast, the way we'd like it,
It were sufficient bargain, could we strike it,
In any woman, were one sure she had
More good among her qualities than bad.
But all this asks some leisure to review;
God knows that many is the tear I too
Have wept in secret since I had a wife.
Praise whoso will the married state of life
I find it a routine, a synthesis
Of cost and care, and wholly bare of bliss.
And yet the neighbours round about, by God,
Especially the women – in a squad –
Congratulate me that I chose to wive
The constantest, the meekest soul alive.
I know where the shoe pinches; but for you,
Why, you must please yourself in what you do.
You're old enough – that's not what I disparage –
To think before you enter into marriage,
Especially if your wife is young and fair.
By Him that made earth, water, fire and air,
The youngest man in this distinguished rout
Will have a busy task – you need not doubt –
To keep a woman to himself. Trust me,
You will not please her more than for, say, three
Years – that is, please her to the point of fervence.
Wives ask a lot in matters of observance.
I beg you not to take it the wrong way.'
Well,' said old January, 'have you said your say?
Straw for your Seneca and proverbial tags;
Not worth a basketful of weeds and rags,
Your pedant-jargon! Wiser men than you,
As you have heard, take quite another view
Of my proposal. What would you reply,
Placebo?' 'An accursed man, say I,
It is that offers an impediment,'
Said he, and so, by general consent,
His friends then rose, declaring it was good
That he should marry when and where he would.
Busy imaginations, strange invention
And soaring fantasy obsessed the attention
Of January's soul, about his wedding.
Came many a lovely form and feature shedding
A rapture through his fancies night by night.
As who should take a mirror polished bright
And set it in the common market-place,
And watch the many figures pause and pace
Across his mirror; in the self-same way,
Old January allowed his choice to play
Mirroring all the girls that lived nearby,

Still undetermined where his thought should lie.
For were there one with beauty in her face
There was another standing high in grace
With people, for her grave benignity,
Whose voices gave her the supremacy.
Others were rich, but had a tarnished name.
At last, and half in earnest, half in game,
He fixed on one, and setting her apart,
He banished all the others from his heart.
He chose her on his own authority,
For love is always blind and cannot see,
And when he lay in bed at night his thought
Pictured her in his heart, for he was caught
By her fresh beauty and her age so tender;
Her little waist, her arms so long and slender,
Her wise self-discipline, her gentle ways,
Her womanly bearing and her serious gaze.
His thought, descending on her thus, was fettered,
It seemed to him choice could not be bettered.
Once he was satisfied in this decision,
He held all other judgement in derision:
It was impossible to disagree
With him in taste, such was his fantasy.
He sent his friends a very strong request
Begging the pleasure – would they do their best? –
Of an immediate visit. In his belief
They needn't be kept long; he would be brief,
For there was no more need to cast around;
His mind made up, he would not shift his ground.
Placebo came and so did all the rest,
And January began with the request
That none should offer any argument
Against the purpose 'which was his intent,
Pleasing to God Almighty, and,' said he,
'The very ground of his prosperity.'
He said there was a maiden in the town
Whose beauty was indeed of great renown;
Her rank was not so great, to tell the truth,
But still she had her beauty and her youth;
She was the girl he wanted for his wife,
To lead a life of ease, a holy life.
And he would have her all – thank God for this! –
There would be shares for no one in his bliss.
He begged them then to labour in his need
And help to make his enterprise succeed,
For then, he said, his mind would be at rest
'With nothing to annoy me or molest,
But for one thing which pricks my conscience still,
So listen to me kindly if you will.
I've often,' he continued, 'heard ere this
That none may have two perfect kinds of bliss,
Bliss in this world, I mean, and bliss in Heaven;
Though he keep clear of sin – the deadly seven
And all the branches of their dreadful tree –
Yet there's so perfect a felicity
In marriage, so much pleasure, so few tears,
That I keep fearing, though advanced in years,
I shall be leading such a happy life,

So delicate, with neither grief nor strife,
That I shall have my heaven here in earth,
And may not that cost more than it is worth?
Since that true heaven costs a man so dear
In tribulation and in penance here,
How should I then, living in such delight,
As every married man, by day and night,
Has with his wife, attain to joys supernal
And enter into bliss with Christ Eternal?
That is my terror. Have you a suggestion,
My worthy brothers, to resolve the question?'

Justinus, who despised his nonsense, said,
Jesting as ever, what came into his head;
And wishing not to spin things out in chatter
Used no authorities to support the matter.
'If there's no obstacle,' he said, 'but this,
God by some mighty miracle of His
May show you mercy as He is wont to do,
And long before they come to bury you
May cause you to bewail your married life
In which you say there never can be strife.
And God forbid that there should not be sent
A special grace that husbands may repent,
And sent more often than to single men.
This, sir, would be my own conclusion then;
Never despair! You still may go to glory,
For she perhaps may prove your purgatory,
God's means of grace, as one might say, "God's whip",
To send your soul to Heaven with a skip
And swifter than an arrow from the bow!

I hope to God that you will shortly know
There's no such paramount felicity
In marriage, nor is ever like to be,
As to disqualify you for salvation,
Provided you observe some moderation,
Tempering down the passions of your wife
With some restriction of your amorous life,
Keeping yourself, of course, from other sin.
My tale is done, but there! My wit is thin.
Be not afraid, dear brother, that's the moral.
Let us wade out, however, of this quarrel;
The Wife of Bath, if you can understand
Her views in the discussion now on hand,
Has put them well and briefly in this case:
And now, farewell, God have you in His Grace!'

He then took leave of January his brother
And they had no more speech with one another.
And when his friends saw that it needs must be
They made a careful marriage-treaty. She,
The girl agreed upon, whose name was May,
(And with the smallest possible delay)
Was to be married to this January.

And I assume there is no need to tarry
Over the bonds and documents they planned
To give her the possession of this land.
Or make you listen to her rich array,
But finally there came the happy day
And off at last to church the couple went

The marriage of Alexander the Great, from the 'Romance of Alexander', is depicted as a Christian union in this medieval illumination. The wedding of January and May in this Tale is celebrated with the ancient pagan gods Bacchus, Hymen and Venus as well as by the Christian priest.

There to receive the holy sacrament.

Out came the priest, with stole about his neck,
And bade her be like Sarah at the beck
Of Abraham in wisdom, truth and grace,
Said all the prayers were proper to the case,
Then signed them with the cross and bade God bless
Them both, and made all sure in holiness.

Thus they were wedded in solemnity,
And at the wedding-banquet he and she
Sat with their worthier guests upon the dais.
Joy and delight filled the entire place,
Stringed instruments, victuals of every kind,
The daintiest all Italy could find.
Music broke forth as with the sound of Zion,
Not Orpheus nor the Theban king Amphion
Ever achieved so sweet a melody.

Feasts were of tremendous importance in medieval social life and their magnificence was an index of social status. January celebrates his wedding with one of appropriate magnificence: 'Joy and delight filled the entire place,/Stringed instruments, victuals of every kind,/The daintiest all Italy could find.'

And yet he felt strong qualms of pity stir
To think he soon must do offence to her,
That very night, and thought, 'O tender creature!
Alas, God grant you may endure the nature
Of my desires, they are so sharp and hot.
I am aghast lest you sustain them not.
God hinder me from doing all I might!
But O I wish to God that it were night,
And the night last for ever! Oh, how slow . . .
I wish these guests would hurry up and go!'
So he began to dedicate his labours
To getting rid politely of his neighbours,
And to detaching them from food supplies.
At last their reason told them they should rise;
They danced and drank and, left to their devices,
They went from room to room to scatter spices
About the house. Joy rose in every man
Except in one, a squire called Damian,
Who carved for January every day.
He was so ravished by the sight of May
As to be mad with suffering; he could
Almost have died or fainted where he stood,
So sorely Venus burnt him with the brand
Which, as she danced, she carried in her hand.
And hastily the boy went off to bed;
No more of him at present need be said.
I leave him there to weep and to complain
Till fresh young May have pity on his pain.
O perilous fire kindled in the bedding,
Domestic traitor, with the danger spreading!
O adder in the bosom, false of hue,
So sly, so homely-seeming, so untrue!
God shield us all from your acquaintanceship!
O January, drunk upon the lip
Of marriage, see your servant, Damian,
Who was your very squire, born your man,
Even now is meditating villainy.
O God unmask your household enemy!
Over the world no pestilence can roam
That is so foul as treachery at home.
The sun had traced his arc with golden finger
Across the sky, caring no more to linger
On the horizon in that latitude.
Night with her mantel which is dark and rude
Had overspread the hemisphere about,
And gone were all the merry-making rout
Of January's guests, with hearty thanks,
And homeward each convivially spanks
To undertake such business as will keep
Him happy, till it should be time for sleep.
Soon after this the restive January
Demanded bed; no longer would he tarry
Except to quaff a cordial for the fire
That claret laced with spice can lend desire;
For he had many potions, drugs as fine
As those that monk, accursed Constantine,
Has numbered in his book *De Coitu*.
He drank them all; not one did he eschew,

A woodcut from the 'Boke of Keruynge' (carving) of a merchant and his family at a feast being entertained by a jester. Marriage was a sacrament and there was a strong association between feasting and the great sacraments of the Christian liturgy.

At every course there came loud minstrelsy
And Joab's trumpets never took the ear
So forcefully as this, nor half so clear
Those of Theodamas when Thebes held out.
Bacchus himself was pouring wine about
And Venus smiled on everyone in sight,
For January had become her knight
And wished to try his courage in the carriage
Of his new liberty combined with marriage.
Armed with a fire-brand she danced about
Before the bride and all the happy rout;
And certainly I'll go as far as this.
And say that Hymen, God of wedded bliss,
Never beheld so happy a wedded man.
Hold thou thy peace, O poet Martian,
Give us no more thy marital doxology
For Mercury on wedding with Philology!
Silence the song the Muses would have sung,
Thine is too small a pen, too weak a tongue,
To signalize this wedding or engage
To tell of tender youth and stooping age,
Such joy it is as none may write about:
Try it yourself and you will soon find out
If I'm a liar or not in such a case.
For there sat May with so benign a face
That but to see her was a fairy-tale.
Queen Esther's eye could never so assail
Ahasuerus, never looked so meek;
Of so much loveliness I dare not speak,
Yet thus much of her beauty I will say
That she was like the brightest morn of May
With every grace and pleasure in her glance.
This January sat ravished, in a trance,
And every time he gazed upon her face
His heart began to menace her and race;
That night his arms would strain her with the ardour
That Paris showed for Helen, aye, and harder.

And to his private friends who lingered on
He said, 'For God's love, hurry and be gone,
Empty the house politely if you can.'
And presently they did so to a man.
A toast was drunk, the curtains back were thrown;
The bride was borne to bed as still as stone.
And when the priest had blessed the wedding-bed
The room was emptied and the guests were sped.
Fast in the arms of January lay
His mate, his paradise, his fresh young May.
He lulled her, sought to kiss away all trouble;
The bristles of his beard were thick as stubble,
Much like a dog-fish skin, and sharp as briars,
Being newly shaved to sweeten his desires.
He rubbed his chin against her tender cheek
And said, 'Alas, alas that I should seek
To trespass – yet I must – and to offend
You greatly too, my spouse, ere I descend.
Nevertheless consider this,' said he,
'No workman, whatsoever he may be,
Can do his work both well and in a flurry;
This shall be done in perfect ease, no hurry.
It's of no consequence how long we play,
We are in holy wedlock, and we may.
And blessed be the yoke that we are in
For nothing we can do will count a sin.
A man is not a sinner with his wife,
He cannot hurt himself with his own knife;
We have the law's permission thus to play.'
And so he laboured till the break of day,
Then took a sop of claret-sodden toast,
Sat up in bed as rigid as a post,
And started singing very loud and clear.
He kissed his wife and gave a wanton leer,
Feeling a coltish rage towards his darling

A wedding procession, from the 'Romance of Alexander'. For all his protestations of love, January is a predatory husband who sees sex as something to be snatched and bringing gratification only to the man: 'His heart began to menace her and race.... God hinder me from doing all I might!/But O I wish to God that it were night.'

And chattering in the jargon of a starling.
The slack of skin about his neck was shaking
As thus he fell a-chanting and corn-craking.
God knows what May was thinking in her heart,
Seeing him sit there in his shirt apart,
Wearing his night-cap, with his scrawny throat.
She didn't think his games were worth a groat.
At last he said, 'I think I'll take a rest;
Now day has come a little sleep were best.'
And down he lay and slept till half-past eight;
Then he woke up, and seeing it was late,
Old January arose; but fresh young May
Kept her apartment until the fourth day
As women will, they do it for the best.
For ever labourer must have time to rest,
For otherwise he can't keep labouring;
And that is true of every living thing,
Be it a fish, a bird, a beast, or man.
Now I will speak of woeful Damian
Languishing in his love, as will appear.
I would address him thus, if he could hear:
'O silly Damian! Alas, alas!
Answer my question; in your present pass
How are you going to tell her of your woe?
She's absolutely bound to answer no,
And if you speak, she's certain to betray you;
I can say nothing. God be your help, and stay you!'
Sick-hearted Damian in Venus' fire
Is so consumed, he's dying with desire;
And so he took his courage in his hand
To end a grief he could no longer stand
And with a pen that he contrived to borrow
He wrote a letter pouring out his sorrow,
After the fashion of a song or lay,
Indited to his lady, dazzling May,
And wrapped it in a purse of silk apart
To hang inside his shirt, upon his heart.
The moon, that stood in Taurus on the day
When January had wedded lovely May,
Had glided into Cancer; she of whom
I speak, fresh May, had meanwhile kept her room,
As is the custom among nobles all.
A bride of course should never eat in hall
Till four days afterwards, or three at least,
But when they're over, let her go and feast.
On the fourth day, from noon to noon complete,
And when high mass was over, in his seat
Sat January in his hall with May,
As fresh and bright as is a summer's day.
And it so happened that this good old man
Exclaimed, as he remembered Damian,
'Blessed St Mary! How can such things be?
Why isn't Damian here to wait on me?
Is he still sick? What's happened? Is he up?'
The squires standing there to fill his cup
Excused him on the grounds that he was ill,
He was in bed, unfit for duty still;
No other reason could have made him tarry.

*In medieval calendars January was often depicted as a time of
carousing at a winter feast.*

'I'm very sorry for it,' said January,
'And he's a gentleman, to tell the truth,'
The old man said, 'and if he died, poor youth,
It were a pity; he's a lad of worth.
I don't know anyone of equal birth
So wise, discreet and secret, and so able;
Thrifty and serviceable too at table.
As soon as possible after meat to-day
I'll visit him myself; and so shall May.
We'll give him all the comfort that we can.'
Then everybody blessed the kind old man
So eager in his bounty and good breeding
To offer anything that might be needing
To comfort a sick squire; a gentle deed.
Madam,' said January, 'take good heed
That after meat you and your women all,
When you have sought your room and left the
hall,
Go up and have a look at Damian
And entertain him; he's a gentleman.
And tell him too that I shall do my best
To visit him myself, after my rest.
Now hurry on, be quick, and I shall bide me
Here, until you return to sleep beside me.'
And on the word he rose and gave a call
To fetch a squire (the marshal of the hall)
And gave him some instructions. Fresh young May
With all her women took the shortest way
To Damian's room and sat beside his bed;
A warmth of comfort was in all she said,
Benignity and beauty in her glance.
And Damian, when at last he saw his chance,
Secretly took his purse and billet-doux,
Couched in the sweetest phrases that he knew,

And put it in her hand with nothing more
Than a long sigh, as deep as to the core;
But in a whisper he contrived to say,
'Mercy, have mercy! Don't give me away!
I should be killed if this were ever known.'
The purse slid from his bosom to her own
And off she went. You get no more of me.
Back to old January then went she;
He was reclining on his bed by this.
He drew her to his arms with many a kiss,
Then settled back to sleep at once; and so
She then pretended that she had to go
Where everybody has to go at times.
There, after memorizing Damian's rhymes,
She tore them into pieces and she cast
Them softly down the privy-drain at last.
Who fell into a study then but May?
And down beside old January she lay
Who slept until awoken by his cough.
He begged her then to strip her garments off
For he would have some pleasure of her, he said,
Her clothes were an encumbrance, to be shed.
And she obeyed, whether she would or no.
Lest I offend the precious, I will go
No further into what he did, or tell
Whether she thought it paradise or hell.
I leave them working thus as I suppose
Till it was evensong, and then they rose.
Whether by destiny or accident,
By starry influence or natural bent,
Or whether some constellation held its state
In heaven to make the hour fortunate
For giving billet-doux and lending wing
To Venus – there's a time for everything,

The learned say – and get a lady's love,
I cannot tell. But God who sits above
And knows that every action has a cause,
Let Him decide, for I can only pause
In silence; this at least is true of May
That such was the impression made that day
And such her pity for that sick young man
She could not rid her heart of Damian,
Or of the wish to see his troubles ended.
'Whoever else,' she thought, 'may be offended,
I do not care; but I can promise this,
To love him more than anyone there is,
Though he mayn't have a shirt. I will be kind.'
Pity flows swiftly in a noble mind.

ere one may see how excellently free
In bounty women, on taking thought, can be.
Some female tyrants – many I have known –
Are pitiless, their hearts are made of stone
And would have rather let him die the death
Than yield their grace or favour by a breath,
And they exult in showing cruel pride,
Calmly indifferent to homicide.

oft May felt pity, you must understand.
She wrote a letter in her own fair hand
In which she granted him her very grace.
There needed nothing but the time and place
To grant the satisfaction he desired;
He was to have whatever he required.

o when she saw occasion one fine day
To visit him, off went the lovely May
And thrust his letter down with subtle skill
Under his pillow, read it if he will.
She took him by the hand and squeezed it hard
(But secretly, for she was on her guard),
Bade him get well, then went without demur
To January who had called for her.

nd up rose happy Damian on the morrow;
Gone was all trace of malady and sorrow.
He preens himself and prunes and combs his
  curls
To take the fancy of this queen of girls.
To January his master, in addition
He was a very spaniel in submission,
And was so pleasant in his general drift
(Craft's all that matters if you have the gift),
That people spoke him well in every way,
But above all he stood in grace with May.
Thus I leave Damian, busy with his needs,
And turn once more to how my tale proceeds.

ome writers argue that felicity
Wholly consists in pleasure; certainly
This noble January, as best he might
In all that was befitting to a knight,
Had planned to live deliciously in pleasure;
His house and all his finery and treasure
Were fashioned to his rank as are a king's,
And among other of his handsome things
He had a garden, walled about with stone;

The traditions surrounding the courtly garden of love are deliberately inverted to create an atmosphere of violence. Priapus was the god of gardens but also the god of orgiastic sexuality, while Pluto was renowned for his rape of Proserpina.

So fair a garden never was there known.
For out of doubt I honestly suppose
That he who wrote the *Romance of the Rose*
Could not have pictured such magnificence;
Priapus never had the eloquence,
Though he be god of gardens, to re-tell
The beauty of this garden and the well
Under a laurel, standing ever-green.
Many a time King Pluto and his Queen
Prosérpina and all her fairy rout
Disported and made melody about
That well and held their dances, I am told.
This January, so noble, and so old,
Found walking in it such felicity
That no one was allowed to have the key
Except himself, and for its little wicket
He had a silver latch-key to unclick it
Or lock it up, and when his thought was set
Upon the need to pay his wife her debt
In summer season, thither would he go
With May his wife when there was none to know,
And anything they had not done in bed
There in the garden was performed instead,
So in this manner many a merry day
Was spent by January and lovely May.
But worldly joys, alas, may not endure
For January or anyone, be sure.

hangeable Fortune, O unstable Chance,
Thine is the scorpion's treacherous advance!
Thy head all flattery, about to sting,
Thy tail a death, and death by poisoning.
O brittle joy, O venom sweet and strange,
O monster that so subtly canst arrange
Thy gifts and colour them with all the dyes
Of durability to catch the wise
And foolish too! Say, why hast thou deceived

Old January, thy friend, as he believed?
Thou hast bereft him of his sight, his eye
Is dark, and in his grief he longs to die.

Alas this noble January, he
So generous once in his prosperity
Went blind; quite suddenly he lost his sight.
Pitiful loss! He wept it day and night,
While fires of jealousy seared his melancholy,
For fear his wife might fall into some folly.
His heart burned hot; he had been nothing loth,
Nay glad, if one had come to slay them both.
For neither on his death nor in his life
Was she to be the mistress or the wife
Of any other, but in weeds of state,
True as a turtle that has lost her mate,
She was to live, the garments on her back
A widow's, never anything but black.

But in the end, after a month or two,
His sorrows cooled a little, it is true,
For when he saw there was no remedy
He took in patience his adversity,
Save that the ineradicable sting
Of jealousy embittered everything,
For so outrageous are the thoughts it rouses
That neither when at home nor in the houses
Of his acquaintance, no, nor anywhere
Would he allow his wife to take the air
Unless his hand were on her, day and night.

Ah, how she wept, fresh as she was, and bright,
Who loved her Damian, and with so benign
A love that sudden death was her design
Unless she could enjoy him; so at first
She wept and waited for her heart to burst.

And Damian too, upon the other part,
Became in turn so sorrowful of heart
That none was ever like him: night or day
There never was a chance to speak to May
As to his purpose, no, nor anything near it,
Unless old January was there to hear it,
Holding her hand and never letting go.
Nevertheless by writing to and fro
And private signals, Damian knew her mind;
And she was well aware what he designed.
O January, what might it thee avail
Though thou couldst see as far as ship can sail?
As well be blind and be deceived as be
Deceived as others are that still can see.
Consider Argus with his hundred eyes
Poring and prying, yet for all these spies
He was deceived, and many more I know,
God wot, who sagely think they are not so.
Least said is soonest mended; say no more.

Now this fresh May of whom I spoke before
Took some warm wax and fashioned an
    impression
Of that same key (in January's possession)
Into the garden, where he often went.
Damian, who knew exactly what she meant,

January's walled garden was conceived as a locked paradise. Such a garden would quickly be equated with the Garden of Eden which was also the context for an allegory about the fall of love and the failure of humanity to respond to the opportunities of Paradise.

Secretly forged a counterfeited key.
That's all there is to say, but presently
A wonder will befall, if you will wait,
Thanks to this key and to the wicket-gate.

O noble Ovid, that was truly spoken
When you affirmed there was no cunning token
Or trickery, however long or hot,
That lovers could not find. For did they not
When Pyramus and Thisbe, I recall,
Though strictly watched, held converse through a wall?
There was a trick that none could have forecast!
But to our purpose; ere a week had passed,
Before July was on them, it befell
That January's thoughts began to swell,
Incited by his wife, with eager wishes
To be at play with her among the bushes
in his walled garden, he and she alone,
And so at last one morning he made moan
To May with this intention: 'Ah,' said he,
'Rise up, my wife, my love, my lady free!
The turtle's voice is heard, my dove, my pet.
Winter is gone with all its rain and wet;
Come out with me, bright-eyes, my columbine,
O how far fairer are thy breasts than wine!
Our garden is enclosed and walled about;
White spouse, come forth to me; ah, never doubt
But I am wounded to the heart, dear wife,
For love of you, unspotted in your life
As well I know. Come forth to take our pleasures,
Wife of my choice and treasure of my treasures!'

He got these lewd old words out of a book.
And May at once gave Damian a look
Signalling he should go before and wait;
So Damian ran ahead, unlocked the gate
And darted in as swiftly as a bird,

He managed to be neither seen nor heard,
And crouched beneath the bushes on his own.

nd then this January, blind as stone,
Came hand in hand with May, but unattended,
And down into the garden they descended
And having entered clapped the wicket to.

ow wife,' he said, 'none's here but I and you,
And you are she, the creature I best love.
For by the Lord that sits in Heaven above,
Believe me I would die upon the knife
Rather than hurt you, truest, dearest wife.
Remember how I chose you, for God's sake;
Not covetously nor in hope to make,
But only for the love I had to you.
And though I may be old and sightless too,
Be true to me and I will tell you why.

hree things for certain you shall win thereby:
First, love of Christ; next, honour to yourself;
Last, your inheritance, my lands and pelf,
Towers and towns; draw the agreement up,
They're yours, it shall be signed before we sup.
But first, as God may bring my soul to bliss,
I pray you seal the covenant with a kiss.
And though I may be jealous, blame me not;
You are so deeply printed in my thought
That when I see your beauty, and engage
That thought with my dislikable old age,
I cannot – though it might be death to me –
Forbear a moment of your company
For very love; I say it with no doubt.
Now kiss me, wife, and let us roam about.'

resh-hearted May on hearing what he said
Benignly answered him with drooping head,
But first and foremost she began to weep.
'Indeed,' she said, 'I have a soul to keep
No less than you, and then there is my honour
Which for a wife is like a flower upon her.
I put it in your hands for good or ill
When the priest bound my body to your will,
So let me answer of my own accord
If you will give me leave, beloved lord;
I pray to God that never dawn the day
– Or let me die as foully as I may –
When I shall do my family that shame
Or bring so much dishonour on my name
As to be false. And if my love grow slack,
Take me and strip me, sew me in a sack
And drop me in the nearest lake to drown.
I am no common woman of the town,
I am of gentle birth, I keep aloof.
So why speak thus to me, for what reproof
Have I deserved? It's men that are untrue
And women, women ever blamed anew.
I think it a pretence that men profess;
They hide behind a charge of faithlessness.'

nd as she spoke she saw a short way off
Young Damian in his bush. She gave a cough
And signalled with a finger quickly where

Like the lady in this woodcut, Pluto sat upon 'a little bench of turfy green'. Turf-topped benches were a feature of late medieval gardens.

He was to climb into a tree – a pear –
Heavily charged with fruit, and up he went,
Perfectly understanding what she meant,
Or any other signal, I may state,
Better than January could, her mate.
For she had written to him, never doubt it,
Telling him all and how to set about it.
And there I leave him sitting, by your pardon,
While May and January roamed the garden.

right was the day and blue the firmament,
Down fell the golden flood that Phoebus sent
To gladden every flower with his beams;
He was in Gemini at the time, it seems,
And but a little from his declination
In Cancer, which is Jupiter's exaltation.
And so it happened through the golden tide
Into the garden from the further side
Came Pluto who is king of Fairyland
And many a lady of his elfin band
Behind his queen, the lady Proserpine,
Ravished by him from Aetna. I incline
To think it is in Claudian you can read
How she was gathering flowers in a mead
And how he fetched her in his grisly cart.
The King of faery sat him down apart
Upon a little bench of turfy green,
And then he turned and thus addressed his queen:

ear wife,' he said, 'what no one can gainsay
And what experience shows us every day
Are the foul treacheries women do to men.

Ten thousand tales, and multiply by ten,
Record your notable untruth and lightness.
O Solomon in thy wisdom, wealth and brightness,
Replete in sapience as in worldly glory,
How memorable are thy words and story
To every creature capable of reason!
Of man's true bounty and of woman's treason
Thou saidst, "Among a thousand found I one,
And yet among all women found I none."

'So said the king who knew your wickedness;
And Jesus son of Sirach, as I guess,
Seldom says much of you in reverence –
Wild fire and a corruptive pestilence
Fall down upon you all to burn and blight!
Do you not see that honourable knight
Who, being blind and old and unobservant,
Is to be cuckolded by his own servant?
Look, there he sits, that lecher in the tree!
Now will I grant it of my majesty
To this blind, old and estimable knight
That he shall instantly receive his sight
Whenever his wife begins her villainy
He shall know all about her harlotry.
Both in rebuke of her and others too.'

'So that,' the queen replied, 'is what you'll do!
Now, by my grandsire's soul, though she is young
I'll put a ready answer on her tongue
And every woman's after, for her sake.
Though taken in their guilt they yet shall make
A bold-faced explanation to excuse them
And bear down all who venture to accuse them;
For lack of answer none of them shall die.
Though a man saw things with his naked eye
We'll face it out, we women, and be bold
To weep and swear, insinuate and scold
As long as men are gullible as geese.

'What do I care for your authorities?
I'm well aware this Jew, this Solomon,
Found fools among us women, many a one;
But if he never found a woman true,
God knows that there are many men who do,
Who find them faithful, virtuous and good.
Witness all those in Christian sisterhood
Who proved their constancy by martyrdom.
And Roman history has mentioned some,
Aye many, women of exceeding truth.
Now keep your temper, sir, though he, forsooth,
Said there were no good women, if you can.
Consider the opinion of this man.
He meant it thus, that sovereign constancy
Is God's alone who sits in Trinity.
Hey! God knows Solomon is only one;
Why do you make so much of Solomon?
What though he built God's temple in the story?
What though he were so rich, so high in glory?
He made a temple for false gods as well,
And what could be more reprehensible?

Plaster him over as you may, dear sir,
He was a lecher and idolater,
And in his latter days forsook the Lord;
Had God not spared him, as the books record,
Because He loved his father, surely he would
Have lost his kingdom, rather than that he should.
And all the villainous terms that you apply
To women, I value at a butterfly!
I am a woman and I needs must speak
Or swell until I burst. Shall I be meek
If he has said that we were wrangleresses?
As ever I may hope to flaunt my tresses,
I will not spare for manners or politeness
To rail at one who rails at woman's lightness.'

'Madam,' he said, 'be angry now no more;
I give it up. But seeing that I swore
Upon my oath to grant him sight again,
I'll stand by what I said, I tell you plain.
I am a king, it fits me not to lie.'
'And I'm the Queen of Fairyland, say I!
Her answer she shall have, I undertake.
Let us have no more words, for goodness' sake.
Indeed I don't intend to be contrary.'

Now let us turn again to January
Who walked the garden with his airy May
And sang more merrily than a popinjay,
'I love you best, and ever shall, my sweet!'
So long among the paths had strayed their feet
That they at last had reached the very tree
Where Damian sat in waiting merrily,
High in his leafy bower of fresh green.
And fresh young May, so shiningly serene,

*The enclosed gardens of traditional courtly romances would, like
January's garden, have gates that could be locked; and they would
be filled with fruit trees – again reminiscent of the Garden of Eden.
The garden in this woodcut also has a pear tree (top left), 'heavily
charged with fruit'.*

A salacious woodcut from the 'Beaute of Women'. At the end of the story Damian ceases to be the stereotyped courtly lover and his sexual desire for May, like January's, is exposed as rapacious and lustful.

Began to sigh and said 'Oh! I've a pain!
Oh Sir! Whatever happens, let me gain
One of those pears up there that I can see,
Or I shall die! I long so terribly
To eat a little pear, it looks so green.
O help me for the love of Heaven's Queen!
I warn you that a woman in my plight
May often feel so great an appetite
For fruit that she may die to go without.'
'Alas,' he said, 'that there's no boy about,
Able to climb. Alas, alas,' said he,
'That I am blind.' 'No matter, sir,' said she,
'For if you would consent – there's nothing in it –
To hold the pear-tree in your arms a minute
(I know you have no confidence in me),

Then I could climb up well enough,' said she,
'If I could set my foot upon your back.'
'Of course,' he said, 'why, you shall never lack
For that, or my heart's blood to do you good.'
And down he stooped; upon his back she stood,
Catching a branch, and with a spring she thence
– Ladies, I beg you not to take offence,
I can't embellish, I'm a simple man –
Went up into the tree, and Damian
Pulled up her smock at once and in he thrust.
And when King Pluto saw this shameful lust
He gave back sight to January once more
And made him see far better than before.
Never was man more taken with delight
Than January when he received his sight.
And his first thought was to behold his love.
He cast his eyes into the tree above
Only to see that Damian had addressed
His wife in ways that cannot be expressed
Unless I use a most discourteous word.
He gave a roaring cry, as might be heard
From stricken mothers when their babies die.
'Help! Out upon you!' He began to cry.
'Strong Madam Strumpet! What are you up to there?'
'What ails you, sir?' said she, 'what makes you swear?
Have patience, use the reason in your mind,
I've helped you back to sight when you were blind!
Upon my soul I'm telling you no lies;
They told me if I wished to heal your eyes
Nothing could cure them better than for me
To struggle with a fellow in a tree.
God knows it was a kindness that I meant.'
'Struggle?' said he, 'Yes! Anyhow, in it went!
God send you both a shameful death to die!
He had you, I saw it with my very eye,
And if I did not, hang me by the neck!'
'Why then,' she said, 'my medicine's gone to wreck,
For certainly if you could really see
You'd never say such words as those to me;
You caught some glimpses, but your sight's not good.'
'I see,' he said, 'as well as ever I could,
Thanks be to God! And with both eyes, I do!
And that, I swear, is what he seemed to do.'
'You're hazy, hazy, my good sir,' said she;
'That's all I get for helping you to see.
Alas,' she said, 'that ever I was so kind!'

'Dear wife,' said January, 'never mind,
Come down, dear heart, and if I've slandered you
God knows I'm punished for it. Come down, do!
But by my father's soul, it seemed to me
That Damian had enjoyed you in the tree
And that your smock was pulled up over your breast.'
'Well, think,' she said, 'as it may please you best,
But, Sir, when suddenly a man awakes,
He cannot grasp a thing at once, it takes
A little time to do so perfectly,
For he is dazed at first and cannot see.

Just so a man who has been blind for long
Cannot expect his sight to be so strong
At first, or see as well as those may do
Who've had their eyesight back a day or two.
Until your sight has settled down a bit
You may be frequently deceived by it.
Be careful then, for by our heavenly King
Many a man feels sure he's seen a thing
Which was quite different really, he may fudge it;

Misapprehend a thing and you'll misjudge it.'
And on the word she jumped down from the tree.
And January – who is glad but he? –
Kissed her and clasped her in his arms – how often! –
And stroked her womb caressingly to soften
Her indignation. To his palace then
He led her home. Be happy, gentlemen,
That finishes my tale of January;
God and his Mother guard us, blessed Mary!

Epilogue to the Merchant's Tale

'EY, mercy of God!' our Host exclaimed thereat,
'May God preserve me from a wife like that!
Just look what cunning tricks and subtleties
There are in woman! Busy little bees
They are, deceiving silly men like us!
They're always sliding and evading thus,
Dodging the truth; the Merchant's tale has shown it
And it's as true as steel – I have to own it.
I have a wife myself, a poor one too,
But what a tongue! She is a blabbing shrew,
And she has other vices, plenty more.

Well, let it go! No sense to rub a sore.
But, d'you know what? In confidence, good sir,
I much regret that I am tied to her.
Were I to reckon her vices one by one,
I'd only be a fool when I had done;
And why? Because it would be sure to be
Reported back to her, by two or three
Among us here; by whom I needn't say;
In all such matters women find a way.
And anyhow my brains would hardly run
To telling you, and so my story's done.'

THE SQUIRE'S TALE

The Squire's Prologue

'SQUIRE, come up and if you feel disposed
Say something about love – it is supposed
You know as much of that as any man.'
'O no, sir,' he replied, 'but what I can

I'll do with all my heart. I won't rebel
Against your pleasure; I've a tale to tell.
Have me excused if I should speak amiss,
My will is good and, look, my tale is this.'

The Squire's Tale
PART I

AT Tzarev in the land of Tartary
There dwelt a king at war with Muscovy
Which brought the death of many a doughty
man.
This noble king was known as Cambuskan
And in his time enjoyed such great renown
That nowhere in that region up or down
Was one so excellent in everything;
Nothing he lacked belonging to a king.

As to the faith in which he had been born
He kept such loyalties as he had sworn,
Then he was powerful and wise and brave,
Compassionate and just, and if he gave
His word he kept it, being honourable,
The same to all, benevolent, and stable
As is a circle's centre; and in a fight
As emulous as any squire or knight,
Young, personable, fresh and fortunate,
Maintaining such a kingliness of state
There never was his match in mortal man.

This noble king, this Tartar Cambuskan,
Begat two sons of Elpheta his wife.
The elder bore the name of Algarsyf,
The other son, the younger, Cambalo.
He had another child, a daughter though,
Youngest of all; her name was Canace.
To tell her beauty is too much for me,
Lying beyond what tongue of mine can sing;
I dare not undertake so high a thing.
My English too is insufficient for it,
It asks a rhetorician to explore it,
A poet in the colours of that art,
To give a fair account of every part.
I am none such, I speak as best I can.

Now it so happened that when Cambuskan
Had borne his diadem for twenty years,
As was his usual custom it appears,
He had the feast of his nativity
Proclaimed throughout the land of Tartary.
It was the Ides of March, in the new year;
Phoebus the sun shone happily and clear
For he was near his point of exaltation
In face of Mars, and there he held his station
In *Aries*, and that's a sultry sign.
Cheerful the weather, vigorous and benign.
And all the birds against the sunny sheen,

Left: The Squire's Tale has an exotic oriental setting. Several accounts of the Mongol Empire were current in Chaucer's time. He knew of the travels of Marco Polo and seems also to have drawn from stories about Prester John. Both the magnificence and the strangeness are established in the opening description.

231

What with the season and the early green,
Sang the loud canticles of their affection,
For, as it seemed, at last they had protection
Against the sword of winter, keen and cold.
This noble Cambuskan of whom I told
Sat on his dais in a royal robe,
High on his throne with diadem and globe,
And there held feast in all his power enfurled,
And there was nothing like it in the world.
If I should pause to tell of his array
The task would occupy a summer's day,
Nor is there any need I should enforce
Attention to his banquet, course on course,
Or number the quaint dishes they put on,
The heron-chick, the richly roasted swan,
For in that country veteran knights report
There are some meats esteemed the daintiest sort
Though in this country their esteem is small,
But there is none who could report it all,
So let me not delay you – it is prime
Of day, it would be fruitless loss of time.

Let me retrace my footsteps to their source.
It happened, close upon the second course,
As the king sat with his nobility
Listening to instruments of minstrelsy
That made delicious music in the hall,
Suddenly at the door in sight of all
There came a knight upon a steed of brass
Bearing a mirror, broad and made of glass.
Upon his thumb he had a golden ring
And at his side a naked sword a-swing,
And up he rode and reached the royal table.
In all that hall not one of them was able
To speak a word for wonder at this knight;
They waited, young and old, and watched the sight.
This stranger-knight so suddenly presented,
Bare-headed, armed and richly ornamented,
Saluted king and queen and nobles all
In order as they sat about the hall
With such deep reverence and comely grace
Not only in his speech but in his face,
That Gawain, ever courteous, ever bland,

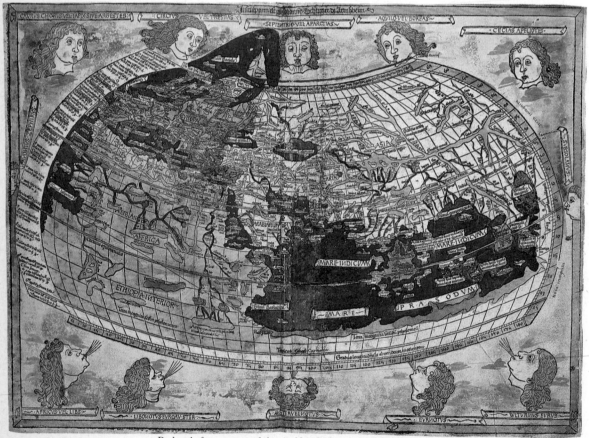

*Ptolemy's famous map of the world, which remained the dominant
conception of a flat earth for some 2,000 years. Of course medieval
travellers like Marco Polo gave more precision to the oriental
location of such stories as that told by the Squire. But the globe did
not begin to take shape for another century.*

And without hurt to you through foul or fair.
If you should wish to fly, and mount the air
As does an eagle when it seeks to soar,
This very steed will bear you as before
In perfect safety on your chosen track,
Though you should fall asleep upon his back,
And, when you twist this pin, return again.

'This steed of brass that easily may run/Within the natural circuit of the sun .../And bear your body to whatever place/Your heart desires.' The brass horse, the mirror, the magic ring and sword all lend a fairy-tale quality to 'The Squire's Tale'.

Though he were come again from fairyland
A greater courtesy could not have shown.
And thus before High Table and the throne
He gave his message in a manly voice
In his own language, with a perfect choice
Of phrase, faultless in syllable or letter;
And, that his story might appear the better,
Gesture and word were fitted each to each,
As taught to those that learn the art of speech,
And though I lack his talent to beguile
And cannot climb over so tall a stile,
I say, as to their general content,
The words I use amount to what he meant,
So far as I can trust my memory.

he King of India and Araby,
    Who is my sovereign lord, this solemn day
    Salutes your Majesty as best he may
And sends you here in honour of your feast,
Through me who am your servant, though the least,
This steed of brass that easily may run
Within the natural circuit of the sun,
That is to say in four and twenty hours,
Wherever you may wish, in drought or showers,
And bear your body to whatever place
Your heart desires, at a gentle pace

he that devised it had a cunning brain;
    He watched through many a change of
        constellation
Ere finding one to suit his operation,
And he knew many a magic seal and spell.

his mirror that I have in hand as well
    Is such that those who look in it may see
    The coming shadow of adversity
Upon yourself and kingdom, it will show
You plainly who is friend and who is foe.
More than all this, if any lady bright
Has set on any man her heart's delight,
If he be false she shall perceive his shady
And treacherous conduct, and the other lady,
So openly, nothing will hide his treason.
And so, against this lusty summer season,
This mirror and this ring are sent by me,
As you behold, to Lady Canace
Your excellent and lovely daughter here.

he virtue of the ring, as will appear,
    Stands in this point; if she be not averse
    To wear it on her thumb or in her purse,
There is no bird that flies beneath the reach
Of heaven but she will understand its speech
And know its meaning openly and plain
And in its language answer it again.
Of every rooted grass that grows on earth
She shall have knowledge too and test its worth
In sickness, or on wounds, however wide.

his naked sword here hanging at my side
    Retains the property to cut and bite
    The armour of whatever man you smite,
Though it were thicker than a branching oak;
And when a man is wounded by its stroke,
Nothing can heal him till the sword is laid
In mercy flat upon the wound it made,
Where he was hurt. This is as much to say
Lay the blade flat, turning the edge away,
And stroke the wound, and you will see it close;
This is the very truth in sober prose.
While it is in your hold it cannot fail.'

he stranger-knight, thus having told his tale,
    Rode out of hall, dismounted and had done.
    His steed of brass that glittered like the sun
Stood in the courtyard still as any stone.
They gave the knight a chamber of his own,
Unarmed and feasted him, and in a while
His gifts were carried forth in royal style,
That is to say the mirror and the sword,
And brought to the high tower under ward
Of certain officers appointed for it.

As for the ring, in solemn pomp they bore it
To Canace herself who sat at table.
But I assure you all it is no fable,
That horse of brass could not be raised or slewed
But stood its ground as if it had been glued.
It was of no avail to drive or bully,
Use windlass, engine, artifice or pulley;
And why? Because they didn't know the dodge.
And so they were obliged to let it lodge
Below until the knight had shown them how
To shift him; you shall hear it, but not now.
Great was the crowd that swarmed about in force
To gaze upon the stationary horse.
It was as tall, as broad, and of a length
Just as proportionable to its strength
As any courser bred in Lombardy,
Quick-eyed, as horsely as a horse can be,
Like an Apulian steed, as highly bred.
And I assure you that from tail to head
Nothing could be improved by art or nature,
So they supposed at least who saw the creature.
But yet the wonder nothing could surpass
Was how it went if it were made of brass.
Some thought it came from fairyland's dominions.
Various men gave various opinions,
As many heads, so many fallacies.
They murmured round it like a swarm of bees
And guessed according to their fantasy,
Or quoted snatches of old poetry
Saying it was like Pegasus of old,
The fabled horse that flew on wings of gold,
Or it was Sinon's horse by whose employ
The Greeks had brought destruction upon Troy,
As one may read in those old epic tales.
Said one of them, 'My spirit fairly quails
To think there may be men-of-arms within it
Plotting to take our town this very minute.
It would be well if such a thing were known.'
Another, whispering to his friend alone,
Muttered, 'He's wrong. More like some apparition
Or trick-illusion made by a magician,
Like what these jugglers do at feasts of state.'
Thus they kept up the jangle of debate
As the illiterate are wont to do
When subtler things are offered to their view
Than their unletteredness can comprehend;
They reach the wrong conclusions in the end.
Some wondered at the mirror and its power
(It had been taken to the master-tower)
And how such things could be foreseen in it.
Another said that such a thing could fit
Quite naturally by the skilled direction
Of angles, by the laws of light-reflection,
And said there was another such in Rome
Then they referred to many a learned tome
By Aristotle and by Alhazen
And Witelo and other learned men
Who when alive had written down directives

For use of cunning mirrors and perspectives,
As anyone can tell who has explored
These authors. Others wondered at the sword
That had the power to pierce through anything,
And spoke of Telephus the Mysian king,
And of Achilles and his marvellous spear,
Able to heal no less than it could shear,
Exactly like this sword, that at a word
Could wound a man or heal him, as you heard.
They spoke of sundry ways of hardening metal
By various ointments, and they tried to settle
The times and methods for this mystery,
Which are unknown, at any rate to me.
And then they spoke about the magic ring
Given to Canace, a marvellous thing,
Concluding thus: 'None such, as one supposes,
Was ever known; but Solomon and Moses
Were said to have been cunning in that art.'
Thus people spoke in little groups apart;
And others said how strange it was to learn
That glass is made out of the ash of fern,
Though bearing no resemblances to glass;
But being used to this they let it pass,
The argument declined, they ceased to wonder,
Like those who speculate on what makes thunder,
Ebb, flood or mist, how gossamer is blown,
Or anything until the cause is known.
And so they guessed and judged as they were able
Until the king began to rise from table.
Phoebus was over the meridian line;
It was the hour of the ascending sign
Of royal *Leo* with his Aldiran,
And this great Tartar king, this Cambuskan,
Rose from the board in all his majesty.
Before him went a blare of minstrelsy
Until he reached the presence-room surrounded
By divers instruments, and these were sounded
So sweetly it was heaven to those that listened.
Children of Venus glided there and glistened
In happy dance, for she was mounted high
In *Piscis*, and looked down with friendly eye.
The noble king was seated on his throne;
The stranger-knight was fetched and he alone
Was chosen forth to dance with Canace.
Great was the revelling and jollity,
It went beyond all dull imagination;
Only a man who knows the exaltation
Of serving love, a man as fresh as May,
A gamesome one, could tell of their array.
For who could paint the circling of their
dances,
So foreign to us, or the countenances
So subtle-smooth in their dissimulations
For fear of jealousy's insinuations?
No one but Launcelot and he is dead.
Pass over them and leave them there to tread
Their long delight, beyond all words of mine.
So on they danced till it was time to dine.

The steward bids them hurry with the spices
And fetch the wine, the minstrelsy entices,
The ushers and the squires in a pack
Run off and bring the wines and spices back.
They ate and drank, and having left the table
They sought the temple, as was reasonable.
The service done, they feasted all day long.
Why should I tell you what they served the throng?
Everyone knows that at a royal feast
There's plenty for the greatest and the least,
And delicacies more than I would know.

His supper done, the king proposed to go
And see this horse of brass, with all his rout
Of lords and ladies standing round about.

Such the amazement at this brazen horse,
Not since the siege of Troy had run its course,
At which another horse amazed her men,
Had there been such astonishment as then.
The king at last put question to the knight
As to this courser's properties and might,
Begging him to explain the beast's control.

This horse began to dance and caracole
Under its master's hand that held the rein;
He answered, 'Sir, there's nothing to explain,
But this; if you would ride it far or near,
Just twirl this pin that's standing in its ear,
As when we are alone I soon can show,
Then name the country where you would wish to go,
Or else the place, wherever you would ride,
And having reached it, if you so decide,
Bid him descend and twirl another pin,
For all the mechanism lies therein,
And down he'll go to carry out your will
And having reached the ground will stand stock-still.
Whatever then the world may do or say
He cannot thence be dragged or borne away.

To make him move or seek some other place
Twirl *this* pin and he'll vanish into space,
Yes, disappear completely out of sight,
Yet will return to you by day or night
If you should please to summon him again
After a manner that I shall explain
To you alone, and that without delay;
Ride when you will, there is no more to say.'

The stranger-knight is compared to Gawain, one of the knights of the Round Table who was distinguished for his courtesy.

The king, informed by what the knight had said,
And once he had it firmly in his head
How to control the beast in everything,
How blithe, how happy was this doughty king!
And he returned to revel as before.
Then they took off the bridle that it wore
And laid it with his treasures in the tower.
The horse then vanished; it's beyond my power
To tell you how, you get no more from me.
And thus I leave, in joy and jollity,
This Cambuskan, feasting with all his train
Till dawn of day had almost sprung again.

PART II

The nourisher of all digestion, Sleep,
Began to wink upon them. 'Drinking deep,'
He said, 'and heavy toil, for slumber call.'
And with a yawning mouth he kissed them all,
Saying, 'To bed, to bed, it is the hour
Of my dominion, blood is in its power.

Cherish your blood,' he whispered, 'nature's friend.'
They thanked him yawningly and in the end
By twos and threes they wandered off to rest
As sleep ordained, they took it for the best.
What dreams they had shall not be told, for me;
Their heads were full of the fumosity

That causes dreams which are of no account.
And so they lay and slept until the fount
Of day filled heaven, all but Canace;
For she was temperate and womanly
And having kissed her father, had departed
And sought her rest before the evening started.
She had no wish to pale her lovely cheek
Or greet the morrow colourless and bleak.

She slept her beauty sleep and then awoke,
And at her waking, in her heart there spoke
Such joy about her glass and magic ring
That twenty times she felt her colour spring.
She had dreamed visions from the deep impression
Made by the magic glass, her new possession.

So ere the sun began its upward glide
She called the waiting-woman at her side
And told her that it was her wish to rise.
Like all old women, glad to be as wise
As are their mistresses, the crone replied,
'What, madam, do you mean to go outside
So early? Everyone is still asleep.'
'I will arise,' she said, 'I cannot keep
In bed or sleep, I want to walk about.'

Her woman called the servants in a rout
And up they got – some ten or twelve there were –
And up rose Canace as fresh and fair,
As bright and ruddy as the early sun
When by some four degrees it has begun
To rise into the *Ram*. It was no higher
When she was ready; forth at her desire
With easy pace, and gowned to greet the May,
She lightly went to walk on foot and play.
Some five or six were with her, and, content,
Forth by an alley through the park she went.

There was a mist that glided from the earth
And gave the sun a huge and ruddy girth,
And yet it was so beautiful a sight
That all their hearts were lifted in delight,
What with the season and the dawn-light springing
And noise of all the birds in heaven singing,
For instantly she knew what they were saying
And understood the meaning in their maying.

The knot and gist of every tale that's told,
If lingered out till all desire be cold
In those that listen and the moment's past,
Savours the less the longer it may last
By fulsomeness of its prolixity,
And for that reason as it seems to me
I ought to reach that knot of which I'm talking
And make an end, and quickly, of her walking.

Amidst a tree so parched it seemed of chalk
Where Canace came dallying in her walk
Above her head a falcon sat on high.
This bird began so piteously to cry
That all the woods re-echoed her distress.
And she had scourged herself with pitiless
Beatings of her wings; a crimson flood
Poured down and painted all the tree with blood,

As ever and again with scream and shriek
She bent and tore her body with her beak.
There is no tiger, no, nor cruel beast
That dwells in wood or forest, west or east,
But would have wept if weep indeed it could
In pity of her, shrieking as she stood.
And never yet has been a man to tell
– If only I could describe a falcon well! –
Of such another bird, as fair to see
Both in its plumage and nobility
Of form and attribute, or find her twin.

It seemed this falcon was a peregrine
From foreign country; bleeding there she stood,
Fainting from time to time from loss of blood,
Till she had nearly fallen from the tree.

This beautiful king's daughter, Canace,
That on her finger bore the curious ring
By which she understood whatever thing
Birds in their language said, and which could teach
Her how to answer in their natural speech,
Had understood the words the falcon said;
The pity of it almost struck her dead.

Up to the tree she hastened at her cries
And looking with compassion in her eyes
Held out her lap towards it, knowing well
The bird was like to faint, and if she fell
For lack of blood, she would be there at hand
Below the branches. Long she seemed to stand
And wait, and then at last began to talk,
As you shall hear, and thus addressed the hawk.

'What is the cause, if you are free to tell,
That puts you to the furious pain of Hell?'
Said Canace to the poor bird above.
'Is it for grief in death, or loss of love?
For as I think these have the greatest part
Among the sorrows of a noble heart.
Other misfortunes one may well contemn,
The way is open for avenging them,
So that it must be either love or loss
That is occasion for your cruel cross,
For none, I see, has hunted you today.
God's love, have pity on yourself, or say
How I can help you. Neither east nor west
Was ever bird or beast so sore distressed
That ever I saw, or in such piteous plight;
It kills my heart to witness such a sight.
I feel such great compassion, come to me,
Come down for love of God and leave the tree,
For as I am the daughter of a king,
If I knew verily the cause and spring
Of your misfortunes, were it in my power
I would make all things well this very hour.
Great God of nature, help me so to do!

Right: 'La dame à la licorne', a French tapestry. When Canace wears the ring, 'There is no bird that flies beneath the reach/Of heaven but she will understand its speech.' The gentleness of virtuous women supposedly gave them an affinity with birds and animals.

I shall find herbs enough and salves for you
To heal your wounds, and quickly if you will.'
The falcon gave a shriek more piteous still
Than any yet and fell to earth; she lay
Stone-still for she had fainted dead away,
Till, lifted up by Canace and taken
Into her lap, the bird began to waken,
And, being recovered, had the strength to talk,
Answering in the language of a hawk:

Marginal illustrations of hunting and hawking at the court of Burgundy, from the Hours of Engelbert of Nassau. Hawking was an aristocratic pastime in which ladies often participated. A male falcon was called a 'tercelet' because he was usually about one-third of the size of the female bird.

That pity is swift to course in noble heart,
Feeling the likeness of another's smart,
Is daily proved, as anyone can see,
Both by experience and authority,
For gentleness of birth and breeding shows
Itself in gentleness; you feel my woes
As I can see, and sure it is a fashion
Well fitting a princess to show compassion
As you have done, my lovely Canace,
In true and womanly benignity
That nature planted in your disposition.
And in no hope to better my condition
But to obey your generosity,
Also that others may be warned by me,
As lions may take warning when a pup
Is punished, I will therefore take it up
And make a full confession of my woe
While yet there is the time before I go.'
And ever while the falcon said her say
The other wept as she would melt away
Until the falcon bade her to be still
And sighing spoke according to her will.
Where I was bred – alas, the cruel day! –
And fostered in a rock of marble grey
So tenderly that nothing troubled me,

I never knew the word adversity
Till I could wing aloft into the sky.
There was a tercelet that lived nearby
Who seemed a very well of gentle breeding;
Yet he was filled with treachery, exceeding
In all that's false. He wore the humble cloak
And colour of true faith in all he spoke,
An eagerness to please me and to serve.
Who could think such a hawk had power to swerve?
Dyed in the grain they were, those treacherous powers,
Just as a serpent hides itself in flowers,
Ready to strike, and waits the moment fit,
Just so this god of love, this hypocrite,
Kept up all ceremonious obligations,
The sweet observances and protestations
That make the music of a gentle love.
But as a sepulchre is white above
The rotting corpse within, as we are told,
Just so this hypocrite blew hot and cold
And in this way pursued his treacherous bent;
None knew, unless the devil, what he meant.
So long I heard his weeeping and complaining,
So long beheld the service he was feigning,
My heart, too foolish-pitiful to sound him,
All innocent of the treachery that crowned him,
Fearing his death (for so it seemed to me),
Believed his oaths, believed him trustworthy,
And granted him my love, on this condition,
That my good name, my honour and position
In public and in private had no hurt;
That is to say according to desert
In him, my heart and thought were his for ever,
But otherwise God knows, and he knew, never.
I took his heart, exchanging it for mine.
How true the saying in the ancient line,
"Thieves' thoughts are not the thoughts of honest
men,"
For seeing things had gone so far by then,
That I had fully granted him my love
In such a way as I have told above
And had as freely given my heart as he
Had sworn his own was given up to me,
Straightway this tiger with his double heart
Fell on his knees and played the humble part
With such devout and bashful reverence
He seemed a noble lover, one whose sense
Was ravished, one would think, for very joy.
Not Jason, no, nor Paris, Prince of Troy
– Did I say Jason? Sure, no other man
Since Lamech was, Lamech who first began,
So it is said, the game of loving two,
Has ever, since the world itself was new,
Thought or contrived the twenty thousandth part
Of counterfeited sophistry and art
As did my love. None fit to tie his shoe
Where there was double-faced deceit to do,
Not one to pay the thanks he paid to me!
And yet his manner was a heaven to see

238

Jason and the Golden Fleece, from the 'Roman de la Rose'. According to classical legend, Jason deserted Medea, Paris betrayed Oenone and Lamech was a bigamist. The falcon cites them as examples of treachery – but surpassed by her own lover.

For any woman, be she ne'er so wise,
Painted and trim and barbered to the eyes
Both in his words and in his countenance.
I loved him, then, for his obedient glance
And for the truth I judged was in his heart,
So that at any time he felt the smart
Of pain, were it so little as a breath,
And I was told, it seemed the twist of death
Tore at my heart. And so it grew to this,
My will became the instrument of his,
That is to say my will obeyed his mood
In everything, as far as reason would,
Within the bounds of honour; nearer, nearer
We grew together, none so dear, none dearer
Than he, God knows, and none shall ever be!
This lasted for two years perhaps, or three,
And I supposed nothing of him but good.
But at its final ending thus it stood:
As fortune willed, he had to leave the land
In which I lived. Ah, never make demand
Of what I felt in sorrow, ask no question,
I cannot picture it, for no suggestion
Would paint the truth, but this I boldly say,
I knew the pain of death that fatal day,
Such was my grief because he had to go.
He took his leave with such a world of woe,
So sorrowfully, that I felt assured
His feelings were no less than I endured
Hearing him speak, seeing his change of hue.
I was so certain he was wholly true,
So certain he would come to me again
And very soon, if ever truth were plain.
And there were reasons too for him to go,
Reasons of honour; it is often so.
I made a virtue of necessity

And took it well, knowing it had to be.
I sought to hide my sorrow, as in fitness
I should, and took his hand – St John my witness! –
And said, "Lo, I am yours, and though we sever,
Be such as I have been and shall be ever."
What he replied I need not now rehearse;
For who could have said better, or done worse?
Yes, what he said was well enough, and soon
The thing was done. Ah, "long should be your spoon
When supping with the devil!" so they say.
And so at last he went upon his way
And forth he flew, whither it seemed him best.
Yet later, when he had a mind to rest,
I think he must have had the text in mind
That "everything, according to its kind,
Seeks its own pleasure," so they say, I guess.
Man by his nature seeks new-fangledness,
As do those birds that people keep in cages;
One cares for them day-long and one engages
To get them straw as fair and soft as silk
And gifts of sugar, honey, bread and milk,
Yet on the instant that the slide is up,
The foot will spurn away the proffered cup
And to the woods they fly for worms to eat,
Such is their longing for new-fangled meat.
The love for novelty their natures gave them;
No royalty of blood has power to save them.

A court lady, from the Book of Hours of Engelbert of Nassau. Canace makes 'a little mew/To house the falcon, hung with velvet blue'. Blue was the colour of constancy and green of lightness in love. The fickle birds were depicted on the outside to imply that they could never enter within the mew, where all was constancy.

'So with this tercelet falcon, woe the day!
Although of gentle birth, though fresh and gay,
Handsome, adoring, good in everything,
One day he saw a kite upon the wing
And suddenly he felt a love so hot

For this same kite my love was clean forgot,
And thus he broke his faith in foul delight
And thus my love is servant to a kite
And I am lost and there's no remedy!'

She ceased and with a scream of agony
She swooned away in her protectress' arms.
Great the lamenting for her falcon's harms
That Canace and all her ladies made,
Not knowing how to soothe her or persuade.

Canace bore her homeward in her lap;
In softest plasters she began to wrap
The falcon's wounds that her own beak had
    torn,
And Canace went delving eve and morn
For herbs out of the ground; new salves she made
From precious grasses of the finest shade
To heal her hawk, indeed both day and night
She lavished on her all the care she might.

Beside her bed she made a little mew
To house the falcon, hung with velvet blue
To signify fair faith, so often seen
In women, and the mew was painted green
Without, with pictures of these treacherous fowls
Like tytyfers and tercelets and owls,
And there were magpies painted too, to chide
Them spitefully, to chatter and deride.

Thus I leave Canace to nurse her hawk
And of her ring at present I will talk
No more, till I return to make it plain
How the poor falcon got her love again
Repentant, as the tale I tell will show,
Through the good offices of Cambalo,
Son of the king of whom I have made mention.
But for the moment it is my intention
To tell adventures and the feats of war,
Such marvels as you never heard before.

First I will tell you about Cambuskan
And all the cities that he overran;
Then I shall speak of Algarsyf his son
And next of Theodora whom he won
To wife, and of the perils he must pass
On her account, helped by the steed of brass.
And after of another Cambalo
Who fought her brothers in the lists and so
At last won Canace by might and main.
And where I stopped I shall begin again.

Peregrine falcons were reputed to be very courteous and exceptionally brave. Although fairly common on mainland Europe, they were rare in England.

PART III

APOLLO whirled his chariot on high
Up through the house of Mercury, the sly –

Words of the Franklin to the Squire and of the Host to the Franklin

WELL! you have done yourself great credit,
  Squire,
  Most like a gentleman! I do admire
  Your powers,' said the Franklin, 'For a youth,
You speak most feelingly, and that's the truth;
In my opinion there is no one here
Will equal you in eloquence, or near,
If you should live. God prosper all that's in you
And may your talents flourish and continue!
It's all so dainty, it delighted me.
I have a son, and by the Trinity
  I'd rather than have twenty pounds' worth land,
  Though it should fall right now into my hand
That he could show the excellent discretion
That you have shown. A plague upon possession!
What use is property if you're a dunce?
I've spoken to him sharply, more than once
And shall again. He doesn't like advice,
All he can do is squander and play dice

And lose his money, at his present stage.
He'd rather romp and chatter with a page
Than entertain a serious conversation
Or learn to be a gentleman. Vocation –'
'Franklin, a straw for your gentility!'
Remarked our Host, 'You know as well as me
That each must tell a tale or two at least
Or break his word and miss the final feast.'
I know it well,' the Franklin said again,
  'I beg you not to hold me in disdain,
  Just for a word or two to this young man.'
Well, no more words, and tell us if you can
  Some story of your own.' 'Glad to obey,
  Since it's your wish; here's what I have to
  say.
Nothing could move me to oppose your will,
Save in so far as I may lack the skill;
I hope you may take pleasure in my stuff,
And if you do, I'll know it's good enough.'

A folio of manuscript depicting the seasons. 'The Franklin's Tale' spans several years and the changing seasons echo the dramatic action. Aurelius declares his love in the traditional Maytime garden. Dorigen faces her cruel choice in 'cold and frosty December'.

THE FRANKLIN'S TALE

The Franklin's Prologue

Of old the noble Bretons in their days
Delighted in adventures and made lays
In rhyme, according to their early tongue,
Which to the sound of instruments were sung,
Or read in silence for their own delight.
And I remember one, if I am right,
Which I will render you as best I can.
But, sirs, I'm not a cultivated man,
And so from the beginning I beseech
You to excuse me my untutored speech.

They never taught me rhetoric, I fear,
So what I have to say is bare and clear.
I haven't slept on Mount Parnassus, no.
Nor studied Marcus Tullius Cithero.
I can't give colouring to my words – indeed
Such colours as I know adorn the mead,
Or else are those they use in dyes or paint.
'Colours of rhetoric' to me seem quaint,
I have no feeling for such things; but still
Here is my story, listen if you will.

The Franklin's Tale

In Brittany, or as it then was called,
Armorica, there was a knight enthralled
To love, who served his lady with his best
In many a toilsome enterprise and quest,
Suffering much for her ere she was won.
She was among the loveliest under sun
And came from kindred of so high a kind
He scarce had the temerity of mind
To tell her of his longing and distress.
But in the end she saw his worthiness
And felt such pity for the pains he suffered,
Especially for the meek obedience offered,
That privately she fell into accord
And took him for her husband and her lord
– The lordship husbands have upon their wives.
And to enhance the bliss of both their lives
He freely gave his promise as a knight
That he would never darken her delight
By exercising his authority
Against her will or showing jealousy,
But would obey in all with simple trust
As any lover of a lady must;

'A house where husband and wife agree.' The Franklin offers a
compromise between the total dominance of her husband, presented
in 'The Clerk's Tale', and the feminism of the Wife of Bath.
Neither Arvéragus nor Dorigen claims dominance over the other, for
'Love will not be constrained by mastery'.

Arvéragus's courtship of Dorigen follows a conventional pattern: he loves her from a distance and he performs many services to prove his worth before he wins her.

Save that his sovereignty in name upon her
He should preserve, lest it should shame his honour.
She thanked him, and with great humility
Replied, 'Sir, since you show a courtesy
So fair in proffering me so free a rein,
God grant there never be betwixt us twain,
Through any fault of mine, dispute or strife.
Sir, I will be your true and humble wife,
Accept my truth of heart, or break, my breast!'
Thus were they both in quiet and at rest.
For there's one thing, my lords, it's safe to say;
Lovers must each be ready to obey
The other, if they would long keep company.
Love will not be constrained by mastery;
When mastery comes the god of love anon
Stretches his wings and farewell! he is gone.
Love is a thing as any spirit free;
Women by nature long for liberty
And not to be constrained or made a thrall,
And so do men, if I may speak for all.
Whoever's the most patient under love
Has the advantage and will rise above
The other; patience is a conquering virtue.
The learned say that, if it not desert you,
It vanquishes what force can never reach;
Why answer back at every angry speech?
No, learn forbearance or, I'll tell you what,
You will be taught it, whether you will or not.

No one alive – it needs no arguing –
But sometimes says or does a wrongful thing;
Rage, sickness, influence of some malign
Star-constellation, temper, woe or wine
Spur us to wrongful words or make us trip.
One should not seek revenge for every slip,
And temperance from the times must take her schooling
In those that are to learn the art of ruling.
And so this wise and honourable knight
Promised forbearance to her that he might
Live the more easily, and she, as kind,
Promised there never would be fault to find
In her. Thus in this humble, wise accord
She took a servant when she took a lord,
A lord in marriage in a love renewed
By service, lordship set in servitude;
In servitude? Why no, but far above
Since he had both his lady and his love,
His lady certainly, his wife no less,
To which the law of love will answer 'yes'.
So in the happiness that they had planned
He took his wife home to his native land
With joyful ease and reached his castle there
By Penmarch Point, not far from Finisterre,
And there they lived in amity unharried.
Who can recount, unless he has been married,
The ease, the prosperous joys of man and wife?
A year or more they lived their blissful life
Until it chanced the knight that I have thus
Described and who was called Arvéragus
Of Caer-rhud, planned to spend a year or so
In Britain (no, not Brittany), to go
And seek high deeds of arms and reputation
In honour; that was all his inclination.
He stayed two years, at least the book says thus.

Despite the marital bliss that follows his courteous behaviour towards his wife, Arvéragus feels obliged to go off to fight in order to sustain his knightly honour: 'to go and seek high deeds of arms and reputation'.

Now I will pause about Arvéragus
And turn to speak of Dorigen his wife
Who loved her husband as her own heart's life.
She wept his absence, sighed for him and pined
As noble wives will do when so inclined;
She mourned, lay wakeful, fasted and lamented,
Strained by a passion that could be contented
Only by him, and set the world at naught.
Her friends who knew the burden of her thought
Brought her such consolations as they might;
They preached to her, they told her day and night,
'You'll kill yourself for nothing.' Such relief
And comfort as is possible to grief
They fuss about to find, and finding, press
Upon her to relieve her heaviness.
Slow is the process, it is widely known,
By which a carver carves his thought in stone,
Yet cuts at last the figure he intended;
And slowly too, thus soothed and thus befriended,
Her soul received the print of consolation
Through hope and reason, and her long prostration
Turned to recovery, she ceased to languish;
She couldn't be always suffering such anguish.
Besides, Arvéragus as it befell
Sent letters to her saying all was well
And that he shortly would be home again;
Only for that her heart had died of pain.
Her friends, seeing her grief began to ease,
Begged her for heaven's sake and on their knees
To come and roam about with them and play
And drive her darker fantasies away,
And finally she granted their request
And clearly saw it would be for the best.
Her husband's castle fronted on the sea
And she would often walk in company
High on the ramparts, wandering at large.
Many a ship she saw and many a barge
Sailing such courses as they chose to go;
But these made part and parcel of her woe
And she would often say, 'Alas for me,
Is there no ship, so many as I see,
To bring me home my lord? For then my heart
Would find a cure to soothe its bitter smart.'
At other times she used to sit and think
With eyes cast downward to the water's brink
And then her heart endured a thousand shocks
To see such jagged, black and grisly rocks,
So that she scarce could stand upon her feet.
Then she would refuge in some green retreat,
Lie on a lawn, and looking out to sea
With long, cold sighs, would murmur piteously:
Eternal God that by Thy providence
Guidest the world in wise omnipotence,
They say of Thee that Thou hast nothing made
In vain; but Lord, these fiendish rocks are laid
In what would rather seem a foul confusion
Of work than the creation and conclusion
Of One so perfect, God the wise and stable;

*Dorigen's home was at 'Penmarch Point, not far from Finisterre',
a stretch of coast still edged by treacherous rocks today.*

Why madest Thou thy work unreasonable?
These rocks can foster neither man nor beast
Nor bird, to north or south, to west or east;
They are a menace, useless, to my mind.
Lord, seest Thou not how they destroy mankind?
A hundred thousand bodies dead and rotten
Have met their death on them, though now forgotten;
Thy fairest work, wrecked on a rocky shelf,
Mankind, made in the image of Thyself.
It seemed that then Thou hadst great charity
Towards mankind; how therefore may it be
That Thou hast fashioned means as these to harm them
That do no good, but injure and alarm them?
I know it pleases scholars to protest
In argument that all is for the best,
Though what their reasons are I do not know.
But O Thou God that madest wind to blow,
Preserve my husband, that is my petition!
I have the learned to their disquisition.
But would to God these rocks so black, so grim,
Were sunk in Hell itself for sake of him!
They are enough to kill my heart with fear.'
Thus she would speak with many a piteous tear.
Her friends could see it gave her no relief
To roam the shore, but added to her grief,
And so they sought amusement somewhere else.
They led her by the water-ways and wells
And many another scene of loveliness;
They danced, they played backgammon, they played chess.
And so one sunny morning, as they'd planned,
They went into a garden near at hand
Where they had staged a picnic and supplied
Victuals enough and other things beside,
And there they lingered out the happy day.
It was the morning of the sixth of May
And May had painted with her softest showers
A gardenful of leafiness and flowers;
The hand of man with such a cunning craft

*Dorigen first meets Aurelius while dancing in the Maytime garden
where her friends try to make her forget her sorrow over Arvéragus's
absence. The squire is the embodiment of youth, gaiety and vigour.*

Had decked this garden out in pleach and graft.
There never was a garden of such price
Unless indeed it were in Paradise.
The scent of flowers and the freshening sight
Would surely have made any heart feel light
That ever was born, save under the duress
Of sickness or a very deep distress;
Pleasure and beauty met in every glance.

And after dinner they began to dance
And there was singing; Dorigen alone
Made her continual complaint and moan
For never among the dancers came to view
Her husband, he that was her lover too.
Nevertheless she had to pass the day
In hope and let her sorrows slide away.

Now in this dance, among the other men,
There danced a squire before Dorigen,
Fresher and jollier in his array,
In my opinion, than the month of May.
He sang and danced better than any man
There is or has been since the world began.
He was, what's more, if I could but contrive
To picture him, the handsomest man alive,
Young, strong and wealthy, mettlesome, discreet,
And popular as any you could meet;
And shortly, if I am to tell the truth,
All unbeknown to Dorigen, this youth
– A lusty squire and servant in the game
Of Venus, and Aurelius was his name –
Had loved her best of any for two years
And longer so it chanced, but still his fears
Had never let him bring the matter up;
He drank his penance down without a cup.

He had despaired of her and dared not say
More of his passion than he might convey
In general terms, by saying that he burned

With love but that his love was not returned;
On all such themes he fashioned many a phrase,
Wrote songs, complaints, roundels and virelays
Saying his griefs were more than he dared tell,
He languished as a fury did in Hell,
And he must die, he said, as Echo did
For young Narcissus and the love she hid.
But in no other way, as said above,
Had he the courage to confess his love,
Save that perhaps from time to time at dances,
Where youth pays love's observances, his glances
It well may be would linger on her face
Beseechingly, as is the common case;
But she was unaware of what he meant.

Nevertheless it happened, ere they went
Out of the garden, since he lived nearby
And was of good position, standing high
In honour and had known her from of old,
They fell in speech and he at last grew bold
And drew towards the purpose in his head.
Taking his opportunity he said:

'Madam, by God's green earth and all its treasure,
Had I imagined it could give you pleasure
That day, on which your lord Arvéragus
Went over sea, then I, Aurelius
Would have gone too, and never come again.
I know the service of my love is vain,
My recompense is but a bursting heart.

'Madam, have pity on the pain and smart
Of love; a word from you can slay or save.
Would God your little feet stood on my grave!
There is no time to say what I would say;
Have mercy, sweetheart, chase me not away.'

She looked at him with closer scrutiny
And answered, 'Are you saying this to me?
Can you intend it? Never,' she said, 'till now

Had I suspected that – what you avow.
But by the Lord that gave me soul and life
I never mean to prove a faithless wife
In word or deed if I can compass it.
I will be his to whom I have been knit.
Take that for final answer, as for me.'

But after that she added playfully,
'And yet, Aurelius, by the Lord above
I might perhaps vouchsafe to be your love,
Since I perceive you groan so piteously.
Look; on the day the coasts of Brittany
Are stone by stone cleared of these hateful rocks
By you, so that no ship or vessel docks
In danger, when, I say, you clear the coast
So clean there's not a single stone to boast,
I'll love you more than any man on earth;'
Accept my word in truth for all it's worth.'

Is there no other way than this?' said he.

No, by the Lord,' she said, 'that fashioned me.
For it will never happen; that I know.
So clear your heart of fancies, let them go.
How can a man find daintiness in life
Who goes about to love another's wife,
That can enjoy her body when he pleases?'

Aurelius sighed again. The long uneases
Of lovers' woe returned on hearing this
And he replied with sorrowing emphasis,
'Madam, it is impossible to do,
So I must die a sudden death, for you.'
And on the word he turned and went away.

Her many other friends came up to play
And wander with her through the leafy walk
Of alleys pleached, but of her lover's talk
They did not know. Revels began anew,
Until the dazzling sun had lost its hue
For the horizon reft it of its light;
This is as much to say that it was night.
So they went home delighted, all in joy
Except, alas, Aurelius, wretched boy.

He sought his house, a sigh at every breath,
And could see no way of avoiding death.
Within himself he felt his heart turn cold
And falling on his knees began to hold
His hands to heaven and the upper air
In raving madness, and he said a prayer.
Excessive suffering had turned his head,
He knew not what he spoke, but this he said,
With pleading heart and pitiful, to one
And all the gods, beginning with the sun:

Apollo, God and Governor, whose power
Tends over every plant and herb and flower
And tree, appointing unto each by reason
Of thy celestial course, his time and season,
According as thy arc is low or high,
Lord Phoebus, in thy mercy cast an eye
On sad Aurelius, wretched and forlorn.

Look on me, Lord! My lady-love has sworn
To prove my death, though for no fault in me,
Unless, O Lord, in thy benignity
Thou pity a dying heart; for well I know,
Shouldest thou please, Lord Phoebus, to bestow
Thy mercy, thou canst help me best of all
Except my lady; listen to my call,
Vouchsafe to hear me, Lord, if I expound
A means of help and how it may be found.

Thy blissful sister, Luna the Serene,
Chief goddess of the ocean and its queen,
Though Neptune have therein his deity,
Is over him and empress of the sea.
Thou knowest, Lord, that just as her desire
Is to be lit and quickened by thy fire,
For busily she follows after thee,
Just so the natural longing of the sea
Follows on her and so is bound to do;
She is its goddess and the rivers' too.

And so, Lord Phoebus, this is my request,
Do me this miracle – or burst, my breast! –
That even now at thy next opposition
Which is to be in *Leo*, thou petition
Thy sister to bring floods so much increased
That they shall rise five fathom at the least
Above the highest rock that now appears
In Brittany, and let this last two years.
Then to my lady I can safely say,
"Keep truth with me, the rocks are all away."

Lord Phoebus, do this miracle for me now!
Beg her to go no faster, Lord, than thou;
I say, beseech thy sister that she go
No faster than thyself two years or so,
Then she will stay at full, and at their height
The spring floods will continue, day and night.
And should she not vouchsafe in such a way
The granting of my lady, then I pray
That she may sink the rocks, that they be drowned
Within her own dark region underground
Where Pluto dwells, for while they are above
I cannot hope to win my lady-love.

Barefoot to Delphi will I go and seek
Thy temple! See the tears upon my cheek,
Lord Phoebus, have compassion, grant my boon!'
And on the word he fell into a swoon
And long he lay upon the ground in trance.

His brother who had heard of his mischance
Found him and caught him up, and off to bed
He carried him. With torment in his head,
I leave this woeful creature, if to die
In desperation, he must choose, not I.

Meanwhile Arvéragus in health and power
Came honourably home, the very flower
Of chivalry, with other noble men.
How art thou blissful now, my Dorigen!
Thou has a lusty husband for thy charms,
Thine own fresh knight, thy honoured man-at-arms

Extreme emotion was one of the conventions of courtly love and the state of mind of an unaccepted lover was always one of acute suffering. Aurelius despairs, is obsessed by the thought of his love, believes his misery will lead to his death and falls into a deranged state and a trance.

That loves thee as his life, in whom there springs
No inclination to imagine things
Or ask if anyone while he was out
Has talked to thee of love. But not a doubt
Entered his head; he had no thought in life
Except to dance and joust and cheer his wife
In blissful joy; and so I leave him thus
And turn again to sick Aurelius.
In furious torment, languishing away,
    Two years and more wretched Aurelius lay
    Scarce with the strength to put his foot to ground.
No comfort during all that time he found
Except his brother, who had been a scholar,
And who knew all about his woes and dolour,
For to no other could Aurelius dare
Ever to say a word of his affair.
More secretly he guarded his idea
Than Pamphilus his love for Galatea.
To all appearances his breast was whole,
But a keen arrow stuck within his soul.
A wound that's only surface-healed can be
A perilous thing, you know, in surgery,

Unless the arrow-head be taken out.
    is brother wept for him and fell in doubt
    Of his recovery until by chance
    It came to him that when he was in France
At Orleans – he was a student then –
He lusted in his heart like all young men
To study things prohibited, to read
In curious arts of magic, and indeed
Search every hole and corner with defiance
To learn the nature of that special science.
And he remembered how he took a look
One morning, in his study, at a book
On natural magic which it chanced he saw
Because a friend, then bachelor-at-law
Though destined later to another trade,
Had hidden it in his desk. This book displayed
The workings of the moon; there were expansions
In detail on the eight-and-twenty mansions
Belonging to her – nonsense such as that,
For nowadays it isn't worth a gnat,
Since holy church has managed to retrieve us
And suffers no illusion now to grieve us.
    nd so, remembering this book by chance,
    His heart as suddenly began to dance
    For joy within him; quickly reassured,
He said, 'My brother surely shall be cured
For I am certain that there must be sciences
By which illusions can be made, appliances
Such as these subtle jugglers use in play
At banquets. Very often, people say,
These conjurers can bring into a large
And lofty hall fresh water and a barge
And there they seem to row it up and down;
Sometimes a lion, grim and tawny-brown,
Sometimes a meadow full of flowery shapes,
Sometimes a vine with white and purple grapes,
Sometimes a castle which by some device,
Though stone and lime, will vanish in a trice,
Or seem at least to vanish, out of sight.
    o I conclude that if I only might
    Discover some old fellow of the kind
    Who has these moony mansions in his mind
At Orleans, or has some power above
All this, my brother might enjoy his love.
A learned man could hoodwink all beholders
With the illusion that the rocks and boulders
Of Brittany had vanished one and all
And ships along the brink could safely call,
Coming and going, and, if this could but last
A day or two, the danger would be past.
She will be forced to recognize his claim
Or else she will at least be put to shame.'
    hy draw my story out? What need be said?
    He went to where his brother lay in bed
    And brought him so much comfort with his plot
To visit Orleans, that up he got
And started off at once upon the road
High in the hope of lightening his load.

248

hey neared the city; when it seemed to be
About two furlongs off, or maybe three,
They met a youngish scholar all alone
Who greeted them in Latin, in a tone
Of friendly welcome, and he struck them dumb
In wonder with 'I know why you have come.'
And ere they went a step upon their way
He told them all they had in mind to say.

he Breton scholar wanted to be told
About the friends that they had known of old
And he replied that they were all now dead;
He spoke with feeling, many tears were shed.

own from his horse Aurelius soon alighted
To follow the magician, who invited
Him and his brother home, set them at ease
And served them victuals; nothing that could please
Was lacking and Aurelius soon decided
He'd never seen a house so well provided.

nd the magician caused there to appear
Before their supper, parks of forest deer
And he saw stags among them, antlered high,
The greatest ever seen by human eye.
He saw a hundred of them killed by hounds
And others, arrow-wounded, lay in mounds.
Next, when the deer had vanished, he was shown
A river bank and there a hawk was flown
By falconers; they saw a heron slain.

hen he saw knights at joust upon a plain
And after that Aurelius was entranced
At seeing his beloved as she danced
And he, it seemed, was dancing with her too.
And when the master of this magic view
Saw it was time he clapped his hands and banished
The figures, and farewell! our revels vanished.
Yet all the time they had not left the house
While being shown these sights so marvellous,
But sat within his study where there lay
His books about them; there were none but they.

he master called the squire who was to set
Their meal, and said, 'Is supper ready yet?
It's very near an hour I could swear,'
He added, 'since I told you to prepare,
When these two gentlemen came in with me
To see my study and my library.'

ir,' said the squire, 'it's ready, and you may
Begin, if it so please you, right away.'
'Then let us eat,' he said; 'that will be best;
These amorous people sometimes need a rest.'

fter they'd eaten, bargaining began;
What payment should this master-artisan
Have to remove the rocks of Brittany
From the Gironde to where the Seine meets sea?
He made it difficult and roundly swore
He'd take a thousand pounds for it or more,
He wasn't too eager even at that price.
Aurelius with his heart in paradise
Readily answered, 'Fie on a thousand pound!
I'd give the world, which people say is round,

The whole wide world, if it belonged to me;
Call it a bargain then, for I agree.
You shall be truly paid it, on my oath.
But look, be sure no negligence or sloth
Delay us here beyond tomorrow, now!'
The scholar gave him answer 'That I vow.'

urelius went to bed in high delight
And rested soundly, pretty well all night.
Tired by his journey and with hope retrieved
He slept, the troubles of his heart relieved.

nd morning came; as soon as it was day
They made for Brittany by the nearest way,
The brothers with the wizard at their side,
And there dismounted having done their ride.
It was – so say the books, if I remember –
The cold and frosty season of December.
Phoebus grew old, his coppered face was duller
Than it had been in *Cancer* when his colour
Shone with the burnished gold of streaming morn,
But now descending into *Capricorn*
His face was very pale, I dare maintain.
The bitter frosts, the driving sleet and rain
Had killed the gardens; greens had disappeared.
Now Janus by the fire with the double beard,
His bugle-horn in hand, sits drinking wine;
Before him stands a brawn of tusky swine,
And *'Sing Noël!'* cries every lusty man.

urelius, using all the means he can,
Gives welcome to the master, shows respect
And begs his diligence, that no neglect
Or sloth delay the healing of his smart,
Lest he should kill himself, plunge sword in heart.

his subtle sage had pity on the man
And night and day went forward with his plan
Watching the hour to favour the conclusion
Of his experiment, that by illusion
Or apparition – call it jugglery,
I lack the jargon of astrology –
She and the world at large might think and say
The rocks had all been spirited away
From Brittany or sunk under the ground.

nd so at last the favouring hour was found
To do his tricks and wretched exhibition
Of that abominable superstition.
His calculating tables were brought out
Newly corrected (he made sure about
The years in series and the single years
To fix the points the planets in their spheres
Were due to reach and so assessed their 'root'
In longitude) and other things to suit,
Such as his astrolabe, and argument
From arc and angle, and was provident
Of fit proportionals for the minor motion
Of planets, and he studied with devotion,
Measuring from the point where Alnath swam
In the eighth sphere, to where the head of the *Ram*
Stood in the ninth, in its eternal station
(As we suppose), and made his calculation.

The magician's skill derives from a mixture of astrology and magic.

He has been rescued from a long dismay.'

And to the temple then he took his way
Where, as he knew, his lady was to be;
And when he saw his opportunity
With terror in his heart, and humbled face,
He made obeisance to her sovereign grace.

'My truest lady,' said this woeful man,
'Whom most I dread and love – as best I can –
Last in the world of those I would displease,
Had I not suffered many miseries
For love of you, so many I repeat
That I am like to perish at your feet,
I would not dare approach you, or go on
To tell you how forlorn and woebegone
I am for you; but I must speak or die.
You kill me with your torture; guiltless, I.
Yet if my death could never so have stirred
Your pity, think before you break your word.
Repent, relent, remember God above you
Before you murder me because I love you.
You know what you have promised to requite
– Not that I challenge anything of right,
My sovereign lady, only of your grace –
Yet in a garden yonder, at such a place
You made a promise which you know must stand
And gave your plighted troth into my hand
To love me best, you said, as God above
Knows, though I be unworthy of your love.
It is your honour, madam, I am seeking;
It's not to save my life that I am speaking.
I have performed what you commanded me
As if you deign to look you soon will see.
Do as you please but think of what you said
For you will find me here alive, or dead.
It lies in you to save me or to slay –
But well I know the rocks are all away!'
He took his leave of her and left the place.

Without a drop of colour in her face
She stood as thunderstruck by her mishap.
'Alas,' she said, 'to fall in such a trap!

And finding the first mansion of the moon,
He calculated all the rest in tune
With that. He worked proportionally, knowing
How she would rise and whither she was going
Relative to which planets and their place,
Equal or not, upon the zodiac face.
And thus according to his calculations
He knew the moon in all her operations
And all the relevant arithmetic
For his illusion, for the wretched trick
He meant to play, as in those heathen days
People would do. There were no more delays
And by his magic for a week or more
It seemed the rocks were gone; he'd cleared the shore.

Aurelius, still despairing of the plot,
Nor knowing whether he'd get his love or not,
Waited for miracles by night and day
And when he saw the rocks were cleared away,
All obstacles removed, the plot complete,
He fell in rapture at his master's feet.
'Wretch as I am, for what has passed between us,
To you, my lord, and to my lady Venus
I offer thanks,' he said, 'for by your care,
As poor Aurelius is well aware,

A weeping woman represents the figure of Sadness in this mid-fourteenth-century French illumination. The plight of Dorigen, like that of Aurelius earlier, is expressed in terms of extreme emotion. 'She wept a day or two,/Wailing and swooning.'

I never had thought the possibility
Of such a monstrous miracle could be,
It goes against the processes of nature.'
And home she went, a very sorrowful creature
In deadly fear, and she had much to do
Even to walk. She wept a day or two,
Wailing and swooning, pitiful to see,
But why she did so not a word said she,
For her Arvéragus was out of town.

A wheel of Fortune, from a late fourteenth-century edition of the 'Roman de la Rose'. Dorigen addresses her lengthy lamentation about her pitiable situation to Fortune which has trapped her unawares and confronted her with the impossible choice between death and dishonour.

But to herself she spoke and flinging down
In pitiable pallor on her bed
She voiced her lamentation and she said:
'Alas, of thee, O Fortune, I complain,
That unawares hast wrapped me in thy chain,
Which to escape two ways alone disclose
Themselves, death or dishonour, one of those,
And I must choose between them as a wife.
Yet I would rather render up my life
Than to be faithless or endure a shame
Upon my body, or to lose my name.
My death will quit me of a foolish vow;
And has not many a noble wife ere now
And many a virgin slain herself to win
Her body from pollution and from sin?
'Yes, surely, many a story we may trust
Bears witness; thirty tyrants full of lust
Slew Phido the Athenian like a beast,

Then had his daughters carried to their feast,
And they were brought before them in despite
Stark naked, to fulfil their foul delight,
And there they made them dance upon the floor,
God send them sorrow, in their father's gore.
And these unhappy maidens, full of dread,
Rather than they be robbed of maidenhead,
Broke from their guard and leapt into a well
And there were drowned, so ancient authors tell.
'The people of Messina also sought
Some fifty maidens out of Sparta, brought
Only that they might work their lechery
Upon them, but in all that company
Not one that was not slain; they were content
To suffer death itself than to consent
To be despoiled of their virginity;
What then's the fear of death, I say, to me?
'Consider Aristoclides for this,
A tyrant lusting after Stymphalis
Who, when her father had been slain one night,
Fled for protection to Diana's might
Into her temple, clung to her effigy
With both her hands and from it could not be
Dragged off, they could not tear her hands away
Till they had killed her. If a virgin may
Be seen to have so loath an appetite
To be defiled by filthy man's delight,
Surely a wife should kill herself ere she
Were so defiled, or so it seems to me.
'And what of Hasdrubal? Had he not a wife
At Carthage who had rather take her life?
For as she watched the Romans win the town
She took her children with her and leapt down
Into the fire; there she chose to burn
Rather than let them do their evil turn.
'Did not Lucrece choose death for her escape
In Rome of old when she had suffered rape
For Tarquin's lust? Did not she think it shame
To live a life that had been robbed of name?
'The seven virgins of Miletus too
Took their own lives – were they not bound to do? –
Lest they be ravished by their Gaulish foes.
More than a thousand stories I suppose
Touching this theme were easy now to tell.
'Did not his wife, when Abradates fell,
Take her own life and let the purple flood
Glide from her veins to mingle with his blood,
Saying, "My body shall at least not be
Defiled by man, so far as lies in me"?
'Since there are found so many, if one delves,
That gladly have preferred to kill themselves
Rather than be defiled, need more be sought
For my example? Better were the thought
To kill myself at once than suffer thus.
I will be faithful to Arvéragus
Or slay myself as these examples bid,
As the dear daughter of Demotion did
Who chose to die rather than be defiled.

'O Skedasus, thou also hadst a child
That slew herself, and sad it is to read
How she preferred her death to such a deed.

'As pitiable or even more, I say,
The Theban maid who gave her life away
To foil Nichanor and a like disgrace.

'Another virgin at that very place
Raped by a Macedonian, it is said,
Died to repay her loss of maidenhead.

'What shall I say of Niceratus' wife
Who, being thus dishonoured, took her life?

'And O how true to Alcibiades
His lover was! She died no less than these
For seeking to give burial to her dead.

'See what a wife Alcestis was,' she said,
'And what says Homer of Penelope?
All Greece can celebrate her chastity.

'Laodamia, robbed of all her joy,
Protesilaus being killed at Troy,
Would live no longer, seeing that he was slain.

'Of noble Portia let me think again;
She could not live on being forced to part
From Brutus whom she loved with all her heart.

'And Artemisia, faithful to her man,
Is honoured, even by the barbarian.

'O Teuta, queen! Thy wifely chastity
Should be a mirror for all wives to see;
I say the same of Bilia and as soon
Of chaste Valeria and Rhodogoun.'

Thus for a day or two she spent her breath,
Poor Dorigen, and ever purposed death.

On the third day, however, of her plight,
Home came Arvéragus, that excellent knight,
And questioned her; what was she crying for?
But she continued weeping all the more.
'Alas,' she said, 'that ever I was born!
Thus have I said,' she answered, 'thus have sworn–'
She told him all as you have heard before.
It need not be repeated here once more.

Her husband, gladly smiling, with no fuss,
But with a friendly look, made answer thus:
'And is there nothing, Dorigen, but this?'
'No, no, so help me God!' with emphasis
She answered. 'Is it not enough, too much?'
'Well, wife,' he said, 'it's better not to touch
A sleeping dog, so I have often heard;
All may be well, but you must keep your word.
For, as may God be merciful to me,
I rather would be stabbed than live to see
You fail in truth. The very love I bear you
Bids you keep truth, in that it cannot spare you.
Truth is the highest thing in a man's keeping.'
And on the word he suddenly burst out weeping
And said, 'But I forbid on pain of death,
As long as you shall live or draw your breath,

That you should ever speak of this affair
To living soul; and what I have to bear
I'll bear as best I may; now wash your face,
Be cheerful. None must guess at this disgrace.'

He called a maidservant and squire then
And said, 'Go out with Lady Dorigen;
Attend upon her, whither she will say.'
They took their leave of him and went their way
Not knowing why their mistress was to go.
It was his settled purpose none should know.

Perhaps a heap of you will want to say,
'Lewd, foolish man to act in such a way,
Putting his wife into such jeopardy!'
Listen before you judge them, wait and see.
She may have better fortune, gentlemen,
Than you imagine; keep your judgements then
Till you have heard my story which now turns
To amorous Aurelius as he burns
For Dorigen; they happened soon to meet
Right in the town, in the most crowded street
Which she was bound to use, however loth,
To reach the garden and to keep her oath.

Aurelius gardenwards was going too;
A faithful spy on all she used to do,
He kept close watch whenever she went out
And so by accident or luck no doubt
They met each other; he, his features glowing,
Saluted her and asked where she was going,
And she replied as one half driven mad,
'Why, to the garden, as my husband bade
To keep my plighted word, alas, alas!'

Aurelius, stunned at what had come to pass,
Felt a great surge of pity that arose
At sight of Dorigen in all her woes
And for Arvéragus the noble knight
That bade her keep her word of honour white,
So loth he was that she should break her truth.
And such a rush of pity filled the youth
That he was moved to think the better course
Was to forgo his passion than to force
An act on her of such a churlish kind,
And against such nobility of mind.
So, in few words, the squire addressed her thus:

Madam, say to your lord Arvéragus
That since I well perceive his nobleness
Towards yourself, and also your distress,
Knowing the shame that he would rather take
(And that were pity) than that you should break
Your plighted word, I'd rather suffer too
Than seek to come between his love and you.

So, Madam, I release into your hand
All bonds or deeds of convenant that stand
Between us, and suppose all treaties torn
You may have made with me since you were born.
I give my word never to chide or grieve you
For any promise given, and so I leave you,
Madam, the very best and truest wife
That ever yet I knew in all my life.

Let women keep their promises to men,
Or at the least remmeber Dorigen.
A squire can do a generous thing with grace
As well as can a knight, in any case.'
And she went down and thanked him on her knees.
Home to her husband then with heart at ease
She went and told him all as I've recorded.
You may be sure he felt so well rewarded
No words of mine could possibly express
His feelings. Why then linger? You may guess.
Arvéragus and Dorigen his wife
In sovereign happiness pursued their life,
No discord in their love was ever seen,
He cherished her as though she were a queen,
And she stayed true as she had been before;
Of these two lovers you will get no more.

'A happy marriage.' The happy marriage of Dorigen and Arvéragus survives, thanks to Aurelius's 'gentilesse' in releasing Dorigen from her promise to become his lover. But Aurelius's behaviour was inspired by Arvéragus's selfless insistence that Dorigen should keep her vow even if it meant her being unfaithful: for 'Truth is the highest thing in a man's keeping.'

Aurelius, all whose labour had been lost,
Cursing his birth, reflected on the cost.
'Alas,' he said, 'alas that I am bound
To pay in solid gold a thousand pound
To that magician! What am I to do?
All I can see is that I'm ruined too.
There's my inheritance; that I'll have to sell
And be a beggar. Then there's this as well;
I can't stay here a shame and a disgrace
To all my family; I must leave the place.
And yet he might prove lenient; I could pay
A yearly sum upon a certain day
And thank him gratefully, I can but try.
But I will keep my truth, I will not lie.'

And sad at heart he went to search his coffer
And gathered up what gold he had to offer
His master, some five hundred pound I guess,
And begged him as a gentleman, no less,
To grant him time enough to pay the rest.
'Sir, I can boast, in making this request,'
He said, 'I've never failed my word as yet,
And I will certainly repay this debt
I owe you, master, ill as I may fare,
Yes, though I turn to begging and go bare.
If you'd vouchsafe me, on security,
A little respite, say two years or three,
All would be fine. If not I'll have to sell
My patrimony; there's no more to tell.'
Then this philosopher in sober pride,
Having considered what he'd said, replied,
'Did I not keep my covenant with you?'
'You did indeed,' he said, 'and truly too.'
'And did you not enjoy your lady then?'
'No . . . no . . .' he sighed, and thought of Dorigen.
'What was the reason? Tell me if you can.'
Reluctantly Aurelius then began
To tell the story you have heard before,
There is no need to tell it you once more.
He said: 'Her husband, in his nobleness,
Would have preferred to die in his distress
Rather than that his wife should break her word.'
He told him of her grief, as you have heard,
How loth she was to be a wicked wife
And how she would have rather lost her life;
'Her vow was made in innocent confusion,
She'd never heard of magical illusion.
So great a sense of pity rose in me,
I sent her back as freely then as he
Had sent her to me; I let her go away.
That's the whole story, there's no more to say.'
Then the magician answered, 'My dear brother,
Each of you did as nobly as the other.
You are a squire, sir, and he a knight,
But God forbid in all His blissful might
That men of learning should not come as near
To nobleness as any, never fear.
Sir, I release you of your thousand pound
No less than if you'd crept out of the ground
Just now, and never had had to do with me.
I will not take a penny, sir, in fee
For all my knowledge and my work to rid
The coast of rocks; I'm paid for what I did,
Well paid, and that's enough. Farewell, good-day!'
He mounted on his horse and rode away.
My lords, I'll put a question: tell me true,
Which seemed the finest gentleman to you?
Ere we ride onwards tell me, anyone!
I have no more to say, my tale is done.

The Second Nun tells a suitably pious tale about the life of St Cecilia, one of the early Christian martyrs. Chaucer includes most of the traditional account, although her martyrdom has been assigned to several different Roman Emperors as well as to Almachius.

THE SECOND NUN'S TALE

The Second Nun's Prologue

THAT nourisher and servant to our vices
Known in our English tongue as Idleness,
The portress at the gateway that entices
To self-abandonment, we should oppress
By her own contrary, a measureless
And lawful industry, with all our power,
Lest the fiend snatch us in an idle hour.

For he with many a cunning cord and bridle
Continually watches us to clap
All whomsoever of us that are idle
And easy to be taken, in his trap.
Not till a man is tossed into his lap
Does he perceive the fiend; let us be loth
To slacken in our work and yield to sloth.

And though we dreaded not what is to be,
That is, our death, reason would teach us keep
From idleness that rots in sluggardry
From whence no harvest comes, which none can reap;
We see that sloth can leash us in a sleep,
To pass the time in sleeping, eating, drinking,
Devouring other people's work, unthinking.

So, to put all such idleness away,
The cause of so much ruin and stagnation,
I have, as diligently as I may,

Idleness, 'the portress at the gateway that entices to self-abandonment'. Idleness was recognized as a brand of sloth in the classification of the seven deadly sins, and the same image of Idleness opening the door to other sins is used in this illumination from the 'Roman de la Rose' where Idleness ushers in 'the Lover'.

Followed the legend in my own translation
Touching thy sufferings and exaltation,
Made of thy garlands, rose and lily-laden,
Cecilia, thine, O martyr, Saint and maiden!

Invocacio ad Mariam

AND thou that art the flower of virgins all,
Of whom St Bernard had such skill to write
To thee at my beginning first I call;
Comfort of sinners, teach me to endite
Thy maiden's death who put the fiend to flight
And won by merit an eternal glory,
As all may find in following her story.

Thou maid and mother, daughter of thy Son,
Thou well of mercy, balm to sinful nature,
In whom God chose His dwelling, as in one
Humblest and highest over every creature,
Who gav'st such nobleness to human feature
That God had no disdain to clothe and wind
His Son in flesh and blood of human kind.

255

ithin the blissful cloister of thy womb
There took man's shape the eternal love and peace,
Lord and guide of the trinal circle, whom
The heavens and earth and sea shall never cease
To glorify, pure virgin, the increase
Of whose fair body, never by man mated,
Was the Creator of all things created.

n thee assembled are magnificence,
Mercy and goodness, with such clemency
That thou, who art the sum of excellence,
Not only helpest those that pray to thee,
But many a time in thy benignity
Thou goest before them freely ere they speak,
O leech of life, and grantest what they seek.

elp me then, fair and meek and blissful maid,
Me, banished in the desert, in the street
Of gall; remember who was not afraid
To say in Cana, 'Lo, the dogs may eat
The crumbs that fall about their masters' feet';
Though I be an unworthy son of Eve,
Accept me for my faith, for I believe.

ince faith is dead that does not live in works,
O therefore give me power to work apace.
Save me from darkness and the fiend that lurks
In darkness, O thou fair and full of grace!
Be thou my advocate in that high place
Where endlessly the angels sing 'Hosanna,'
Mother of Christ, dear daughter of St Anna!

hed thou thy light upon my soul in prison,
Troubled by the contagion of the flesh,
Weighed down by lusts of earth that have arisen
Of false affection, tangled in their mesh;
Haven of refuge, O salvation fresh
And comforting to all by sorrow shaken,
Help me in that which I have undertaken!

nd you, all you that read what I shall write,
Forgive me if I show no diligence
To ornament my story or endite
A subtle style; I take the words and sense
From one who held in holiest reverence
The saint of whom he wrote, and tell her tale,
Begging you to amend it where I fail.

Interpretatio Nominis Ceciliae

IRST let me tell you whence her name has
sprung,
Cecilia, meaning, as the books agree,
'Lily of Heaven' in our English tongue,
To signify her chaste virginity;
Or for the whiteness of her constancy,
The greenness of her conscience, of her fame
The scent and sweetness, 'lily' was her name.

ecilia may betoken 'path to the blind'
From the example given in her story;
Or in Cecilia some would have us find
A union as it were of 'Heaven's glory'
And Leah, the Active Life, in allegory;
'Heaven' is set for thoughts of holiness
And 'Leah' for ceaseless labour and address.

ecilia may be also said to mean
'Wanting in blindness,' as she had the light
Of sapience and a bearing calm and clean;
Or, as the maiden was beloved and bright,
To say from 'Heaven' and 'leos' would be right
And mean 'a Heaven for people,' so to call
The good example of her works to all.

After the conversion and baptism of Valerian, Cecilia's husband, an angel from paradise appears at their house bearing 'two coronals'. These are their crowns of glory, their reward from Heaven. In Chaucer's version they receive them not at the moment of martyrdom but after they determine to live a life of virginity.

or 'leos' means 'people' in the English tongue,
And just as one may look to heaven and see
The sun and moon, and where the stars are hung,
So in this maiden, spiritually,
We see her faith and magnanimity
And the whole clarity of her wisdom thence
In many works of shining excellence.

nd just as these philosophers will write
To prove that heaven is swift and round and burning,
Just so was fair Cecilia the White,
As swift and ceaseless, turning and returning
To works of mercy, and round in her discerning
And perseverance, burning with the flame
Of charity, and so I read her name.

The Second Nun's Tale

HIS maiden, bright Cecilia, so I read,
Was Roman born and came of noble kind
And from her cradle fostered in the creed
Of Christ, and bore His gospel in her mind;
She never ceased in prayer, or so I find
It written of her, to God in love and dread,
Beseeching Him to guard her maidenhead.

nd when this maid was given to a man
In wedlock – he was young and bore the name
(Her legend tells us) of Valerian –
Upon the day of marriage, when it came,
She was devout and humble, still the same;
For there, beneath her robe of golden mesh,
She wore a shirt of hair upon her flesh.

nd while the organs made their melody,
To God alone within her heart there sounded
This prayer, 'Lord, keep my soul and body free
From all defilement, lest I be confounded.'
On Him who died upon a tree she grounded
Her faith in love, and every second day
Or every third she fasted and would pray.

et the night came and she must go to bed
Beside her husband, as is oft the way,
And turning to him privately she said,
'Sweet and beloved husband, if I may,
There is a thing I dearly wish to say
If you will hear, and yet I would conceal it;
Swear to me, then, you never will reveal it.'

irmly Valerian on his honour swore
That for no cause, whatever it might be,
Would he betray her, he could say no more.
And she began to speak. 'I have,' said she,
'A guardian angel, one that tenders me
So great a love, that whether awake or sleeping
My body is committed to his keeping.

ere he to feel – and O, believe it true –
That you had touched me either in love or lust
He instantly would bring your death on you;

Young as you are you would go down to dust.
But if you love me cleanly, as you must,
He will love you, even as he loves me,
And show the glory of his ecstasy.'

St Cecilia (left) in a Book of Hours. Her remains were supposed to
have been taken from the catacombs to a church in Trastevere,
named after her, in 891.

alerian, corrected by God's grace,
Answered again, 'That I may trust in you,
Show me that angel, let me see his face,
And if indeed he be an angel true
Then I will do as you have begged me to,
But if you love another man, on oath
I say this sword of mine shall slay you both.'

ecilia answered, 'You are well advised,
And you shall see the angel if you will,
But first believe in Christ and be baptized.
Go by the Appian way,' she said, 'until
You reach, some three miles hence upon a hill,

A village where the poorer people live.
Go up to them and speak the words I give.

Tell them that I, Cecilia, sent you there
    That they might show you Urban, old and good,
    For secret needs and say your thoughts are fair.
And when you meet Saint Urban, as you should,
Repeat my words; they will be understood
And when he has confessed and purged your heart
You then shall see the angel, ere you part.'

Valerian went out to seek the place
    And just as she had told him there he found
    Holy Saint Urban, met him face to face
At work upon a Christian burial ground,
And told him on what errand he was bound.
And Urban, when his message had been given,
Was filled with joy and raised his hands to heaven.

And from his eyes the tears began to fall.
    'Almighty Lord, O Jesu Christ,' said he,
    'Sower of chaste thought, shepherd of us all,
Take thou the fruit, whose seed of chastity
Thou sowedst in Cecilia, unto Thee!
Lo, like a busy bee that knows no guile
Thy thrall Cecilia serves thee all the while!

Her very spouse, that she but now has taken
    Fierce as a lion hither has she sent
    Meek as a lamb, his violence forsaken
For Thee, dear Lord!' Now, as he spoke, there went
A man before them clad in white and bent
With age; a golden book was in his hand.
Before Valerian he took his stand.

Valerian fell down for very dread
    On seeing him. He raised him from his fall,
    Opened the golden book and thus he read:
'One Lord, one Faith, one God above us all,
One Christendom, and One that we may call
Father, supreme both here and everywhere.'
These were the words in golden letters there.

Thus having read, then said this ancient man,
    'Believest thou these sayings? Yes or no?'
    'All this I do believe,' Valerian
Replied. 'For nothing is more truly so
In Heaven above or in the earth below.'
The ancient vanished then, he knew not where;
Urban the Pope baptized him then and there.

Home to Cecilia then he went and found
    Her standing with an angel in his room;
    The angel held two coronals that were bound
With lily-flowers and roses in full bloom
And to Cecilia then he turned, to whom
He gave the first, the second with its weight
Of roses to Valerian, her mate.

With a clean body and with spotless thought
    Cherish these coronals for ever. They,'
    The angel said, 'from Paradise were brought
For you, and they shall never rot away
Or lose their savour, trust to what I say.
And they are such as none shall see, unless
His heart is chaste and hates all filthiness.

And thou, Valerian, that wert so soon
    Glad to pursue what good advice began,
    Say what thou wouldest; thou shalt have thy boon.'
'I have a brother,' said Valerian,
'In all the world there is no other man
I love so well. I pray he may find grace
To know the truth as I do, in this place.'

The angel said, 'God liketh thy request;
    You both shall bear the palm of martyrdom
    And come hereafter to His blissful rest.'
Now while the angel spoke, Tiburce had come,
Valerian's brother, and aware of some
Sweet savour which the rose and lily cast
About the chamber, felt his heart beat fast,

And 'Where, I wonder, at this time of year
    Can such a fragrance come from? Can you tell?
    The scent,' he said, 'of rose and lily here –
Why, if I had them in my hands their smell
Could pierce no deeper, could not pierce so well.
I find a savour in my heart, and seeing
Nothing, I know that it has changed my being.'

Valerian said, 'Two coronals have we,
    Snow-white and rosy-red and shining fair,
    Such as your eye has never learnt to see;
As you have smelt their savour at my prayer
So, dearest brother, you shall see them there,
If without tardiness you will receive
The very truth, and knowing it, believe.'

Tiburce replied, 'Do you say this to me
    In truth or do I hear it in a dream?'
    'Dreaming,' Valerian said, 'we used to be,
Till now we were in sleep, so it must seem,
But now awake, in truth.' 'Yet how to deem,'
Tiburce replied, 'Whether we're dreaming now?'
Valerian answered, 'I will tell you how.

The angel of God has taught me truth. Your eyes
    Shall also see if you renounce the power
    Of idols and be clean, not otherwise.'
(As to the miracle of these crowns of flower,

Right: This magnificent stained glass window at Bourges cathedral in France recounts the whole of St Cecilia's legend. The top centre shows her marriage to Valerian; in the centre the angel arrives bearing his coronal; at the bottom St Cecilia faces martyrdom in her bath; on the right Valerian with the Blessed Saint Urban.

St Ambrose speaks of it to strengthen our
Belief, commends it solemnly indeed;
The noble Doctor's preface, if you read,

ays thus, "To gain the palm of martyrdom,
   Cecilia, being filled with Heaven's grace,
   Forsook the world, her chamber and her groom,
Witness Valerian and Tiburce, in face
Of whose conversion we may judge her case,
Which God in bounty honoured with a crown
Of flowers for each, brought by an angel down.

his maiden brought these men to bliss above:
   The world well knows the worth, you may be sure,
   Of a devoted chastity in Love.
This St Cecilia showed him, and secure
In faith he held all idols as impure,
Vain, dumb and deaf, even as those that make them;
And so it was she charged him to forsake them.")

ho thinks not so is but a brute at best,'
   Tiburce gave answer, 'if I do not lie.'
   Cecilia turned and kissed him on the breast
In joy that he beheld with inward eye
And saw the truth. Said she, 'Though we should die

This woodcut, printed by Wynkyn de Worde at the end of the fifteenth century, shows a late-medieval view of 'Saints in Glory'. Many figures with nimbuses surround the feet of God the Father who is seated in glory on his heavenly throne surrounded by eleven seraphim. A significant aspect of pre-Reformation Christianity was the panoply of saints, martyrs and other intermediaries between heaven and earth. The prayer addressed to Mary (seated here on God's right hand, crowned but with no nimbus) at the beginning of the Tale closely echoes the prayer of St Bernard in Dante's 'Paradiso'.

For it, let us ally ourselves today.'
Blissful and lovely she went on to say:

ust as the love of Christ has fashioned me
   To be your brother's wife, that love devised
   A new alliance as for you and me,
And so I take you now that have despised
Your idols; therefore go and be baptized,
Make yourself clean and then you shall behold
The angel's face of which your brother told.'

iburce for answer turned and said, 'Dear brother,
   First tell me whom I am to seek and where?'
   'Whom you should seek? Be happy,' said the other.
'None but Pope Urban; I will take you there.'
'Urban, my brother?' He began to stare.
'Is that where you will take me, then?' said he.
'That would be very strange, it seems to me.

ou cannot mean that Urban,' he went on,
   'That has so often been condemned to die
   And lives in holes and corners, here and gone,
   And daren't put forth his head if one goes by?
People would burn him, they would have him fry
If he were seen and caught. To seek him thus
Would surely make them do the same to us.

o, in our search after the Deity
   That Heaven in her secrecies may hide,
   We shall be burnt on earth, most certainly.'
To which Cecilia valiantly replied:
'Men might fear death and would be justified
In seeking to preserve their lives, dear brother,
If there were only this life and no other.

ut there's a better in another place
   That never shall be lost. Be not afraid;
   God's Son has told us of it, by His grace,
The Father's Son, by whom all things were made;
Those creatures in whom reason is displayed
The Holy Ghost proceeding from the Father
Dowers with a living soul, believe it rather.

y word and miracle the Son of God,
   When in this world, declared and we have learned
   There was an after-life for all who trod
The path He chose.' 'Dear sister,' he returned,
'Did you not say just now, in what concerned
The Being of God, there was but One, and He
Was Lord in truth? Yet now you speak of three.'

hat too I shall explain,' she said, 'in season.
   Just as the wisdom in a man is three,
   Having invention, memory and reason,
So also in God's nature there can be
Three Persons that are One in Deity.'
And she began to preach in eager fashion
Of Christ's first coming and His pain and passion,

Prayer, of course, was central to Christian life. But from Chaucer's time onwards the search for a more direct relationship with God began to challenge the hierarchy.

And all He underwent in our condition,
    And how the Son of God had been withheld
    On earth from making man a full remission,
Bound as he is in sinfulness and quelled
By many cares, and when she had dispelled
His lingering doubt, Tiburce in eager hope
Went with Valerian to seek the Pope.

Urban thanked God; with happy heart and light
    He christened him and within little space
    Perfected him in learning as God's knight;
And after that Tiburce was filled with grace
And every day thereafter saw the face
Of God's bright angel, and if he was stirred
To ask of God a boon, his prayer was heard.

It would be hard to tell in order due
    How many wonders for them Jesus wrought,
    But lastly, if I may be brief with you,
The officers of Rome went out and sought
These brothers. To the prefect they were brought,
Almachius named. He questioned them and strove
To search their will, and to the idol of Jove

He sent them. 'Make them sacrifice,' he said,
    'Or strike their heads off; so my orders are.'
    One Maximus, his officer, the head
Among the prefects and his registrar,
Took these two saints together, whom so far
I have described, and brought them through the city,
And as he led them forth he wept for pity.

When Maximus had listened to their teaching
    He got the torturers to give him leave
    To take them to his house, and by their preaching
He was converted ere the fall of eve.
Their faith was found sufficient to retrieve

The torturers too and bring them to disown
Their false beliefs and trust in God alone.

Cecilia came when evening drew to night
    With priests who christened all with one accord,
    And afterwards when morning had grown light
She gravely said, 'O you that are restored
In Christ and are the soldiers of the Lord,
Cast off the works of darkness and put on
The armour of righteousness, the night is gone.

You have done battle greatly and prevail,
    Your course is done, your faith has never swerved;
    Go to the crown of life that cannot fail.
    The righteous Judge and Saviour you have served
Shall give it you, for you have well deserved.'
And then they led them forth to sacrifice
As I have told you, or to pay the price.

But, taken to the temple, no advice
    – To tell the matter briefly – could persuade
    These men to offer incense, sacrifice
Or bow to Jove, but on their knees they prayed
To God with humble hearts and unafraid.
Their heads were severed in that very place;
Their souls went upward to the King of Grace.

And Maximus who saw it testified
    With piteous tears that he had seen the sight;
    High into Heaven he saw their spirits glide
With angels, full of clarity and light.
His words converted many before night.
And when Almachius heard what he had said
He had him scourged to death with whips of lead.

Cecilia buried him beside her own,
    Beside Tiburce, beside Valerian,
    In her own burial-place beneath a stone.
Almachius therefore hastily began
To issue orders; officer and man
Were sent to fetch Cecilia before him
To honour Jove with incense and adore him.

But they, converted by her holy lore,
    Wept and affirmed their fullest confidence
    In all she said, and cried out, more and more,
'Christ is God's Son, without a difference,
Verily God; we cite in evidence
That He has saints to serve him, such as these,
And, though we die, proclaim it on our knees.'

Almachius (for these doings made a stir)
    Ordered her to be fetched that he might see
    Cecilia for himself and question her.
'What sort of woman, then, are you?' said he.
'I am a gentlewoman born,' said she.
'I'm asking you,' he said, 'of your belief,
About your faith, though it may cause you grief.'

For prick it with a needle when it's blown
And the inflated boast is overthrown.'

'Well, you began most contumaciously,'
He said, 'and you continue turbulent.
Do you not know the Principality
Has given ordinance to this intent
That every Christian shall have punishment
Unless he will deny his Christian creed,
And that denying it he shall be freed?'

'Your princes err, and so your nobles do,'
Cecilia said, 'and by some crazy law
Would make us guilty, but it is not true.
You know us innocent; because you saw
That we held Christ in reverence and awe
And bore the name of Christians, down you sat
And put a crime upon us, just for that.

'But we, that know the name for virtuous,
Renounce it not, whatever be the price.'
Almachius answered her, 'The choice stands thus;
Abjure your Christendom, or sacrifice!
There's no escaping; follow my advice.'
At this the beautiful and blessed maid
Began to laugh and answered, unafraid,

'O Judge, confused for all your subtlety,
Would you that I denied my innocence?
Is it your wish to make a sinner of me?
Look at him there upholding this pretence
In open court, a madman lost to sense
In his endeavours!' He answered, 'Sorry wretch,
Do you know how far my power may stretch?

'Is there no force or power in my breath?
Have not our mighty princes given to me
Authority and power of life and death?
Why do you speak so proudly then?' said he.
'I do not speak in pride but steadfastly,'
She answered; 'I, and those upon my side,
Have deadly hatred for the sin of pride.

'If you are not afraid to hear the truth
I will be open and expose to view
Your monstrous lies. Authority forsooth!
You say your princes have bestowed on you
Power of life and death; but that's not true.
You can take life, have power to destroy,
But that's the only power you enjoy.

'But you may say your princes in their might
Made you death's minister. Say more than so
And you will lie. Your power is very slight.'
'Muzzle your boldness,' said Almachius, 'go!
And pay our gods the sacrifice you owe.
Your insults to myself can be endured,
I'm a philosopher and am inured.

*God the father, a detail from a late-medieval stained glass window.
Martyrdom is the theme of this tale and was a powerful thesis of the
whole medieval religious canon. Sainthood and martyrdom were
virtual synonyms. This, of course, comes most explicitly from the
greatest of all martyrdoms, the sacrifice by God the Father of his
own Son on behalf of mankind, re-enacted by priests every day in
the Sacrament of the Mass.*

'You have begun your questions foolishly,'
Answered Cecilia, 'seeking to conclude
Two points in one, which shows stupidity.'
He, vexed at her rejoinder, then pursued,
'How is it that your answer is so rude?'
'How!' she replied on being thus arraigned,
'Of conscience and pure heart and faith unfeigned.'

Almachius answered, 'Do you take no heed
Of my authority?' And she returned,
'Your power is little to be feared indeed;
Power of mortal man is soon discerned
To be a bladder full of wind and spurned;

ut there are insults that I will not swallow
That you have levelled at our gods,' said he.
Cecilia cried, 'Your sophistries are hollow,
There's not a word in what you've said to me
That did not publish your obliquity
And prove yourself, I say it without grudge,
An ignorant official, a vain judge.

othing you lack to make your outward eye
Totally blind, for what is seen by all
To be a stone you seek to glorify,
A senseless piece of stone that you would call
A god! Put out your hand and let it fall
Upon it, touch it, taste it! You will find
Your hand says "Stone!" although your eyes are blind.

eople will laugh at you to hear such stuff
As you have uttered, they will think you mad,
For it is known, and commonly enough,
That God Almighty is in Heaven, clad
In glory, and these idols – if you had
The eyes to see it – offer no delight
To you or to themselves; not worth a mite.'

ll this she said and more it well may be,
Till he grew angry. 'Take her whence she came
Home to her house, and in her house,' said he,
'Burn her to ashes in a bath of flame.'
Thus he commanded and they did the same,
They shut her in a bath and set alight
A mighty fire beneath it. Day and night

hey stoked it and from night to day again,
And yet in spite of all the flame and heat
She sat there cool and neither feeling pain

Nor sweating, not a drop from head to feet.
Yet it was in that bath she was to meet
Her death, for this Almachius in his wrath
Sent a man down to kill her in the bath.

hree grievous strokes upon her neck he smote,
This torturer, but by no circumstance
Could he succeed in cutting through her throat;
Now at that time there was an ordinance
Forbidding executioners to chance
Smiting a fourth stroke, whether soft or sore,
And so this torturer dared do no more.

alf dead with carven neck she perished there;
He left her lying and he went his way.
But all the Christian folk, or such as were
About her then, bound her with sheets to stay
The flow of blood, and she, to the third day,
Lingered in pain yet never ceased in teaching
The faith she fostered, and continued preaching.

oods, movables, her rights in everything
She then bequeathed to Urban, saying, 'Lo,
There was a boon I asked of Heaven's King;
Three days of respite I desired that so
I might commend these souls before I go
To you that you may guide them in their search
And build my house for a perpetual church.'

t Urban and his deacons secretly
Fetched forth her body and buried it by night
Among his saints. Her mansion came to be
The Church of St Cecilia, hers by right;
St Urban hallowed it, as well he might.
And in that Church in every noble way
Christ and his saint are honoured to this day.

An alchemist seated at his table while his assistants stoke the furnace. 'The Canon's Yeoman's Tale' shows how the hope of transmuting base metals into gold could be made a bait for the greedy and credulous.

THE CANON'S YEOMAN'S TALE

The Canon's Yeoman's Prologue

WHEN St Cecilia's life had reached the
            close,
        Some five miles further on, as I suppose,
        At Boughton-under-Blean we saw a hack
Come galloping up. Its rider was in black
And under that a dingy surplice lay.
The hackney horse he rode was dappled grey
And sweating hard, it was a sight to see;
It must have galloped miles, it seemed to me.
His yeoman's horse was also puffed and blowing,
And sweated so it hardly could keep going.
The foam stood high upon its collar, flecked
Just like a magpie – that was the effect.

A wallet on the crupper, doubled tight,
        was fastened and it seemed he travelled light
        To suit a summer day, this worthy man.
And as he came towards us I began
Wondering about him till I understood
His cloak was sewn together with his hood,
And pondering this it needed no research
To write him down a canon of the church.

h is hat hung down behind him on a lace
        As he had ridden at more than trotting-pace,
        In fact he had been galloping like mad.
To keep him cool and catch the sweat, he had
Beneath his hood a dock-leaf, dripping wet.
It was a joy to see that canon sweat!
His forehead dropped down moisture like a still
For plantain, pellitory-juice or squill.
When he came up with us he gave a hearty
Shout and he said, 'God bless this jolly party!
How fast I've spurred,' he said, 'all for your sake;
I was determined I would overtake
Your happy crowd and ride in company.'

h is man was just as full of courtesy
        And said, 'My lords, I saw the day begin
        With your departure, when you left the inn,
And so I warned my lord and master, who
Is very eager, sir, to ride with you
Just for enjoyment; he is fond of fun.'

'G od bless you, friend, for warning him. Well done!'
        Our Host rejoined. 'And one may well suppose
        Your lord is wise, he looks it, goodness knows;
I'll wager he's high-spirited as well.
D'you think he has a tale or two to tell
To brighten up our company this morning?'

'W ho? He? My lord? Rather! I give you warning
        He's a great joker, all for jollity,
        Not half he is, you can rely on me.
If you had studied him as well as I,
You'd be amazed how capable and sly
When he gets down to work my master is.
All sorts of enterprise! Those jobs of his
Are more than any of you here and now
Could bring about unless he showed you how.
Homely as he may look among your crowd,
If you but knew him you would all be proud;
You wouldn't forgo acquaintance with my lord,
Not for a fortune; if I could afford
To bet, I'd wager all in my possession.
He is a man of very great discretion,
I warn you, sir, he's a superior being.'
'Well,' said our Host, 'while I'm not disagreeing,
What is he then? A clerical? Or what?'

'O nly a cleric? Him? I should say not!'
        The Yeoman said. 'Much more, or else I'm daft.
        Let me inform you briefly of his craft.

I say my master has such subtle powers
        – Although I help him in this work of ours
        I can't explain them all, he's so far on –
That all this blessed road we ride upon
From here as far as Canterbury town,
Why, he could turn it all clean upside down
And pave it all with silver and with gold!'

T he Yeoman paused as if his tale was told.
        Our thoughtful Host said, '*Benedicite!*
        All that you say sounds wonderful to me,
For if your lord is truly so sagacious,
So much to be respected, goodness gracious,
Why does he take his dignity so light?

That gabardine is hardly worth a mite
– Well, for a man like that; God bless my wits,
It isn't even clean, it's torn to bits!
Why is your lord so sluttish, may I say?
With all those magic powers can't he pay
For better cloth, if what you say is so?
Answer me that, that's what I'd like to know.'
hy?' said the Yeoman. 'Need you ask me that?
God help us all, the thing he's working at
Can never be successful – this remark
I can't make openly, so keep it dark –
He knows too much, I think. Easy to scoff,
But things when overdone just don't come off,
The learned tell us, it's a waste endeavour;
That's why he's such a fool – he's far too clever.
Often enough a man with too much brain
Is likely to misuse it. What's the gain?
I'm very sorry for it, but that's his way;
God help him! I have nothing more to say.'
ell, never mind, my man,' replied our Host,
'But what's this subtlety of his you boast,
If I may ask? What does he do all day,
If he's as sly and crafty as you say?
Where do you live now, if you don't mind telling?'
'In slums,' he answered, 'suburbs are our dwelling;
We lurk in holes and corners and blind alleys,
Places where every thief and robber rallies
By nature, fear-stricken and secret places
Where those reside who dare not show their faces;

This woodcut, printed by Wynkyn de Worde, gives a good impression of late-medieval London – its crowded buildings almost bursting through the walls – where Chaucer's tale is set.

That, to tell truth, is where we go a-walking.'
ow,' said the Host, 'if I may go on talking,
Why are you so discoloured round the face?'
'God was unkind to it, that's about the case,'
He said; 'I'm used to blowing up the fire
And that's what changed my colour. I don't enquire
Into complexions, mirrors leave me cold.
I work like mad at learning to make gold.
We're always blundering, spilling things in the fire,
But for all that we fail in our desire
For our experiments reach no conclusion,
Yet we keep plenty under that illusion
And borrow money, say a pound or two,
Or ten or twelve and even more, we do,
And make them think that at the very least
Their money will be doubled or increased.
Yet it's a lie but still we live in hope
It might be managed somehow; on we grope.
But the whole science lies so far ahead
It can't be overtaken, though we said
On oath it could, it slides away so fast.
It will make beggars of us all at last.'
ow while his Yeoman was enlarging thus
In came the Canon, hearing him discuss,
To listen closer; his suspicious head
Distrusted anything that people said.
Cato has said a guilty conscience delves;
The guilty think all talk is of themselves.
That was the cause the Canon drew in near
His Yeoman; he was very keen to hear,
And he addressed his Yeoman, having heard,
'You hold your tongue, don't speak another word
Or if you do you'll pay for it, d'you see?
You're slandering me before this company.
What's more, you're telling things that should be hidden.'
eah?' said our Host. 'Go on, don't be forbidden,
I wouldn't mind his threats if I were you,
They're not worth anything.' 'No more I do,'
He answered. When the Canon realized
That all his secrets were to be surprised
He fled away in very grief and shame.
'Ha!' said the Yeoman. 'Now we'll have a game,
Now I can talk, and I've a lot to tell.
He's gone, the foul fiend carry him off to Hell!
We'll never meet again, I'll tell you flat,
For pound or penny, I can promise that.
He was the one first brought me to the game,
Grief strike him down, before he dies, in shame!
For it's a serious thing to me I say,
As I am well aware, think as you may.
And yet for all my misery and grief,
Long hours and injuries without relief,
I never could leave the business, any price.
O that I had a brain that would suffice
To tell you all that's proper to that art!
Nevertheless I'll try to tell you part,
And since my master's gone I will not spare;
All that I know about it I'll declare.'

The Canon's Yeoman's Tale

PART I

I'VE served this canon seven years and more,
Yet am no nearer science than before.
All that I ever had I've lost thereby,
And so, God knows, have many more than I.
Time was when I was fresh and fond of cheer,
Liked decent clothes and other handsome gear;
Now I might wear my hose upon my head,
And where my colour was a lively red
My face is wan and wears a leaden look;
If you try science you'll be brought to book.
My eyes are bleared with work on preparations,
That's all the good you get from transmutations.
That slippery science stripped me down so bare
That I'm worth nothing, here or anywhere.
Added to that I am so deep in debt
From borrowing money, you can lay a bet
Long as I live I'll never pay it, never!

Chaucer shows considerable knowledge of alchemy (top right). Some scholars believe this Tale was inspired by a personal grievance as a result of his own dealings with an alchemist. One of the canons of the King's Chapel at Windsor was reputed to be an alchemist and Chaucer, in his capacity as Clerk of the King's Works, an appointment he received in 1389, may well have had some dealings with him. This theory receives some support from the fact that in his later years Chaucer was repeatedly borrowing small amounts of cash.

Let every man be warned by me for ever;
Whoever tries his hand at such behavings,
If he goes on I say will lose his savings.
What's more, so help me God, his only gains
Are empty money-bags and addled brains.
And by the time the man's gone raging mad
And risked and lost whatever goods he had,
He then eggs others on and off they run
To lose their goods, as he himself has done.

A spiteful wretch takes pleasure when he sees
That others suffer from the same disease,
So I was told once by a learned man.
But what's the odds? I'll on as I began.

When we had fixed a place to exercise
Our esoteric craft, we all looked wise;
Our terms were highly technical and quaint.
I blew the fire up till fit to faint.

As for proportions, why should I rattle on
About the substances we worked upon,
The six or seven ounces it may be
Of silver, or some other quantity,
Or bother to name the things that we were piling
Like orpiment, burnt bones and iron filing
Ground into finest powder, all the lot,
Or how we poured them in an earthen pot?
(You put in salt and pepper, be it stated,
Before these powders I enumerated,
Securely covered by a sheet of glass,
And plenty of other things, but let them pass.)
And how the pot and glass were daubed with clay
For fear the gases might escape away,
And then the fire, whether slow or brisk,
We had to make, the trouble and the risk
We took to sublimate the preparation
Or in the amalgaming and calcination
Of quicksilver, crude mercury that is?

We always failed, for all those tricks of his.
Our orpiment, our mercury sublimate,
Our lead protoxide ground on a porphyry plate
And measured out in ounces, grain by grain,
Gave us no help. Our labour was in vain.
Neither the gas that rose as things grew hot
Nor solids at the bottom of the pot
Were the least use in what we tried to do,
Lost was our trouble, lost our labour too,
And all the money, in the name of Hell,
That we'd laid out on it was lost as well.

And there was also many another thing
Pertaining to the trade we had to bring,
Though I can't name them in an ordered plan

Because I'm an uneducated man;
Yet I will list them as they come to mind,
Though not distinguishing their class and kind:
Armenian clay, borax and verdigris,
Earthen and glass-ware vessels piece by piece,
Our urinals, our pots for oil-extraction,
Crucibles, pots for sublimative action,
Phial, alembic, beaker, gourd-retort,
And other useless nonsense of the sort
Not worth a leek, needless to name them all;
Water in rubefaction, bullock's gall,
Arsenic, brimstone, sal ammoniac,
And herbs that I could mention by the sack,
Moonwort, valerian, agrimony and such,
Which I could number if it mattered much.
Our lamps – we had them burning day and night
To help us to succeed, if we but might!

For all Chaucer's obvious dislike of alchemy, it had originated as a scientific study. Gold was regarded not merely as the most precious of metals but as the noblest of substances. This led to a belief that metals formed a hierarchy with gold at the apex and that other metals differed from each other in terms of absolute worth. But they were, it was believed, all representative of intermediate stages in the production of gold. In time the warmth of the earth would bring them to perfection (i.e. turn them into gold) so if this process could be accelerated by the alchemist, then gold could be produced.

Our furnace too for calcifying action,
Our waters in a state of albefaction,
Chalk, quicklime, ashes and the white of eggs,
Various powders, clay, piss, dung and dregs,
Waxed bags, saltpetre, vitriol and a whole
Variety of fires of wood and coal;
Alkali, tartar, salt in preparation,
Matters combust or in coagulation,
Clay mixed with horse-hair, sometimes with my own,
Crystallized alum, oil of tartar thrown
With tartar crude and unfermented beer,
Yeast and a dozen more than you shall hear,
Realgar, various absorbent batters
And, I may add, incorporative matters;
Our silver in a state of citrination,
Things sealed in wax and things in fermentation,
Our moulds, our vessels for assaying metal
And many other things I learnt to settle
I'll tell as I was taught, if you want more.

There were the bodies seven and the spirits four
Which my instructor frequently rehearsed;
Among the spirits quicksilver came first
And orpiment came second, then he passed
To sal ammoniac and brimstone last.
As for the seven bodies I should mention,
Here they all are, if they are worth attention:
Gold for the sun and silver for the moon,
Iron for Mars and quicksilver in tune
With Mercury, lead which prefigures Saturn
And tin for Jupiter. Copper takes the pattern
Of Venus if you please! This cursed trade
Robs one of all the money one has made,
And all one spends on it or round about it
Will certainly be lost, I cannot doubt it.

If you would publish your infatuation
Come on and try your hand at transmutation;
If one of you has money in his fist
Step up and make yourself an alchemist.
Perhaps you think the trade is easy learnt?
Why then, come on and get your fingers burnt;
Monk, friar, priest, canon, let them come who may,
And study books and papers night and day
To learn the weird directions verse by verse,
They'll find it's all in vain, God knows, and worse.
And as for trying to teach a simpleton,
Pooh! No use talking of it; can't be done.
Whether you know your alphabet or not,
All's one for all the good that may be got.
Learned and simple by my soul's salvation
Achieve the same results from transmutation
Equally well when all is said and done;
They all fail absolutely, every one.

And still I have forgotten my intention
To speak of iron filings and to mention
Corrosive liquids, ways of mollifying
Or hardening substances, or of supplying
Oils and ablutions, stores of fusible metal,
And so on. It's beyond a book to settle

These matters, any book; it would be best
To give this catalogue and myself a rest,
For I imagine I have said enough
To raise the devil, be he never so rough.

Ah no, let be! For the Philosopher's Stone,
Called the Elixir, never can be known.
We seek and seek, and were it once discovered
We should be safe enough – expenses covered.
But there's no way; whatever paths we trod
The search was useless and I swear to God,
For all our cunning, when all's tried and done
That stone won't yield itself to anyone.
It's made us squander all we ever had,
Losses enough to drive us nearly mad
But for the hope that crept about our heart
Always supposing, when we felt the smart,
It would relieve us of our sad condition;
Sharp was the hope and hard the supposition.

I give fair warning you may search for ever;
A golden future lures one on to sever
Oneself from all one ever had, and trust
An art for which one cannot lose the lust;
People will always find it bitter-sweet,
Or so it seems. With nothing but a sheet
To cover one at night, with no array
Other than some outlandish cloak by day
One yet would sell them both and be bereft.
No one can stop until there's nothing left.

Go where they may a man can always tell
Such people by their pungent brimstone smell;
For all the world they stink as will a goat,
A hot and ram-like smell that seems to float
About them, and a man a mile away
Will catch the foul infection, I dare say.
See? By the smell and by the threadbare cloak
You're pretty sure to recognize these folk.

If privately you ask them to confess
Why they go round in such a shabby dress,
They'll turn at once and whisper in your ear
That if they should be spotted they must fear
Death for their learning, such is their pretence.
That's how these people trade on innocence.

Well, pass on to the story you require;
Before the pot is placed upon the fire
My master takes a certain quantity
Of metals which he tempers, none but he
– I can speak boldly now he's gone away –
For he's a cunning worker as they say,
At any rate he's made himself a name;
He blundered very often just the same.
And how, d'you think? It happens, like as not,
There's an explosion and good-bye the pot!
These metals are so violent when they split
Our very walls can scarce stand up to it,
Unless well-built and made of stone and lime –
Bang go the metals through them every time.
And some are driven down into the ground
– That way we used to lose them by the pound –

And some are scattered all about the floor;
Some even jump into the roof, what's more.
Although the devil didn't show his face
I'm pretty sure he was about the place.
In Hell itself where he is lord and master
There couldn't be more rancour in disaster
Than when our pots exploded as I told you;
All think they've been let down and start to scold you.

Some said the way the fire was made was wrong;
Others said, 'No – the bellows. Blown too strong.'
That frightened me, I blew them as a rule.
'Stuff!' said a third. 'You're nothing but a fool,
It wasn't tempered as it ought to be.'
'No!' said a fourth. 'Shut up and listen to me;
I say it should have been a beech-wood fire
And that's the real cause, or I'm a liar.'

I cannot tell you why the thing went wrong;
Recriminations though were hot and strong.
'Well,' said my lord, 'there's nothing more to do.
I'll note these dangers for another brew;
I'm pretty certain that the pot was cracked.
Be that as may, don't gape! We've got to act.
Don't be alarmed, help to sweep up the floor
Just as we always do, and try once more.
Pluck up your hearts!' The muck was gathered up,
A canvas then was laid to form a cup
And all the muck was thrown into a sieve;
He sifted it for what it yet might give.

'By God,' says one, 'I saw some metal fall,
Some's saved although we haven't got it all.
If things went wrong just now and acted tough,
Another time they may go well enough.
We've got to risk our goods if we're to gain.
What about merchants? Lord! They don't maintain
A fixed prosperity, believe you me.
Sometimes their goods are swallowed by the sea,
And sometimes they come safely back to port.'
'Well, calm yourself,' my master would retort;
'Next time I shall have things in proper frame,
I'll see our ship comes home, or take the blame.
Something went wrong I know, I'll find out what.'

Another said the fire was too hot.
But whether hot or cold you may depend
We always met with failure in the end.
Yet, though we never reached the wished conclusion
We still went raving on in our illusion,
Sitting together, arguing on and on
And every one as wise as Solomon.

However, all that glitters is not gold,
And that's the truth as we're so often told.
It isn't every apple on the spray
Is good to eat, lament it how you may.
It's just the same with us. Though it may please us
To think we're wise, the wisest one, by Jesus,
Will prove the biggest fool, that's my belief,
And he that seems the honestest, a thief.
That will be clear enough to you, my friends,
Before I leave you and my story ends.

PART II

HERE is a canon going up and down
Amongst us, one who could infect a town
As large as Nineveh and Rome spread flat
With Troy and three or four on top of that.
The endless tricks and cunning of this crook
Are more than could be written in a book
Though you sat down and wrote a thousand years;
He has no equal in this vale of tears.
The terms he uses wriggle, wind and scuttle
In tones of voice so infinitely subtle,
A man engaged with him in conversation
Soon finds his brain is dizzy with rotation,
Unless the man's a devil like himself.
Many a man he's cozened of his pelf
And will again, if he should live awhile.
Yet there are men will travel mile on mile
To seek this canon out and be acquainted,
Not knowing everything he does is tainted.
So if you care to listen to what I say
You shall hear all about it right away.

I f, holy canons of the church, it rouses
The thought that I am slandering your houses,
Since it is of a canon I am speaking,
Reject the thought! God knows, there is some sneaking
Rascal in every house and God forbid
That all were judged by what one madman did.
Slandering you's no part of my intention,
But to set right the evils that I mention.

N or is my tale aimed specially at you;
It will apply to many others too.
Among the twelve apostles our Creator
Found faith in all but one, who was a traitor.
Then why should the remainder be to blame
That stood in innocence? I say the same
Of you, except for this, if you will hear:
If any lurking Judas should appear
Among you, fling him out I say betimes,
Before you're shamed and beggared by his crimes.
And therefore take no umbrage, sirs, I pray,
And in this instance listen to what I say.

T here was a chantry priest, it would appear,
One who had lived in London many a year,
So pleasant in his manner and so able,
The lady in whose house he sat at table
Refused to take a farthing's worth of pay
For board and clothes, whatever his display,
And she allowed him pocket-money as well.
No matter for that; I shall proceed to tell
My story of the canon, whose intrusion
Brought this unhappy priest to his confusion.

T his treacherous canon, then, came in one day,
Entered the priest's apartment where he lay
And begged him to advance a certain sum,

A sixteenth-century alchemist in his den with his furnace. Alchemists recognized seven metals corresponding with the seven planets of the medieval astronomers.

Which was to be repaid him, saying, 'Come,
Lend me a mark, it's only for three days,
I'll pay you on the nail – I'm one who pays.
And if I fail you when you come to check,
Another time just hang me by the neck!'

T his priest produced the money on the spot;
The canon, after thanking him a lot,
Took leave of him and went upon his way
And brought his money back the proper day.
When it had been paid back and matters righted
This foolish priest of course was quite delighted
And said, 'Trust me, I never take offence
If someone comes to borrow a few pence
Or anything I have in my possession
When he's a honest man of good profession
And doesn't break his day if he should owe;
To such a man I never can say no.'

W hat!' said the canon. 'I not pay when due?
That would be something altogether new!
My honour is a thing I hope to keep
For ever till the moment when I creep
Into my grave. God send I do indeed;
You can trust that as surely as the creed.
And I thank God – in good hour be it spoken –
No one can say my word was ever broken
For any gold or silver I was lent;
I never stole a farthing with intent.

N ow, sir,' he said, 'to speak of my concerns,
Since you are fond of doing kindly turns
And were particularly kind to me,
To pay you back the coin of charity
I'll tell you something, if you care to learn,
In simple language how I came to turn
My talents towards alchemy and science.
Watch! You can place an absolute reliance

On seeing me work a miracle ere I go.'
    hat!' said the priest. 'Can that be really so?
    Mother of God! I beg you to proceed!'

'   t your commandment, sir, I will indeed,'
    He answered, 'God forbid that I should not.'
    D'you see? This thief's kind service was a plot.
How true it is that proffered service stinks!
So say the wise, and anyone who thinks.
I'll verify that saying in a while
Upon this canon, root of fraud and guile.

An alchemist and his assistant in a woodcut attributed to Holbein.
Repeated failure and disappointment could not shake medieval faith
in the possibility of manufacturing the philosopher's stone, that
would be capable of transmuting base metal into gold merely by
touch. Successive failures were always attributed to technical
difficulties or to miscalculations – as Chaucer brilliantly parodies in
this Tale. 'Yet, though we never reached the wished conclusion/We
still went raving on in our illusion,/Sitting together, arguing on and
on/And everyone as wise as Solomon.'

He took a special pleasure and delight,
Such was his fiendish heart, and appetite
For bringing Christian people to destruction;
God keep us from his treacherous seduction!
    he priest had no idea with whom he dealt,
    And what was coming to him never felt.
    O foolish priest! O innocent in bliss,
Soon to be blinded, and by avarice!
O God-abandoned, blind in a complete
And thoughtless ignorance of the deceit
This wily fox is putting into shape!
You're in the snare, there will be no escape;
And therefore to press on to a conclusion
That only can refer to your confusion,
Unhappy man, I hurry on to volley
Anathemas upon your witless folly
And on the treachery of that other wretch
As far as my abilities will stretch.
    ou think this canon was my master, eh?
    Sir Host, by Mary of Heaven let me say
    It was another canon and not he,
    A hundred times more skilled in trickery.
His frauds have cozened people many a time;
It dulls my wits to speak of it in rhyme.

Whenever I think of them it brings a rush
Of blood for very shame, I have to blush
– At any rate my cheeks begin to glow
Though there's no colour in them, well I know;
My face is tarnished, fumes of the diverse
Metals you heard me latterly rehearse
Have wasted and consumed and turned it yellow.
Now take account of this accursed fellow:
'   ir,' he addressed the priest, 'send out your man
    For quicksilver, as quickly as you can;
    Let him bring several ounces, two or three,
And when he's back I promise you shall see
A miracle you never saw before.'
'   ertainly,' said the priest, 'he's at the door,
    It shall be done at once.' The man was sent,
    Ready to do his bidding; off he went
And, to tell truth, returned immediately
Bringing three ounces of the mercury,
And gave them to the canon for a start.
    he canon laid them carefully apart
    And sent the servant out again for coal,
    In order to start work towards his goal.
    he man came back and brought a scuttleful;
    This canon then drew forth a crucible
    Out of his bosom, showed it to his dupe,
'And now,' he said, 'be good enough to stoop
And measure out an ounce of mercury.
This is our instrument, as you can see.
Open your hand; now put the mercury in,
That's it . . . and in the name of Christ begin
The study of science, be an alchemist!
    ew, very few indeed, I would enlist
    With those who share the secrets of my science.
    But you shall watch me, using this appliance,
Do an experiment. I shall reduce
Or mortify this metal – no abuse
Of your good faith – before your very eyes.

This woodcut represents the alchemical symbolism of the process of
transmutation whereby one metal turned into another. The king
(gold) is here being killed by his son (mercury) in order that he and
the five 'servant' metals (lead, tin, copper, iron and silver) may be
transmuted into gold through the king's resurrection.

An alchemist and his furnace. The heat of the furnace was supposed to accelerate the process whereby the heat of the earth, over the years, was thought to transmute baser metals into gold. This illustration comes from Elias Ashmole's 'Theatrum Chemicum Britannicum', a treatise on chemistry and alchemy. Much of this book was based on the manuscript of Thomas Norton's 'Ordinal', an alchemical treatise written in about 1477 but never printed.

Yes, you shall watch it as it mortifies
And changes into silver just as fine
And good as any in your purse or mine
Or anywhere else, and just as malleable.
If not, call me a liar and unable
To show my face, a subject for your mirth!
I have a powder here that cost the earth
And it will make all good, for it's the basis
Of all my power – I'll show you – in these cases.
Send your man off, tell him to wait outside,
And shut the door on him. I won't be spied
Upon at work, for no one else must see
The way we set to work in alchemy.'
He gave his orders and the thing was done,
The servant was sent packing at a run,
The chamber door was bolted with a jerk
And these philosophers got down to work.
At the accursed canon's fell desire
The priest then set the thing upon the fire
And grabbed the bellows busily and blew.
Into the crucible the canon threw
This powder – what it was I cannot tell;

Possibly chalk, or glass would do as well,
Or anything else indeed, not worth a fly
To hoodwink him – and urged him to look spry
And cover up the crucible with coal.
'To demonstrate my love for you, dear soul,'
The canon said, 'in what we're going to do,
I'll leave the handling of it all to you.'
'Oh, thank you!' said the priest, who was delighted,
And couched the coals just as he was invited.
And while he busied himself this fiendish wretch,
This treacherous canon, whom the devil fetch,
Produced a bit of beech-wood, charred to coal,
In which there had been subtly bored a hole
That held an ounce of silver filings, stopped
With wax securely, lest a filing dropped.
Please understand this treacherous invention
Was not made then, but made of long intention;
The canon had devised it all before,
And other dodges too. I'll tell you more
Hereafter of those other things he brought,
For long before he came he had the thought
Of tricking him. So he did before they parted.
He couldn't wait to skin him, having started.
It dulls my wits, I say, to speak of him.
Oh, to take vengeance on this treacherous, trim
Liar! If only I knew how! But there,
He's slippery – here and there and everywhere.
Now listen, gentlemen, for God's dear love.
He took this coal for which I spoke above
And palmed it dexterously, while the priest,
Still busy as I said, had nearly ceased
Poking, as I have told you, with a prong
Among the coals. 'You're doing it all wrong!'
The canon said, 'Here's how it ought to be,
Dear chap, I'll fix it; give the thing to me,
Just let me interfere a little. There!
St Giles, I'm sorry for you! I declare
You've got quite hot – why, man, you're pouring sweat,
Here, take this cloth and wipe yourself, you're wet.'
And while the priest was mopping up his face
The canon took his coal – the damned disgrace! –
And stuck it in the middle, somewhat higher
Than was the crucible, and blew the fire
Till up it flamed and all the coals were red.
'And now let's have a drink,' the canon said;
'All will be well quite soon, I'll undertake.
Sit down, let's cheer ourselves for goodness' sake.'
After a while this canon's beechen coal
Burnt up; out came the silver from the hole
Into the crucible and began to run
As you'd expect. What else could it have done?
Couched well above the flames it couldn't miss.
The priest, alas, knew nothing of all this,
Thinking the coals were all alike and good;
It was a trick he had not understood.
And when this alchemist saw all was ready
'Rise up,' he said, 'Sir priest, beside me – steady,
We haven't got a mould. Let's take a walk

For we shall need to buy ourselves some chalk
Which I can carve, if I may make so bold,
Into the shape required for a mould.
And you must get me out a bowl or pan
With water in it, for I tell you, man,
Our business here is just about to sprout.
And just to disabuse you of all doubt,
While you're away, to clear me of suspicion
I shall go with you on your expedition
And stay with you till we return once more.'

And to be brief he then unlocked the door,
Went out and shut it, turning to re-lock it,
And off they went. The key was in his pocket.

Presently back they came with no delay.
Why should I drag my story out all day?
He took the chalk when they got back again
And made a mould of it. Let me explain:
Out of his sleeve I say he took a rod
Of silver – pour thy vengeance on him, God! –
Which weighed an ounce exactly; this he took
(Watch for the tricks of this accursed crook),
And carved his mould to make a perfect fit
For this same silver rod, depend on it,
So furtively the priest, you may believe,
Saw nothing. Then he tucked it up his sleeve,
Turned to the fire, took out the preparation
And poured it in the mould with great elation.
He cast the mould into the water-pan
When ready, saying to the priest, poor man,
'Look what we've got, put in your hand and grope
And you will find some silver there, I hope.'

Hell's devils! What else could have been the stuff?
Silver filings are silver right enough.

The priest put in his hand and took a scoop
And out he brought the metal with a whoop,
Thrilled to the veins to see this silver rod.
'God's blessing on you, and the Mother of God
And all his saints preserve you, worthy master!'
He cried. 'And may they bring me to disaster
Unless you will vouchsafe your kind compliance
In teaching me this noble art and science.
I'll work for you with all my might and main!'

Well,' said the canon, 'let me try again;
We'll have a second shot; pay careful heed
And you'll become an expert, and at need
Can try it in my absence, once you're in
The ways of scientific discipline.
Let's take another ounce of mercury,
This is no time for chattering,' said he,
'And do the same with it as we have done
Already with the first, our silver one.'

The priest then set to business and began
To do precisely what this cursed man
Commanded of him, puffing at the fire
In the mad hope of reaching his desire.
Meanwhile the canon, if I need explain,
Stood ready by, to gull the priest again,

Dandling, to give him countenance in this,
A hollow stick – observe the artifice! –
Into the end of which an ounce, no more,
Of silver filings had been stuffed before,
As in the beech-wood coal, with wax no doubt,
To stop the silver filings falling out.

And while the priest was busy at his job
The canon came and touched him with the knob
And with a flourish cast the powder in
Just as before – the devil scrape his skin,
Hear me, O God, and flay him for the trick! –
And stirred the crucible with this same stick
Primed in the treacherous way that you have heard;
He always was a crook in deed and word.

He stirred the coals until the wax began
To melt over the flame, as any man
Except a fool of course would know it must.
Out of the stick slid all the silver dust
And down into the crucible it fell.

What can be better, gentlemen, than well?
For when this priest had been deceived again
And taken it all for gospel, right as rain,
He was so happy that I can't express
In words of ecstasy of happiness.
He proffered to the canon on the spot
Body and soul. 'Eh,' said the canon. 'What?
I have some powders, though I seem poor to some,
But let me tell you there is more to come.
D'you happen to have some copper here?' said he.
'Yes,' said the priest, 'I think I have, maybe.'
'If not you'll have to buy some right away,
Be off with you, dear sir, be quick I say.'

He went away and came back with the copper;
The canon took it from him, as was proper,
And carefully weighed out a measured ounce.

My tongue is all too simple to pronounce
Words that could serve my thoughts or match my
        feelings
About his bloody-minded double-dealings.
Friendly he seemed to those he hadn't caught
But was a fiend in what he felt and thought.
It wearies me to say how false he was,
Yet I must try to speak of it because
It may help others to beware his treason
In time, and truly that's my only reason.

Within the crucible the canon placed
His ounce of copper, set it then in haste
Among the flames and cast the powder in,
Telling the priest to stoop down and begin
Blowing the fire, and it was all a hoax;
He made a monkey of him with his jokes.

He cast the molten copper in his mould
And put it in the water to get cold;
Leaning above it, in he put his hand.
Now in his sleeve – as you will understand,
You heard me say so – was a silver rod.
He took it slyly out, the filthy sod,
– The priest knew nothing of his treacherous plan –

And left it in the bottom of the pan.
He fumbled in the water, groped about
And with amazing sleight-of-hand took out
And hid the copper rod. With friendly charm
He took the unsuspecting victim's arm
And said to him, as if it were a joke,
'By God, you're much to blame! Stoop down and poke;
Help me as I helped you. That's only fair;
Come on, put in your hand and see what's there.'

The priest took out the silver there and then.
The canon said, 'We must go out again
Taking these rods, all three, that we have made,
And ask some fellow in the goldsmith trade
Whether they're anything. I should be distressed
To find them less than silver of the best.
Well, it's a thing that can be proved forthwith.'

So off they went to find a silversmith
And gave their metal to the man to try it
With fire and hammer; no one could deny it,
All were as should be, silver unalloyed.

Was that besotted cleric overjoyed?
Never was bird gladder to greet the day,
Never was nightingale in depth of May
More joyful in her eagerness to sing,
Nor lady lustier in carolling
Or in her talk of love and womanhood,
Nor knightly soul more eager to do good
In deeds of arms to please his chosen lady
Than was the priest to learn that graceless, shady
Business; and he addressed the canon thus:
'For love of God who died for all of us,
And if I may deserve so much of you,
What will that powder cost me? Tell me, do!'

'By our Lady,' said the canon, 'for a buyer
I warn you it's expensive; save one friar
And I myself there's no one who can make it,
Not in all England.' 'Never mind, I'll take it,'
The priest replied; 'for God's sake, what's the price?'
'It's dear,' he said, 'but at a sacrifice,
Since you're a friend and really want to bid,
God help me, it is yours for forty quid.
But for the kindness that you showed before
In lending me a mark it would be more.'

This priest at once collected forty pound
In golden pieces and he took them round
To give the canon for his recipe,
Whose work in life was fraud and treachery.
'Sir priest,' he said, 'I look for no renown
In this my art; in fact I play it down.
So, if you love me keep the matter quiet;
If people knew my skill there'd be a riot.
By God, there'd be such envy and defiance
Against me for philosophy and science,
I should be killed; there'd be no other way.'

'Why God forbid!' the priest said. 'Killed, you say?
Better to squander all the wealth I had
To save you – if I didn't, send me mad,
Dear God! – than see you suffer such an ill.'

'You have a solid reason for good will,'
The canon said. 'Good-bye and many thanks!'
And off he went, this prince of mountebanks;
The priest never set eyes on him again
After that day. I hardly need explain
That when he tried experiments the priest
Had no success whatever, not the least.
The powder wouldn't work, it was a mock;
He had been tricked and made a laughing-stock.
That was the canon's way of introduction
When bringing down poor people to destruction.

Gentlemen, think, there has been strife of old
In every class waged between men and gold,
So fierce there's hardly any to be had.
Alchemy has made many people mad
And on my word I think it may well be
The greatest reason for its scarcity.

An astrological table, also reproduced from Elias Ashmole's treatise 'Theatrum Chemicum Britannicum'. The affinity of the base metals with the seven planets posed a constant problem for alchemists: how to secure the most favourable influences for success.

Their scientific jargon is so wholly
No one can hope to understand it fully,
Not as intelligence goes nowadays.
And they may go on chattering like jays

And take delight and trouble in their chatter
But for all that they'll never solve the matter.
If you are rich it's easy to be taught
How to transmute and bring your wealth to naught.
There's so much lucre in this fine affair
One's joy can be transmuted to despair.
It can impoverish the heaviest purses,
Yet all it does for one is buy the curses
Of those that lend their goods before they've learnt.
Oh fie, for shame! When people have been burnt
Cannot they learn, alas, to shun the fire?
And you that use it, master your desire
Lest you lose all; for better late than never.
Long is the ruin that can last for ever!
Prowl as you may, the secret can't be found,
Though you're as bold as Dobbin blundering round;
Poor blind old horse, in dangers all unknown,
He's just as liable to hit a stone
As keep along the highway, and I hold
It's just the same transmuting into gold.
Should, then, your outward eye see incorrectly
Let the mind's eye behold more circumspectly.
You may be wide awake, but though you stare
You will make nothing of that business there,
Rather will waste all you can grab or earn.
Slacken a fire that is quick to burn;
Meddle no more with alchemy, I mean,
For if you do all thrift will be swept clean.
I should at once inform you if I may
What genuine philosophers would say.
Arnold is one of those that make the quorum;
He wrote *Rosarium Philosophorum*
And came from Villa Nova. Thus says he:
'There is no mortifying mercury
Without the use of sulphur, brother to it.'
The first of all philosophers that knew it
Was Hermes Trismegistus and he said:
'Doubtless the dragon never can be dead
Or mortify, unless you also slay
His brother with him. Put another way,
The dragon stands for Mercury, none other,
And sulphur, known as brimstone, is his brother,

And these are drawn from *Luna* and from *Sol*.
Therefore,' he said, 'observe this protocol:
Let no man busy himself to seek this art
Unless he knows the language and the heart
Of science, both in aim and technical term,
For, without these, he is an ignorant worm.
This is a craft and science that is furled
As secrets of the secrets of the world.'
Plato had a disciple once, and he
Said to his master – if you care to see,
It is recorded in the *Chimica
Senioris Zadith Tabula* –
'Tell me the name, sir, of the Secret Stone?'
And Plato said in answer, 'It is known
As Titan Stone upon the tongues of men.'
'And what is that?' said the disciple then.
'Magnesia,' answered Plato. 'Is it thus?
Then it's *ignotum per ignotius*!
What then may be Magnesia, master, pray?'
'Magnesia is the liquid, I would say,
Composed of the Four Elements,' he said.
'What's its root-principle or fountain-head?
Will you be pleased to indicate that fount?'
'No, no,' said Plato then, 'on no account.
Philosophers are under strict control
Never to tell that secret to a soul
Or write it in a book; it is unpriced,
Being a secret very dear to Christ.
It is His will that no discovery
Be made of it, save where His Deity
Wills to inspire His servants, else forbidden.
No more; from whom He wills He keeps it hidden.'
So I conclude; since God will not allow
Philosophers to tell their pupils how
To find this stone, no doubt it's better so,
And my advice would be to let it go.
Make God your adversary for a whim
And work at what is contrary to Him
And to His will, and you will never thrive
Though you transmute as long as you're alive.
Aye, there's the point for which my tale began,
And may God prosper every honest man!

Amen.

THE MANCIPLE'S TALE

The Manciple's Prologue

DON'T you all know where stands a little town,
The one that people call Bob-up-and-down,
Near Blean Woods on the way to Canterbury?
Well, it was thereabouts our Host turned merry.
'Dun's in the mire!' he said. 'Behold King Log;
For love of money drag him from his bog!
Will no one wake our friend asleep behind?
A thief could rob him and he wouldn't mind.
Look at him napping . . . Forty winks? Cock's bones!
He'll tumble off his horse and hit the stones.
Is that the London Cook, the devil take him?
Make him come here, he knows the fine, we'll make him
Tell us a story, though I'm bound to say
It won't be worth a barrow-load of hay.
Wake up, you Cook!' he said. 'God give you sorrow,
What's up with you to sleep this sunny morrow?
Have you had fleas all night, or else got drunk,
Or spent the night in toiling with a punk,
And haven't got the strength to raise your head?'

The Cook was drunk, pale-drunk, no touch of red,
And answered from a stupor, 'Bless my soul!
I feel all heavy, haven't got control;
I'd rather sleep,' he said, 'I don't know why,
Than drink a gallon of wine, the best you buy
In all Cheapside.' The Manciple said, 'Well,
If I can make things easier for a spell
For you, and not offend the company,
And if the Host extends his courtesy
To let me, I'll excuse you from your tale.
Upon my word, your face is pretty pale,
Your eyes are somewhat dazed, I can't help
    thinking,
As for your breath, I'm bound to say it's stinking,
Which shows you indisposed for such a matter.
Blunt words are best, I never was one to flatter.

---

*Left: Pilgrims from Canterbury Cathedral. The duties of a
manciple were to purchase provisions for an institution such as a
college or a monastery. The hostility between manciples and cooks
was often a topic for stock jokes.*

Look at him yawning there, the drunken sot!
You'd think he meant to swallow us on the spot.
Keep your mouth shut, man! Mercy, what a
    socket!
The devil of Hell's own hoof would hardly block it;
Your cursed breath may well infect us all.
You stinking swine, fie, how you gape and sprawl!
(Look out, take care, sir, he's a powerful man)
I'd like to see a punch-ball hit his pan!
He's about ripe for trouble in that line;
You'd think he had been drinking monkey-wine,
And that's when one goes playing with a straw!'

This speech annoyed the Cook who, turning raw,
Craned at the Manciple with so much force
For want of speech, he tumbled off his horse
And there he lay for all the care they took;
Fine cavalry performance for a cook!
Pity he couldn't have held on by his ladle.

They got him back at last into the cradle
After a deal of shoving to and fro
To lift him up, it was a sorry show;
Poor, pallid soul, unwieldier than most!

But to the Manciple at last our Host
Turned and remarked, 'Drink is in domination
Over the fellow; by my soul's salvation
I think he'd only tell a lousy tale.
Whether it's wine or maybe new-brewed ale
That's in him, he is talking through his nose;
Like someone with a cold, one would suppose,
Snuffling like that. I think he's going to spew.
It's just about as much as he can do
To keep his horse from falling in the ditch
And if his horse should fall, he'll follow, which
Gives us as much as we can do to strain
And lift his drunken body up again.
Carrying corpses would be just as grim.
Tell on your tale, I've had enough of him.

But, Manciple, it wasn't very nice
Of you to scold the fellow for his vice.
Another day those chickens you have loosed

May very likely all return to roost.
I mean he might allude to small amounts
That could be criticized in your accounts
As not quite honest, if it came to proof.'
'That might be awkward; I shall keep aloof.
He easily could catch me in the snare,'
The other said, 'I'd rather buy the mare
Between his drunken legs than start a row,
I mustn't make him angry anyhow.
The things I said were only meant in jest.
Do you know what? I've something of the best
Here in this gourd, wine of the ripest grape;
Just watch and we shall have another jape.
I'll give the Cook some liquor if I may,
On pain of death he shall not say me nay!'
And certainly, to tell you what occurred,
The Cook, alas, drank freely from the gourd.
What was the need? He'd had enough before,

Yet spluttered in the mug and drank some more,
Giving it back when he had had enough.
The Cook, who was delighted with the stuff,
Thanked him as best he could for some time after.
Our Host went off into a roar of laughter
And said 'Well, now I see how necessary
It is to bring one's drink to keep us merry,
For it can turn all rancour and dissension
To love and harmony and stop contention.
O Bacchus, thou! A blessing on thy name
That so convertest earnest into game;
Our thanks and worship to thy deity!'
My prayers are done, you get no more of me.
Now, Manciple, on with your story, pray.'
'Well, sir,' he said, 'attend to what I say.'

The Manciple's Tale

WHEN Phoebus had his dwelling here on earth
As ancient books report, for what they're
   worth,
He was a paladin of lustiest marrow,
Better than anyone with bow and arrow.
He slew the serpent Python as it lay
Coiled in the sunshine and asleep one day,
And many a noble and distinguished deed
His bow performed for him, as you can read.
And every instrument of minstrelsy
He well knew how to play, while melody
Poured from his throat, clear joy to hear him sing.
Even Amphion, famous Theban King
Who built the town's defences by his singing,
Was not so skilled in setting echoes ringing.
Added to that he was the handsomest man
That ever was heard of since the world began.
Why should I make description of his features?
He was the fairest living of earthly creatures.
And therewithal he was of noblest bearing,
Filled with high honour, excellence and daring.
This Phoebus, flower in the cap of youth,
Renowned for bounty, chivalry and truth,
To please himself and signalize his glory
In having vanquished Python, says my story,
Was wont to carry in his hand a bow.
It happened that this Phoebus kept a crow
Lodged in a cage, and there for many a day
He taught it speech, as one can teach a jay,
And fostered it with care. This crow was white,
White as a snowy swan; it could recite
With perfect mimicry of tone and word

This illustration of a caged bird plotting its escape is from the 'Roman de la Rose'. The idea that it would value its freedom, no matter how well it was treated, was a common one.

What any man had uttered, and the bird
Would use this talent when it told a tale.
In all the world there was no nightingale,
Moreover, with a hundred thousandth part
Of what it had in merriness and art.
Now in his house this Phoebus had a wife
Who lived with him; he loved her more than life
And night and day he gave his diligence
To pleasing her and showing reverence,
Except for this, if it's the truth they tell us,

I have to say he was extremely jealous
And wished to guard her, lest an exhibition
Be made of him, as those in his condition
Commonly do – in vain, it can't succeed.
A good wife who is pure in thought and deed
Should not be checked and spied on, that is plain,
And truly it is labour all in vain
To check a wicked wife; it can't be done.
It's imbecility, say I for one,
For men to waste their labour checking wives,
And so the ancients say who wrote their lives.

But to my purpose, as I first began;
This excellent Phoebus does the best he can
To please her, thinking by his kind address
And by his management and manliness
That no one could extrude him from her graces.
But God knows, none can compass in such cases
The power to restrain a thing which nature
Has naturally implanted in a creature.

Take any bird and put it in a cage
And let your heart's intention then engage
To foster it tenderly with food and drink,
With every dainty mess that thought can think,
And keep it clean as nearly as you may,
Caged in a cage of gold however gay,
That bird would rather twenty thousand fold
Be in a forest which is rough and cold,
Feeding on worms and other wretched trash.
It's on the watch, and ready in a flash
To escape out of the cage and to be gone.
Freedom is what it sets its heart upon.

Or take a cat, nourish it well with milk
And tender meat, make it a couch of silk,
But let it see a mouse along the wall
And it abandons milk and meat and all,
Aye, every other dainty in the house,
Such is its appetite to eat a mouse.
You see, a natural lust is in possession
And appetite has banished its discretion.

She-wolves are also of this baser kind;
They choose the lowest wolf that they can find,
The least in reputation, to be mated,
When the time comes to have their passion sated.

These parallels are all produced to show
The faithlessness of men, they do not go
For women, not at all. The foul delight
Of men is wrecking lecherous appetite
On lower things than wives however fair,
However true, however debonair;
Flesh pines for the new-fangled, curse upon it,
And nothing with the stamp of virtue on it
Will pleasure us for more than a short while.

This Phoebus who was innocent of guile
Was well deceived, for all his excellent features.
She had a man, one of the lowest creatures
Beneath him and of little reputation,
Worth nothing next a man of Phoebus' station.
And more's the harm it happens often so

A virtuous wife provides a good feast for her husband before the Lenten fast. As soon as he has killed his wife, Phoebus becomes convinced of her innocence. Of the ten manuscript fragments that Chaucer left of 'The Canterbury Tales', the Manciple's Prologue and Tale form a separate group and some scholars believe Chaucer intended them to be the first of the Tales told by the pilgrims on their return journey – but of course this huge enterprise was never completed.

And is a common source of human woe.

It chanced his wife, when Phoebus was away,
Sent for her bully – bully, did I say?
Tut-tut, that was a very knavish speech!
Your pardon, lords and ladies, I beseech.

Wise Plato says, as those who can may read,
Words should be in accordance with the deed.
In tales told properly a word should bring
The sense of being cousin to the thing.
I'm a blunt, boisterous man and tell you all
There is no real difference at all
Between a lady-wife of high degree
Dishonest of her body, if she be,
And some poor wench, no difference but this
– That's if so be they both should go amiss –
That since the gentlewoman ranks above
She therefore will be called his 'lady-love',
Whereas that other woman, being poor,
Will be referred to as his wench or whore.
And as God knows (and so do you, dear brother),
One name is just as low as is the other.

Nor is there difference in my belief
Between a tyrant and an arrant thief
Or outlaw, when the tyrant has no claim.
They told great Alexander just the same,
That just because a tyrant has the might
By force of arms to murder men downright
And burn down house and home and leave all flat,
They call the man a captain, just for that.
But since an outlaw with his little band
Cannot bring half such mischief on a land
Or be the cause of so much harm and grief,
He only earns the title of a thief.

Well, I'm no scholar and you shan't be vexed
By hearing me enlarge on any text;
Back to the tale I started, but more fully.
When Phoebus' wife had notified her bully
They wrought their will in all its transient rage.
Now the white crow, still hanging in its cage,
Beheld their work and never said a word.
But once Lord Phoebus had returned, the bird
Unlocked its throat and sang, 'Cuckoo! Cuckoo!'
What, bird!' said Phoebus. 'That's no song for you!
Were you not wont to sing your songs so gaily
That it rejoiced my heart to hear you daily
In tuneful voice? Alas, what song is this?'
By God,' it said, 'I do not sing amiss.
Phoebus,' it said, 'in spite of all your worth,
Of all your beauty and your gentle birth,
Of all your minstrelsy and singing too,
And all your watching, someone's hoodwinked you,
Has bleared your eyes – a man whose reputation
Compared with yours has little estimation,
Not worth a gnat indeed; upon my life,
On your own bed I saw him plumb your wife.'
What more d'you want? The crow, in his behoof,
Boldly informed him, giving serious proof,
Of how his wife had done her lechery
And had put shame on him and villainy;
He swore he had seen it with his very eyes.
Phoebus fell backward at the crow's replies;
It seemed to him his sorrowful heart was
    breaking.
Setting an arrow to his bow and taking
Aim as he bent it in his rage to slay,
He killed his wife; there is no more to say.
And all his instruments of minstrelsy
He broke in sorrow for it, psaltery,
Lute, harp, guitar, and then he broke his bow
And arrows, and he thus addressed the crow:
Traitor,' he said, 'it was thy scorpion-tongue
Brought my confusion. Oh, my heart is wrung
With grief! Why was I born? Would I were dead!
O dearest wife, O gem of joy that shed
So grave, so true a light upon our love!
Now thou art dead and pale of face, O dove
Of innocence, that I can swear! O speed
Of hand too rash, to do so foul a deed!
O mind confused, O thoughtless rage surprised
That smote a guiltless creature unadvised!
O fainting trust, O prompting to suspect,
Where was your thought and wisdom to direct?
O every man, beware how you are moved,
Never believe but what is strongly proved!
Strike not too soon, ere you can reason why,
Be soberly advised before you try
To execute your justice and assuage
Suspicion by the acting of your rage.
Alas, a thousand in their hasty ire
Have been undone and brought into the mire.
O sorrow! I shall kill myself for grief!'

An early fourteenth-century illumination. The general theme of the Tell-Tale bird appears in several stories and can be traced back to Ovid. A briefer version was also used by Chaucer's contemporary, John Gower.

And to the crow he said, 'O wicked thief,
Now I shall pay you for your lying tale!
Once you sang sweetly like a nightingale,
But now, false thief, your liquid song is done
And all your snowy feathers, every one;
Never in all your life to utter word,
Vengeance shall fall upon you, traitor-bird.
You and your issue ever shall be black;
Their sweetest music, like your own, shall crack
And you shall croak, foretelling storm and rain
In token that through you my wife was slain.'
And up he started at the crow and tore
The fair white feathers out that once it bore
And made it black, and took away its song
And power of speech, and flung it forth headlong
Down to the devil, nor do I wish it back.
And that's the reason why all crows are black.
My lords, this is a parable conveying
A moral; pray take heed of what I'm saying.
Never tell anyone in all your life
That any other has enjoyed his wife,
For he will hate you mortally, believe it.
Solomon said – the learned so receive it –
'Teach every man how to refrain his tongue.'
But as I said, you won't find me among
The scholars, but my mother long ago
Would say, 'My son, reflect upon the crow;
My son, you hold your tongue and hold your friends.
A wicked tongue but serves the devil's ends.
My son, the cross can save you from his net;
My son, God in His endless goodness set
A wall about the tongue of teeth and lip:
Take counsel ere you speak, let nothing slip.
My son, too often by some babbling speech
Many are blasted, so the scholars teach.
A little wisely spoken as a rule
Will save a man from being cursed for fool.

My son, restrain your tongue in self-denial
On all occasions, save in making trial
Of prayer or speaking in the honour of God.
The first of virtues, if you will kiss the rod,
My son, is to restrain and guard your tongue;
So teach your children this when they are young.
My son, superflous, unthinking speech,
When to say less is still within your reach
And would suffice, will harm you, I was taught.
Much chatter is the food of sinful thought.
Are you aware what hasty tongues can do?
Just as a sword can cut an arm in two
Or slice it into bits, dear son, just so
A tongue can sever friendship at a blow.
A chatterbox is hateful to the Lord;
Here Solomon the wise is in accord
With David in his psalms, and Seneca too.

My son, say nothing when a nod will do.
Feign to be deaf if you should hear the chatter
Of any fool that broaches dangerous matter.
And add this Flemish proverb to your diet
If you will learn it, "Little speech, much quiet."
My son, if you have said no wicked word
You need not fear to have been overheard,
Whereas a wicked word, I tell you plain,
Once said can never be recalled again.
What's said is said and goes upon its way,
Like it or not, repent it as you may.
He is a slave to any that has heard
Him tell a tale, he'll suffer for that word.
My son, be cautious, fashion nothing new
By way of tidings, whether false or true;
Wherever you may be, with high and low,
Refrain your tongue and think upon the crow.'

THE PARSON'S TALE

The Parson's Prologue

THE story of the Manciple had ended.
From the south line the sun had now
    descended
    So low, it stood – so far as I had sight –
At less than twenty-nine degrees in height.
Four o'the clock it was, to make a guess;
Eleven foot long, or little more or less,
My shadow was, as at that time and place,
Measuring feet by taking in this case
My height as six, divided in like pattern
Proportionally; and the power of Saturn
Began to rise with *Libra* just as we
Approached a little thorpe. Our referee,
Our Host, that is, and trusted guide, who made
Decisions for our happy cavalcade,
Turned round and said, 'Matters, my lords, stand thus;
There's but one story lacking now to us.
We've carried out my sentence and decree.
We've heard a tale from each in his degree,
What I ordained is nearly done, I say.
God send the best of fortune, so I pray,
On whomsoever is last to pour the liquor.
Sir Priest,' he said, 'are you by chance a vicar?
Or else a parson? Tell the truth, I say;
Don't spoil our sport though, be you what you may,
For every man but you has told his tale.
Unbuckle now and show what's in your bale,
For honestly, to judge you by your looks,
You could knit mighty matters out of books.
So up and tell a story, by cock's bones!'

The parson said at once in level tones,
    'You'll get no fable or romance from me,
    For Paul in his Epistle to Timothy
Reproves all those who waive aside the truth
For fables that are wretched and uncouth.
And why unclench my fist on your behalf,

I that can scatter wheat, to give you chaff?
And therefore if you care to hear my preaching
I'll offer virtuous matter, moral teaching.
So if you'll hear me, granting that sufficed,
I would be glad in reverence of Christ
To give you lawful pleasure if I can.

But trust me truly, I'm a southern man,
    I can't romance with rum-ram-ruf by letter,
    And rhyme, God knows, I hold but little better;
I won't embellish things with tricks like those
If you'll excuse me, but I'll speak in prose,
A happy thing, to knit and make an end
Of all our feast. Jesu in mercy send
Me wit to guide your way one further stage
Upon that perfect, glorious pilgrimage
Called the celestial, to Jerusalem.
These are my thoughts; if you approve of them
I'll start my tale at once, so tell me pat
If you agree. I can't say more than that.

Nevertheless I put this meditation
    In full submission to the castigation
    Of learned men. I am not skilled in texts,
I only take, as each of you expects,
The moral of it, and for your protection
As I protest, submit it to correction.'

These words had gained assent from everyone,
    For that, we thought, was just what should be
      done,
To close upon a virtuous persuasion,
And give him both an audience and occasion;
Our Host was then requested to prevail
On our behalf with him to tell his tale.

Our Host was ready and found words for all,
    And said, 'Now, master Parson, fair befall
    Your reverent meditation! But I'm thinking
You'd better hurry, for the sun is sinking.
Be fructuous and brief in what you tell
And may God send you grace to do it well!
Say what you please; you will be gladly heard.'
So he began his sermon, on the word.

Left: The Parson's Tale was a sermon about the preparation for confession and the true nature of the Seven Deadly Sins. These illustrations of six of them are from 'Piers Plowman'.

The Parson's Tale

THE Parson's tale is a prose sermon on the proper preparation for Confession and the true nature of the Seven Deadly Sins. It seems therefore to lead naturally to Chaucer's Retractions which follow it. On the literal plane of meaning it seems to be offered as an appropriate ending to a pilgrimage before the Saint's shrine is reached. On the allegorical plane, referred to by the Parson when first called upon for a story, it may be deemed a preparation for a last confession to be made on 'that perfect, glorious pilgrimage' that is called the celestial, to the Heavenly Jerusalem.

A brief summary of the Parson's sermon here follows:

God desires no man to perish and there are many spiritual ways to the celestial city. One noble way is Penitence, the lamenting for sin and the will to sin no more. The root of the tree of Penitence is contrition, the branches and the leaves are confession, the fruit satisfaction, the seed grace, and the heat in that seed the Love of God.

Contrition is the heart's sorrow for sin. Sin may be venial or deadly. Venial sin is for one to love Christ less than he ought. Deadly sin is to love a creature more than the Creator. Venial sin may lead to deadly sin. There are seven deadly sins of which the first is pride.

Pride is shown in many forms: arrogance, impudence, boasting, hypocrisy, joy in having done harm, etc. It may be inward or outward. Outward pride is like a tavern sign that shows there is wine in the cellar. It may show itself in too many clothes or too few, or in the carriage of the body, as when the buttocks jut as it were the hinder parts of a she-ape in the full of the moon. One can show sinful pride in retinue, in ostentatious hospitality, in one's strength, in one's gentility. The remedy for Pride is Humility or true self-knowledge.

Envy is sorrow at the prosperity of others and joy in their hurt. It is the worst of sins as it sets itself against all other virtues and goodness, and is flatly against the Holy Ghost, source of Bounty. Backbiting and grumbling are the Devil's Paternoster.

The remedy for Envy is to love God, your neighbour, and your enemy.

Anger is the wicked will to vengeance. Anger against wickedness, however, is good, wrath without bitterness. Wicked anger is either sudden or premeditated; the latter is the worse. Malice aforethought chases the Holy Ghost out of the soul. It is the devil's furnace and heats hatred, manslaughter, treachery, lies, flattery, scorn, discord, menaces, and curses. The remedy for Anger is Patience.

Accidie does all tasks with vexation, slackly and without joy, and is encumbered by doing good. It restrains one from prayer. It is the rotten-hearted sin of Sloth. It leads to despair. The remedy is Fortitude.

Avarice is a lecherous desire for earthly things, a kind of idolatry. Every florin in one's coffer is a mommet, an idol. It leads to feudal extortions by lords from their villeins, to fraud, to simony, gambling, theft, false-witness, sacrilege. The remedy is Mercy or 'pity largely taken'.

Gluttony is an immeasurable appetite to eat or drink. Drunkenness is the horrible sepulchre of man's reason. The remedy is Abstinence, Temperance, and Sobriety.

Lechery is near cousin to Gluttony. It has many forms and is the greatest sin of theft there is, for it steals body and soul. The remedy is Chastity and Continence, and not to eat or drink too much. When the pot boils strongly the best remedy is to withdraw the fire.

Confession must be freely willed and made in full faith. A man must only confess his own sins, and truthfully with his own mouth, not painted with subtle words. It must be a considered, not a hasty act, and frequent.

Satisfaction consists generally in alms-giving, penance, fasting, and bodily pains. Its fruit is endless bliss in Heaven.

CHAUCER'S RETRACTIONS

The Maker of this Book here takes his Leave

NOW I beg all those that listen to this little treatise, or read it, that if there be anything in it that pleases them, they thank Our Lord Jesu Christ for it, from whom proceeds all understanding and goodness.

And if there be anything that displeases them, I beg them also to impute it to the fault of my want of ability, and not to my will, who would very gladly have said better if I had had the power. For our Book says 'all that is written is written for our doctrine'; and that is my intention. Wherefore I beseech you meekly for the mercy of God to pray for me, that Christ have mercy on me and forgive me my sins: and especially for my translations and enditings of worldly vanities, which I revoke in my retractions: as are the book of *Troilus;* also the book of *Fame;* the book of *The Nineteen Ladies;* the book of *The Duchess;* the book of *St Valentine's Day of the Parliament of Fowls; The Tales of Canterbury,* those that tend towards sin; the book of *The Lion;* and many another book, if they were in my memory; and many a song and many a lecherous lay; that Christ in his great mercy forgive me the sin.

But the translation of Boethius *De Consolatione,* and other books of Saints' legends, of homilies, and morality and devotion, for them I thank our Lord Jesu Christ and His blissful Mother, and all the Saints of Heaven; beseeching them that they henceforth, to my life's end, send me grace to bewail my sins and to study the salvation of my soul; and grant me the grace of true penitence, confession and satisfaction, that I may perform them in this present life, through the benign grace of Him that is King of kings and Priest over all priests, who bought us with the precious blood of His heart; so that I may be one of those that at the Day of Judgement shall be saved. *Qui cum Patre,* etc.

Here ends the book of the *Tales of Canterbury* compiled by Geoffrey Chaucer, on whose soul Jesu Christ have mercy.

Amen.

SOURCES OF ILLUSTRATIONS

The miniatures at the head of each tale come from the 1911
facsimile edition of the Ellesmere Manuscript of the
Canterbury Tales

228. *Beaute of Women*, London 1525
230. Victoria & Albert Museum, facsimile of 'Les Tres Riches Heures du Duc de Berry' (Bridgeman Art Library)
232. National Maritime Museum, Greenwich. (Michael Holford)
233. British Library. Ms. Add. Roy. 18.D.11, f.74
235. *Le Livre des Verteux Faix de Plusiers Nobles Chevaliers*, Rouen 1488.
237. Musée Cluny, Paris. (Giraudon)
238. Bodleian Library, Oxford. Ms. Douce 219/220, f.63
239. Bodleian Library, Oxford. Ms. Douce 195, f.94v
239. Bodleian Library, Oxford. Ms. Douce 219/220, f.68v
240. Emmanuel College, Cambridge. Ms. 112, f.180v (by kind permission of the Master and Fellows)
242. Biblioteca Statale, Lucca. Codex Latinum 1942, f.38 (Scala)
243. Bodleian Library, Oxford. Ms. Douce 195, f.67v
244. *Storia di Uberto e Filomena*, Florence, late 15th century
244. Bodleian Library, Oxford. Ms. Douce 195, f.48
245. Bodleian Library, Oxford. Ms. Douce 195, f.15v
246. Bodleian Library, Oxford. Ms. Douce 332, f.8v
248. Bodleian Library, Oxford. Ms. Douce 332, f.1
250. *Lunare* by Bernardino de Granolachis, Florence 1491
250. Bodleian Library, Oxford. Ms. Selden Supra 57, f.3
251. Bodleian Library, Oxford. Ms. Douce 332, f.58
253. Bodleian Library, Oxford. Ms. Douce 195, f.151v
254. Archivio Torre de Tombo, Lisbon. Livre d'Heures de Don Duarte, f.144v. (Giraudon)

255. Bodleian Library, Oxford. Ms Douce 195, f.5
256. Keble College, Oxford. Ms. 49, f.268
257. British Library. Ms. Egerton 1070, f.107v
259. Bourges Catherdal (Giraudon)
260. *Thordinary of Crysten men*, London 1506
261. *Tractato di Oratione mentale* by Savonarola, Florence
262. St Mary's Church, Orchardleigh, Somerset. (Bridgeman Art Library)
264. Bodleian Library, Oxford. Ms. Ashmole 971, f.41
266. *View of London*, printed by Wynken de Worde, 1497
267. *De Proprietatibus Rerum* by Bartholomaeus Anglian, London
268. British Library. Ms. Harley 3469, f.4
270. *Tripus Aureus* by Michael Maier, Frankfurt, 1678 (Ann Ronan Picture Library)
271. *The Alchemist* by H. Holbein, 1527 (Ann Ronan Picture Library)
271. *Pretiosa Margarita Novella* by Petrus Bonus, Venice 1546 (Ann Ronan Picture Library)
272. Bodleian Library, Oxford. Ms. Ashmole 971, f.76v
274. Bodleian Library, Oxford. Ms. Ashmole 971, f.68
276. Canterbury Cathedral (Sonia Halliday)
278. Bodleian Library, Oxford. Ms. Douce 332, f.131v
279. *Contrasto di Carnevale e Quaresima*, Florence late 15th century
280. Bodleian Library, Oxford. Ms. Douce 308, f.98
282. Bodleian Library, Oxford. Ms. Douce 104, ff.24, 26, 26v, 27 and 29

Front cover picture: British Library. Ms. Roy. 18.D.11, f.148
(Michael Holford)
Back cover picture: British Library. Ms. Add. 5141, f.1
Endpapers and front cover border by Studio Briggs
Silhouettes of the pilgrims throughout by Philip Hood